Statistics

Frank Owen
Ronald Jones

POLYTECH PUBLISHERS LTD STOCKPORT

First published 1977
Reprinted 1978

© Copyright Polytech Publishers Limited
   36 Hayburn Road, Stockport SK2 5DB

ISBN 0 85505 021 7

Printed in Great Britain by
Butler & Tanner Ltd, Frome and London

CONTENTS

PREFACE

Recent years have seen many changes in both the content and style of examinations of the standard which used to be called 'Introduction to Statistics'. These changes reflect the growing belief that it is not enough to be able to perform statistical calculations. Important as it is to have some degree of calculative ability, this alone is no longer sufficient to ensure a pass in the examination room. More and more it is becoming necessary for the student to understand, not only what he is doing, but also the meaning of the results he obtains.

In surveying the literature, it seems to us that although there are many excellent books on statistical method there is a marked deficiency of textbooks designed to cover the present first-year syllabus of the major professional bodies. It is this gap that this book is designed to fill. We hope that it will prove to give full coverage of the Ordinary National Certificate Statistics examinations in both Business Studies and in Public Administration, the examinations of the Institute of Certified Accountants, and the Institute of Secretaries and Administrators. Additionally it covers the content of the Statistics section of the Institute of Cost and Management Accountants paper in Mathematics and Statistics, and should prove useful for large parts of the Quantitative Methods paper of the Institute of Public Finance and Accountancy.

Every author knows that his book is never entirely his own work. We owe a great deal to the comments and criticisms of our colleagues at Liverpool Polytechnic; we believe that all students using this book will have reason to be as grateful as we are to the many bodies who have so willingly allowed us to use their past examination questions. We are deeply appreciative of the encouragement and practical help of our publishers without which this work might never have seen the light of day.

The debt we owe to previous writers is beyond measure. If we have not acknowledged every single one it is because their ideas are so much a part of our own that it is impossible to identify with certainty what is theirs. We hope that each one of them will accept our acknowledgement of their contribution to the existing state of knowledge.

Such merits as this book may have are a direct result of the help we have received from these and from many others. But the final manuscript is ours and the responsibility for undetected errors that remain must be ours alone.

Above all our gratitude is expressed to our wives, who have endured many hours of loneliness during the writing of this book. Their forbearance and encouragement have contributed in no small part to the completion of this manuscript. To them it is dedicated.

Frank Owen
Ronald H. Jones

Liverpool Polytechnic

ACKNOWLEDGEMENTS

We would like to express our thanks to the following examinations bodies who have allowed us to make such a liberal use of their past examination questions:

The Royal Society of Arts
The Union of Lancashire and Cheshire Institutes
The Union of Educational Institutes
The Northern Counties Technical Examinations Council
The East Midlands Educational Union
The Yorkshire and Humberside Council for Further Education
The Welsh Joint Educational Committee
The Scottish Business Education Council
The Association of Certified Accountants
The Chartered Institute of Secretaries and Administrators
The Institute of Cost and Management Accountants
The Association of International Accountants
The Chartered Institute of Public Finance and Accountancy

Chapter One

The Raw Material of Statistics

Most people are vaguely aware that Statistics is concerned with figures in one way or another. Equally, we think, most people are rather distrustful of the statistics that they see quoted in the press or on television. We must admit that we ourselves have some sympathy for the housewife who is told on the news one evening that the cost of living has gone up by only 2% this month, and then finds in the shops next morning that everything she buys has, in fact, risen in price by between 5% and 10%. When this sort of thing happens it is no wonder that people get the impression that statistics can be made to prove anything. And yet – if our figures are accurate and the information is presented properly – how can this be so? We would like you to believe right from the start that no genuine statistician will ever deliberately misrepresent information or use it to mislead people. It can be done of course. In life many people are unscrupulous, and later in this course we will tell you how they misrepresent information, with the strict warning that *you* must never do it.

The great weakness of this subject, Statistics, is that to the man in the street who has never studied it, the methods used by statisticians are a closed book. We hope that as you work through this course your own personal book will be opened and that you will understand the dilemma in which our housewife finds herself.

But before we begin to think of the techniques you will use and the calculations you will perform, let us stop for a minute to consider the raw material you will be dealing with.

Suppose that the student union in your school or college wishes to obtain information about its members – their age, sex, home area, whether they live in a flat, or at home, or in lodgings and so on. How would the union secretary go about collecting this information? The most obvious way is for each student to be issued with a questionnaire, posing the relevant questions, and asking for it to be returned to the secretary's office. No doubt some of the forms will be incorrectly completed: some students may genuinely misunderstand the questions: some may refuse to answer certain questions which they regard as personal: doubtless some, in the fashion of the great petitions of the nineteenth century, will be signed by Queen Victoria or Karl Marx. Yet, with all its faults, this mass of completed questionnaires is the basic raw material for the statistical report that the union secretary wishes to produce.

Raw material such as this, collected at first hand, in response to specific questions is known as *primary data*; its characteristics are that it is obtained directly for the purpose of the survey which is being undertaken, and is, as yet, unanalysed.

Now, if your union secretary is lucky, he may also be able to obtain a great deal of information from the College administration, who, using enrolment forms as their primary data, may already have produced for their own purposes a fair amount of statistical information about students. Such information will, of course, have been produced for college purposes and may not be exactly what the union wants: but it is often useful additional information. Such data, which has already been collected for another, and different purpose, we know as *secondary data*. Usually it is of less use than primary data since it has already been processed and the original questionnaire is unlikely to have asked all the questions you would like to have asked. Without exception, all the data you will work on in this book is secondary data. But whether it is primary or secondary, there can be very little statistical information which was not at one time to be found only in a pile of completed forms or questionnaires. The main task of any writer on statistics is to explain what the statistician does with his raw data between collecting it and presenting his report. So let us go back to your union secretary.

It is obvious that no-one would sit down and write a report in the form of

'Mary Smith is 17, lives in Durham, and is in lodgings here; Susan Yeung comes from Singapore and is in lodgings here...'

We might just as well hand over the completed forms to anyone who is interested since all that this type of report does is detail the information which is already given in detail on the questionnaire.

We can get a clue about the next stage of the analysis if we ask ourselves what it is that the union really wants to know. Surely the sort of information that is really wanted is how many students are 16, how many are 17 and so on; what percentage of students live at home; what proportion of students come from overseas. It is not the individual we are interested in so much as total numbers in given categories. The categories in this investigation may be age, sex, type of residence, number of hours a week spent on study and so on. Within each category students will vary. Some are 16; others are 17;

some live at home, others in lodgings. We call each of these categories a *variable* because within each category students will vary. So we may now say that we are interested in a number of variables such as age, and more specifically in the value we can assign to each student within the range of values over which the variable extends. We may find, for example, that when we consider the variable 'age', 267 students are aged 17, 164 are aged 18 and so on up to the eldest student. The numbers of students whom we can place at each value of the variable we will call the *frequency*, because it tells us how often we will come across a student with this particular characteristic (that is, aged 18, or doing 27 hours a week private study, or travelling more than 15 miles to college). Thus the first step we must take is to decide what aspects of student life we are interested in and count up how many students are found within each of these categories. In so doing we are simplifying our data – reducing it to a more manageable form. In the process some detail is lost. We no longer know how old Brenda Jones is; but if we are interested we still have her completed questionnaire. On the other hand we do know that 267 students are aged 17 as well as much other general information.

Once we have reached this stage we are in a position to summarise our results in the form of a table and our work begins to look more like that of a statistician. Probably as a first tentative step we would produce a simple table dealing with only one variable. It might appear like this:

Age of Students attending ABC College

Age (the Variable)	Number of Students (the Frequency)
17	267
18	164
19	96
20	74
21 and over	23
	624

There is nothing wrong with our producing 15 or 20 tables like this, each concerned with a single variable, but surely it is better for presentation purposes if we could produce a small number of compound tables each showing several variables at once. Thus we could construct a double table showing the two variables, age and sex of students at the same time.

We have constructed this table by listing one of our variables vertically (age) and the other horizontally (sex). There is no golden

Age	Number of Students		
	Male	Female	Total
17	151	116	267
18	98	66	164
19	70	26	96
20	52	22	74
21 +	18	5	23
Total	389	235	624

rule, but it generally looks better if we tabulate the variable with the greater number of values vertically and that with the smaller number of values horizontally. Notice too that we have totalled both the vertical and the horizontal columns and that this adds to our information. We not only have the age distribution of male students and of female students but also the age distribution of the entire student population, and the total number of male and female students.

You may of course still argue that the table is still concerned with only one variable, age, and that all we have is two age distributions. Let us then extend our table to consider three variables, age, sex and type of accommodation. Obviously now we must further subdivide either the horizontal or the vertical columns. Again it is a good general guide to say that we believe it better to subdivide the horizontal rather than the vertical columns. But in doing this the variable in the vertical column tends to become the more important. So we must consider which is the most important variable, and this often depends on what we are trying to show. Let us suppose that in this case we are aiming to show that the type of accommodation a student occupies depends on his or her age. In this case we will list the ages vertically and subdivide the horizontal columns. Our table may now appear like this:

Age	Number of Students						Total
	At Home		In Lodgings		In Flat		
	M	F	M	F	M	F	
17	112	92	16	20	23	4	267
18	64	42	24	16	10	8	164
19	31	12	28	7	11	7	96
20	8	4	16	10	28	8	74
21 +	2	3	3	1	13	1	23
Total	217	153	87	54	85	28	—
	370		141		113		624

You will readily appreciate what a vast amount of information a table such as this can give us: the number of students who live at home, subdivided into male and female and classified according to age, as well as the same information for those who are living in lodgings or living in a flat. You can understand too how much more information could be incorporated if we subdivided further the horizontal axis as well as some subdivision of the vertical axis such as the area of origin followed in each case by the age range.

There is one problem – the more we subdivide, the more complicated our table becomes, and there comes a time when it is so difficult to read it and understand it that we find that clarity has been lost rather than gained. It is true that one treble table, such as the one above, is better than three single tables. It is equally true that if we are considering eight or nine variables, three treble tables are better than one very complex one. And if you are wondering why clarity is so important think again what we have been doing. We have collected primary data, simplified it and classified it, and are now trying to present it to our union executive in a readily digestible form. How much notice do you think the executive will take of us if they cannot understand what our tables are all about?

Just in case you are ever in the position of having to construct tables to present the raw material you have collected, there are several points you should bear in mind. Let us call them the 'Principles of Good Tabulation'.

(a) Every table should have a short explanatory title at the head. At the end you should put a note of the source of the information you have used, whether it is based on your own survey or secondary data.
(b) The unit of measurement should be clearly stated, and if necessary defined in a footnote. Not many people, for example, would know offhand what a 'Long Ton' is. In addition the heading to every column should be clearly shown.
(c) Use different rulings to break up a larger table – double lines or thicker lines add a great deal to the ease with which a table is understood.
(d) Whenever you feel it useful insert both column and row totals.
(e) If the volume of data is large, two or three simple tables are better than one cumbersome one.
(f) Before you start to draft a table be quite sure what you want it to show. Remember that although most people read from left to right, most people find it easier to absorb figures which are in columns rather than rows.

As with most things practice is the best way of learning, and these principles will soon become second nature after you have drafted a few tables for yourself.

You might well ask at this stage whether this is all there is in this subject of Statistics. If it were you would all end up with distinctions. But the most important part of the work is still to come. No statistician (or student) worth his salt is content with a mere list of figures. He now begins to ask questions, the most important of which is, 'What do the figures tell me?' We now begin, that is, to analyse the figures, and statistical techniques are largely methods of extracting the utmost possible information from the data we have available. We could, for example, calculate the average age of students living at home, and compare it with the average age of students living in flats to try to determine whether we are right in assuming that the younger student will tend to live at home and the older student tend to be a flat-dweller. We can do the same thing for both male and female students to see if they behave differently. Let us simply say that there are many questions that the statistician can ask even from the simple data we have used so far.

We said earlier that the most obvious way for the union secretary to collect his data was to issue a questionnaire to each and every student. The results of his enquiry would cover every single student in the college – it will refer to what statisticians call the *population* of students. Beware of this term population. In statistics it does not mean the number of people living in a particular area. What it implies is that we have examined or obtained information about every single member of a particular group we are investigating. Thus we can talk of a population of telegraph poles, a population of shaggy-haired dogs, a population of ball-bearings and so on.

But is there any need for us to examine the population of students attending the college? If we wish to save time and money can we not do as so many public opinion polls do and take a sample of students? We could issue the questionnaire to, say, 60 or 70 students only, or perhaps to every tenth student, and so reduce our raw data considerably. The *sample results* we obtain can then be applied to the population of students: if 12% of the sample live at home, we will argue that about 12% of all students in the college live at home.

Now, you may well argue that this can lead to wildly inaccurate results; and if you consider some of the results of public opinion polls in recent years it is apparent that things can, and do, go wrong. The sample chosen may be too small; it may not be representative of the population; the error arising as a result may mislead us. We will explain later how to overcome such problems and set up a sample survey which is likely to give satisfactory results. We will explain

too how to estimate the degree of error that may arise as a result
of sampling. For the moment we will merely point out that in taking
a sample we are in good company: an extremely high percentage
of government statistics such as the statistics of Household Expenditure are based on samples which, on the face of it, appear to be ludi-
crously small.

If you think back now to the questions we suggested that you
might ask about what our tables can tell us, you will realise that
most of them involve a more detailed study of one variable only –
the age of females living at home; the age of males living in flats.
When we do begin to analyse you will appreciate that this is usual.
The table presents several variables at once, but we extract just one
of them at a time for further examination. In a few cases we will use
two variables at once, when we are asking if there is a relationship
between them such that one affects the other or that both move in
sympathy. But in this foundation course we will never ask you to
get involved in the analysis of three or more variables at once – which
is indeed a complex matter.

The Frequency Distribution

The problems we have met so far are simple. We have had to deal
with only five age groups of students, and hence our tables are compact and easily presented. Let us now turn to far more complex data
collected from the community as a whole. Government departments
collect a mass of detailed information on which to base future policy
and one of the areas which they investigate closely is the weekly earnings of adults aged 21 and over who are in full-time employment
each April. In the United Kingdom it seems that earnings in the
recent past ranged from about £10 a week to £80 a week and more.
You can imagine how cumbersome a table we would have if we listed
every single wage level as we listed each age. Theoretically we might
have to list earnings at intervals of a penny, and so have a table of
over 70,000 lines – a ridiculous situation. Fortunately we can simplify
this. Do you think it really matters to us as statisticians whether a
worker is receiving £11.90 or £12.15 a week? We would probably
be content to say that they both receive about £12 a week. Extending
this further, we could argue that if we are looking at the pattern of
wages we would be satisfied to combine together all those who received between £10 and £12 per week, or even between £10 and £15
per week. Now this is precisely what the government does in many
of its published statistics. It does not say that 157 people receive
£10.21 a week, 362 receive £10.37 and so on, but merely that 100,000
people receive over £10 but less than £15 per week. Earnings are

stated in convenient bands or classes, and certainly we get a much better picture of earnings from this than we could ever get from a table listing 70,000 different levels of earnings.

To show you the effect of combining different values of the variable into a single class we reproduce below a table taken from the Annual Abstract of Statistics for the United Kingdom.

Distribution of Earnings of Adults in Full-time Employment

Earnings (£)		No. of Workers (millions)
10 and under	15	0.1
15	20	1.1
20	25	2.1
25	30	2.3
30	35	1.9
35	40	1.4
40	45	0.8
45	50	0.5
50	60	0.4
60	70	0.3
70	80	0.1
		11.0

Source: U.K. Annual Abstract of Statistics

A table such as this is known as a *frequency distribution* and is very common in statistical work. The variable we are considering, earnings, can take any value within the relevant group – it need not be an integer (or whole number). You might object of course that a worker cannot be paid £12.3762 a week, and in this sense it is not true to say that wages can take *any* value. On the other hand, subject to the minimum currency unit of Britain being £0.005 or a half penny, it is a fair statement to make. This type of data is known as *continuous* data. Other examples of continuous data are ages, petrol consumption per week, miles travelled by British Rail, and you can probably think of dozens of others yourself.

We might, on the other hand, be considering a data variable which can have only set values. If we are considering the number of seats in a cinema there can only be a certain number, 875 or 358, not 364.34 or 786.93. Similarly, the number of journeys made by bus, the population of a city, the number of students sitting an examination, must be integers. Data of this kind which can have only a limited number of values is known as *discrete* data. An example of a frequency distribution using discrete data would be a frequency distribution showing the value of orders received by a departmental store during the winter months.

Orders Received

Value of Order (£000)		Number of Orders Received
0 and under	5	20
5	10	51
10	15	139
15	20	116
20	25	31
25	30	14
30 and over		5
		376

Few people would prefer to be faced with a table thousands of items long when they can have instead a manageable frequency distribution like these. Yet, something is lost. Most distributions are constructed, as was our table of wages, using groups or classes which may in some cases be very wide indeed. We have sacrificed detail for the sake of presenting a picture which can be absorbed fairly simply. It might seem, of course, that the use of class intervals will prevent our using the frequency distribution as the basis for further work. Naturally it does create a problem, and to overcome it we have to make an assumption. Going back to our wage data, we do not know the exact wages of the 1.9 million people earning between £30 and £35 a week. To enable further work to be carried out we assume that all the 1.9 million workers earn a wage precisely at the centre of the class we are considering, i.e.

$$\frac{30 + 34.99}{2} = 32.495 \text{ or } £32.50$$

Since you will be using this mid-point of a class times without number in statistics, let us stress the importance of accuracy here. You must firstly consider whether the distribution is continuous or discrete. Consider a table showing cinema size determined by number of seats. One class may be cinemas ranging upwards from 200 seats but having less than 300 seats. Here the data is discrete; the minimum number of seats is 200 and the maximum is 299. The mid-point of this class is

$$\frac{200 + 299}{2} = 249.5$$

But if the same class, 200 and under 300, referred to continuous data, say the number of miles travelled by car, the minimum and maximum values of the group are 200 and 299.999. Hence the mid-point of the class becomes

$$\frac{200 + 299.999}{2} = 250$$

You will find, if you look at any published statistical tables, that in many cases no limits are given for the first and last classes. An income distribution showing annual income might begin merely with 'Under £660' and end up with the group 'Over £50,000'. Such open-ended classes create problems and we will give you a few hints on how to handle them later.

One of the most difficult problems you will have in building up a frequency distribution from raw data is to decide on what class intervals to use. Obviously, a great deal will depend on the data you have available, but a few general guidelines may help. Firstly, try not to choose class intervals which will reduce the number of groups below five or six. If you do the data will be so compressed that no pattern emerges. Naturally the rule is not infallible – E.E.C. have published statistics of farm sizes giving only three classes. These three, however, correspond to a generally accepted international definition of small, medium and large farms. Our advice is that you should not try to emulate E.E.C. Equally, at the other extreme, do not have too many classes. About fifteen or sixteen is the maximum. The problem here is not only the difficulty of absorbing lengthy tables, but also the fact that each group will have a very low, or in some cases, even a zero frequency. And this leads to another point. At the upper end of the table, if you stick slavishly to a single class interval you may well find that several consecutive groups have no members while a higher group has a frequency of two or three. In these circumstances you should sacrifice the idea of equal class widths and combine the several classes into a single wider class.

A good general guide is to take the difference between the minimum and maximum value of the variable (which we call the *range*), and divide by ten. This will give you the right class width (or thereabouts) for the majority of classes, provided that you realise that a class width of five, or ten, or fifty is better than one of four, or seven or sixty-two, and provided that you take care with the extreme values of the variable.

One final word of caution. Your table must be so constructed that each item of data falls clearly into a given class. Far too many tables have class intervals such as 10–20, 20–30, 30–40 and so on. But suppose an item is exactly 20 or exactly 30, which group do you place it in? If the distribution is continuous it is better to say, 10 and under 20, 20 and under 30; or possibly 10–19.9, 20–29.9: if the table is discrete you can give the exact limits, 10–19, 20–29 and so on.

Before we leave this brief description of the frequency distribution it would be an advantage if we show you how to tackle examination questions which ask you to construct a frequency distribution from a mass of figures. For this purpose we will look at a question recently set for the Scottish National Certificate in Business Studies examination.

EXAMPLE

The following is a record of the percentage marks gained by candidates in an examination:

65	57	57	55	20	54	52	49	58	52
86	39	50	48	83	71	66	54	51	27
30	44	34	78	36	63	67	55	40	56
63	75	55	15	96	51	54	52	53	42
50	25	85	27	75	40	37	46	42	86
16	45	12	79	50	46	46	59	57	50
56	74	50	68	52	61	40	38	57	31
35	93	54	26	67	62	51	52	54	61
93	84	28	66	62	57	45	43	47	33
45	25	77	80	91	67	53	55	51	36

Tabulate the marks in the form of a frequency distribution, grouping by suitable intervals.

Looking at these figures we find that there are 100 marks given ranging from 12 to 96. We have laid down a principle of aiming at somewhere in the region of 10 classes in our frequency distributions and it certainly seems that the best class width in this example would be 10 marks. If we were to use 5 mark intervals we would end up with some 18 classes which is too many; if we use 15 mark intervals we end up with only 6 classes which is too few.

We now have to find out how many of these marks fall within each class, and we recommend that you should do this in this way. Firstly list every class vertically; now take each candidate's marks in turn, and place a dash or a 1, or some other suitable mark against the class into which it falls. Having done this for every mark we can now take each class in turn and add up how many candidates fall into each class. Your rough working will appear something like this.

You will notice that for ease of counting we have divided our dashes into groups of five.

10 and under 20	111							3
20 and under 30	⫰⫰⫰ 11							7
30 and under 40	⫰⫰⫰ ⫰⫰⫰							10
40 and under 50	⫰⫰⫰ ⫰⫰⫰ ⫰⫰⫰ 1							16
50 and under 60	⫰⫰⫰ ⫰⫰⫰ ⫰⫰⫰ ⫰⫰⫰ ⫰⫰⫰ ⫰⫰⫰ 1111							34
60 and under 70	⫰⫰⫰ ⫰⫰⫰ 111							13
70 and under 80	⫰⫰⫰ 11							7
80 and under 90	⫰⫰⫰ 1							6
90 and under 100	1111							4
								100

Before you do anything else now, check that the total frequency (that is, the number of dashes) in your rough working is the same as the number of items given in the question. Having done this you are now ready to construct your frequency distribution. Remember, though, all the things that are necessary: the heading of the table, the column headings and the source, if it is available. Getting the table correct is only one part of the answer, although it is an important part. Your final frequency distribution will appear something like this:

Percentage Marks gained by Examination Candidates
...... Examination .... 19 ..

Marks Awarded		Number of Candidates
10 and under 20		3
20	30	7
30	40	10
40	50	16
50	60	34
60	70	13
70	80	7
80	90	6
90	100	4
		100

Source: Examiners' Report 19 .

We will spend a great deal of time later on examining frequency distributions such as this to see what further information it can give us. But whatever distribution we study it has one thing in common with all other frequency distributions – it tells us the magnitude of a variable at a given point in time. There are times however when we need to look at the way the magnitude of a variable changes over fairly long periods of time – for example, we might be considering the way in which the volume of British exports to Hong Kong has changed year by year since 1960. Such a table is called a *time series*, and later we will show you how to analyse the pattern that such a series shows. It follows from the nature of the time series that it consists of a series of time periods: years, quarters, months, or even days, with the value of the variable given against each time period. Thus, recently, Barclays Bank conducted a survey of the output of motor vehicles quarter by quarter in each of the Common Market countries. The figures for France represent a typical time series with the value of the variable given quarterly.

Output of Motor Vehicles – France
(monthly averages – thousands)

Year 1	1st quarter	150
	2nd quarter	165
	3rd quarter	104
	4th quarter	113
Year 2	1st quarter	173
	2nd quarter	180
	3rd quarter	124
	4th quarter	184

Source: Barclays Bank Briefing No. 12

In much statistical work a time series of this nature may extend over many years, but you will find it surprising what such a series can tell us.

What is Statistics?

If you have followed carefully the argument of this chapter it should now be apparent that statistics is concerned with the collection, simplification, presentation and analysis of information which can be expressed quantitatively. If you do your work well you will get an accurate picture of the data you are studying. There will still be some of you who may claim that Statistics can be made to prove anything, and to be fair, if the data is misused this may be true. If you ignore parts of the data, and conveniently forget to include calculations and information which is inconvenient or does not support your preconceived ideas, most things are possible. But if you follow your analysis through to the bitter end, using all the information which is available, keeping an open mind and interpreting only what your figures throw up, you cannot but be somewhere near the truth. In a world in which so much reliance is placed on the work of statisticians, where government policy often depends on their findings, and where industrial decisions involving millions of pounds are taken on the basis of statistical analysis, it is important to remember that whether you like what your figures show or not, your task is to interpret what the available data tells us as honestly as you are able.

EXERCISES TO CHAPTER 1

1.1   Describe in detail the steps in a statistical investigation; include in your description a brief summary of the various methods of presenting conclusions. Illustrate your answer with examples of statistical investigations that might be carried out in a business environment.   O.N.C.

1.2   (a) Prepare a summary of the tasks involved in conducting a statistical investigation.

(b) State three methods of presenting the results of such an investigation.   A.I.A.

1.3   What is the difference between primary and secondary data? Why is it important that statisticians should make a distinction in their use of these categories of data?   A.C.A.

1.4   *Average Weekly Earnings* of Administrative, Technical and Clerical Staff in the Public Sector and in Insurance and Banking*

MALES

October	National and Local Government including Education (Teachers) and National Health Service	Nationalised Industries	Insurance and Banking
	£	£	£
1966	26.69	26.25	26.63
1967	27.88	27.13	27.73
1968	29.65	28.95	29.11
1969	32.03	31.18	30.88
1970	36.00	35.83	34.63

* Including earnings of monthly-paid employees converted to a weekly basis.

Source: Department of Employment.

Write a short report in which you bring out the main features of the data given above. Include appropriate derived statistics and illustrate your report with a suitable diagram or graph.   O.N.C.

1.5   In 1951, 207 thousand persons received unemployment benefit, 906 thousand persons sickness benefit, 1437 thousand males retirement pensions, 2709 thousand females retirement pensions, 457 thousand received widows' benefit. 217 thousand persons received other National Insurance benefits. In 1971 the corresponding figures for unemployment benefit was 457 thousand, for sickness benefit was 969 thousand, for male retirement pensions 2611 thousand, for female retirement pension 5196 thousand, for widows' benefit 448 thousand, for other National Insurance benefits 387 thousand. (Source: *Social Trends* 1972.) Tabulate this data, calculate appropriate secondary statistics and include those statistics in your tabulation. Comment briefly on your tabulation.   O.N.C.

1.6   An inquiry into the population of a town at 1st April 1974 showed that the total was 297,500 persons of whom 60% were females and 40% males. 50,000 females were aged thirty and under, 60,000 were aged from 31 to 60 and the remainder were over 60 years of age. The corresponding figures for males were 60,000, 39,000 and 20,000. The average family size was 3.5. 75% of the female population lived in the northern area of the town and the remainder in the southern area. Of the males, 20% lived in the southern area. Tabulate the data given showing the analysis of each class of person into areas and age groups. Include actual figures and percentages. Show also the number of families for the town in total.   O.N.C.

1.7   The Saturn Finance Company wishes to study for several years (1971, 1972, 1973, 1974) the distribution of its loans according to size of loan (under £100, £100 and under £250, £250 and under £500, £500 and over) and the purpose of the loan (home improvement, car purchase, durable household goods purchase, other).

  (a) Prepare a table in which the data can be presented cross-classified by year, size of loan and purpose of loan. Include summary rows and columns for all classifications given.
  (b) Insert the following figures in the appropriate cells:
      (1) In 1972, 42.7 per cent of all loans made for home improvements were for £100 and under £250.
      (2) In 1971, 31.4 per cent of all loans made for purchase of cars were for £250 and under £500.
      (3) In 1974, 29.7 per cent of all loans were under £100.
                                                                    O.N.C.

1.8   While the population of the United Kingdom grew from 38.2 millions in 1901 to 55.8 m in 1972, the increase was not uniform between the regions. Seventy years ago, the south-east was the most populous region with 10.5 m. In mid-1972, its population was an estimated 17.3 m. Both the West Midlands and East Midlands have also grown quickly; the former from 3.0 m to 5.1 m and the latter from 2.1 m to 3.4 m. During the same period, East Anglia's population grew from 1.1 m to 1.7 m, whilst the south-west increased from 2.6 m to 3.8 m.

Despite its generally high birth rate, Northern Ireland's population, whilst growing from 1.2 m in 1901 to 1.5 m in mid-1972, fell as a proportion of total U.K. population. A similar trend is revealed in other economically depressed regions, and both Wales and Scotland, because of losses due to migration, have grown much more slowly than average, Wales from 2.0 m to 2.7 m and Scotland from 4.5 m to 5.2 m. (Source: *New Society and Social Trends*, Modified.) *Note:* not all regions have been included.

Arrange the above data in a suitable table, providing additional columns, in blank, appropriately headed, in which could be inserted derived statistics enabling comparisons to be made.   O.N.C.

1.9   The total number of employees of Core and Peel Ltd. at 31st December 1971 was 10,590, of which 6721 were men, 3106 women and the rest juniors. During 1971 108 men resigned and 74 men were engaged. The corresponding figures for women were 29 and 87 and for juniors 17 and 23. 1386 men, 976 women and 16 juniors were absent sometime during the year due to illness, 509 men, 876 women due to domestic circumstances and 366 men, 272 women and 3 juniors due to other causes. The average weekly wage rate paid to men was £32.00, to women £20.13 and to juniors £18.25. The company worked 50 weeks in the year. Tabulate these details showing suitable totals and sub-totals. Include also:

   (a) the numbers employed at 1st January 1971,
   (b) an estimate of the total annual wages paid per grade of labour
        and for the employees in total.   O.N.C.

1.10   (a) The records of the Family Expenditure Survey of 1971 show that in 4642 households interviewed in the survey, the head of the household was in employment. In 1236 households the occupation of the head of the household was 'professional'; 101 earned less than £30 per week; 153 earned £30 but under £40 per week; 194 earned £40 but under £50 per week; the remainder earned £50 or over per week. In 470 households the occupation of the head of the household was 'clerical'. 119 earned less than £30 per week; 129 earned £30 but under £40 per week; 90 earned £40 but under £50 per week; the remainder earned £50 or over per week. In the remaining households the occupation of the head of the household was 'manual'. 930 earned less than £30 per week; 814 earned £30 but under £40 per week; 638 earned £40 but under £50 per week; the remainder earned £50 or over per week. Tabulate this data.

(b) Using your table as an example list the basic rules which should be observed when tabulating statistical data. O.N.C.

1.11 In 1970, 44,000 houses were purchased with a local authority mortgage (total sum advanced = £154 m) and 32,000 with the help of insurance companies (£154 m advanced) whilst building societies lent £1986 m to 540,000 purchasers. These figures compare with 56,000 (£168 m), 34,000 (£124 m) and 504,000 (£1,477 m) in 1967, and 19,000, 40,000 and 460,000 houses purchased in 1969 with the help of loans of £69 m, £179 m, and £1556 m from local authorities, insurance companies and building societies respectively (abridged from *New Society*).

(a) Arrange the above data in concise tabular form.
(b) Prepare a table in blank, with suitable headings in which could be inserted derived statistics from the above figures which would facilitate the making of comparisons. O.N.C.

1.12 (a) List clearly the steps taken in forming a frequency distribution from a set of about 1000 observations giving reasons where necessary.

(b) Construct a frequency distribution using the following 100 observations:

Lives of electric light bulbs, in hours, to the last complete hour.

690	701	722	684	662	699	715	742	726	716
728	705	693	691	688	706	707	691	701	713
740	662	676	738	714	703	695	692	699	685
698	687	703	726	699	692	714	724	664	689
694	705	717	682	717	707	696	697	681	708
712	733	705	673	694	716	745	692	719	701
679	680	654	691	669	685	725	704	724	714
689	702	710	696	697	709	721	677	680	671
685	724	736	696	688	692	728	656	690	695
702	696	708	698	710	682	694	676	700	663

O.N.C.

1.13 The following is a record of the heights in centimetres of a sample of 85 servicemen:

169	179	183	186	166	181	177	173	167	193	176	183	162	170	186	174
188	165	168	174	170	176	186	177	185	175	179	166	190	182	182	180
194	177	184	175	168	181	180	172	178	192	175	189	180	175	183	191
172	188	180	176	185	178	179	173	165	170	178	181	181	189	187	191
179	196	179	182	171	169	171	184	198	182	175	190	187	176	164	187
167	185	177	184	178										

Tabulate the above data in the form of a frequency distribution, using as intervals 160 cm and under 165 cm, 165 cm and under 170 cm, 170 cm and under 175 cm, and so on. Illustrate the table by means of a histogram. O.N.C.

1.14   The lengths of telephone calls from a certain office were noted and the results are shown below giving the times in seconds.

141	43	203	104	82	63	24	84	41	86	47	43
100	53	139	147	137	186	214	106	150	109	170	172
194	124	175	177	162	129	128	219	40	105	48	65
105	154	154	35	149	54	104	109	119	74	140	104
168	127	191	30	109	88	104	207	38	164	182	120
166	53	145	29	112	143	49	199	130	52	109	77
142	75	146	105	125	112	40	126	67	49	90	140
132	118	134	133	159	123	161	112	157	104	92	112
151	98	156	117	156	190	122	135	116	96	163	116
186	155	106	153	69	105	136	106	131	118	94	121

Arrange these figures in a grouped frequency distribution using the intervals 0–19, 20–39, etc. O.N.C.

1.15   The data below are the times for completion, rounded to the nearest hour, of a sample of fifty houses.

911 902 900 867 897 915 945 940 917 883 874 880 932 919 899 903 872
901 874 925 886 928 917 906 925 913 898 888 912 896 921 908 933 903
920 885 901 892 931 902 893 887 928 907 916 895 907 864 891 890

Classify these data into a frequency distribution. O.N.C.

1.16   The following is a record of marks scored by candidates in an examination:

77	59	84	73	51	43	50	81	61	53	69
37	58	63	67	61	90	61	50	60	84	56
77	57	42	43	41	49	37	21	24	35	34
50	11	52	30	16	33	67	87	64	47	59
37	92	88	30	38	22	22	49	46	50	64
23	73	73	48	26	36	51	85	71	57	45

(a) Tabulate the marks in the form of a frequency distribution, grouping by suitable intervals.
(b) Construct a histogram from your frequency distribution.
(c) Explain the essential differences between a histogram and a bar chart. Scot. A.S.C.

1.17   A person's socio-economic status can be classified as either A, B, C1, C2, D or E in descending order. A random sample of 60 individuals taken in 1973 gave the following information on weekly earnings (£) in relation to socio-economic class:

45 (B)	20 (E)	16 (D)	61 (C2)	18 (E)
32 (C2)	22 (C2)	64 (C1)	62 (C1)	33 (D)
49 (D)	28 (C1)	60 (C2)	74 (B)	50 (C2)
49 (C2)	64 (B)	33 (D)	29 (C2)	21 (E)
24 (C1)	48 (C2)	23 (D)	27 (C2)	26 (E)
26 (D)	37 (C2)	85 (A)	18 (C1)	42 (C2)
43 (C1)	37 (C2)	67 (B)	19 (E)	22 (D)
17 (C2)	17 (C2)	19 (D)	23 (D)	50 (C2)
66 (C1)	74 (C1)	17 (E)	37 (C2)	55 (C1)
52 (C2)	37 (C2)	26 (D)	42 (C1)	40 (C2)
79 (B)	23 (E)	24 (D)	31 (D)	44 (C1)
15 (E)	18 (E)	40 (C2)	65 (C1)	17 (E)

Required:

(1) Compile a frequency distribution of earnings with intervals of a suitable width.

(2) By considering earnings to fall into one of three groups of less than £25, £25–45, and more than £45, compile a two-way table showing the frequencies in each earnings group/socio-economic class combination.

(3) Describe the main features of the data as observed from the table compiled in answer to (2) above.　　　　　　　　　A.C.A.

Chapter Two

Diagrams and Graphs

Watch any television education programme and almost certainly one of the first things to strike you will be the number of devices used to present information in a vivid and arresting fashion. Graphs, diagrams, blocks of wood, animated cartoons – all play their part in putting the subject over.

Of course, television is the ideal medium for this type of visual presentation, and one of the more important developments of the second half of the twentieth century may well turn out to be the impact of television as a means of imparting information. Yet, in all this, the television producer is doing little more than statisticians have already been doing for a considerable period of time. The scale is more grandiose; the impact is probably many times greater; but the techniques are the same.

It is, perhaps, a sad commentary on our ability and our patience that, when we are confronted by a large and complicated mass of figures, few people can grasp them in their entirety – no matter how well they are presented. Any series of numbers becomes less comprehensible as its length increases. Ten numbers can possibly be absorbed; twenty we may grasp with a great deal of effort; beyond this the list will leave hardly any impression on our minds at all. In fact, one of the main jobs of a statistician is to identify the main features of the information given by the figures, and to present them in such a way that they become readily and quickly intelligible. For this purpose, graphs and diagrams are invaluable. Naturally, some detailed information is lost, but what we gain in understanding far outweighs this loss.

We would like, at this point, to be able to say to you that we are going to give you a few simple rules which will enable you to master the technique of presenting diagrammatic information quickly and easily. It is not, however, as simple as that. The diagram you draw depends in part on the information you have, and what you are trying to stress. If you are trying to stress how much the government is spending annually you will produce a very different diagram from one which sets out to examine what the government spends the money on. It might also depend on the readers you are aiming at. A diagram suitable for the readers of a mass circulation daily newspaper will be very different from one in an economic journal; a diagram intended to extol the qualities of a particular brand of soap powder will be far removed from one designed to show the changing composition of agricultural output in the Common Market. Effective presentation is a question of flair and experience, and there is only one guideline – does the diagram present clearly and vividly the information it is designed to present?

We cannot pretend that the way in which we illustrate the presentation of particular information is the only way. You may, in fact, think that it is not the best way. What we will do is to indicate the weapons you have available. The rest is up to you!

1. *The Bar Chart*

One of the most common of all techniques for presenting data is the use of the bar chart, in which the length of the bar is proportional to the size of the items we are considering. Suppose we are considering the population of some E.E.C. countries; we could be presented with a table like this:

	Population (million)		Population (million)
France	50	Denmark	4.9
Benelux	10	Britain	56
Germany	61	Holland	12.9
Italy	54		

Now, shut your eyes, and without reference to the table state which country has the highest population, which the lowest, and where Britain comes in the league table. If you have played fair we are prepared to bet that a high proportion of you cannot answer all three questions correctly. Why? Simply because experience shows that people do not absorb lists of figures. A very different result would be obtained if we presented the same information in the form of a bar chart.

The immediate impression we get is of four giant members accompanied by a number of very small members; and it hits the eye that Britain is a giant, second only to Germany.

You will notice that the bar diagram has a heading, as should all diagrams. It is no use presenting information unless the reader knows what the information is. Note, too, that the source of the information

Millions

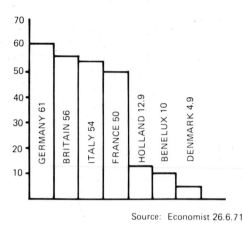

Population of E.E.C. countries 1969 (millions)

Diagram 2.1

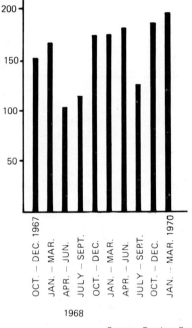

Population of motor vehicles – France (monthly average – thousands)

Diagram 2.2

is given as we are using secondary data. This enables the reader, if he is interested, to go back to the original figures and delve more deeply.

Here we were looking at one variable factor at a particular point in time, but we may equally use the bar diagram to show how the value of something, say the output of motor vehicles in France, has varied over time.

Here you will notice that the bars are separated – this is a matter of personal preference. It is probably neater, but many statisticians say that it is more difficult to compare the height of the bars. Looking at the diagram it is immediately apparent that production in three quarters was exceptionally low; in April–June of year 2 and in the July–September quarter in years 2 and 3. Further examination may show that in the July–September quarter production is low every year, possibly due to its being the holiday season, but the April–June quarter of year 1 is clearly exceptional and one is constrained to make a more detailed examination of what happened at that time.

The bar chart is a most versatile instrument and capable of adaptation to almost any data. Three further modifications will, we think, convince you of this versatility.

Often the data we are examining includes negative figures. Profits in one year, for example, might be converted into losses the next; the balance of payments may be in surplus or deficit. Such negative figures can be represented on the bar chart quite simply by extending the bar below the zero base line as in Diagram 2.3 on page 24.

Sometimes, of course, we may be less interested in an absolute total than we are in the way that total is made up. We may wish to find out how the final cost of production is made up, where sales revenue goes to, what the government does with the money it collects. Again the bar chart proves itself equal to the task, since we can always subdivide the bar as shown in Diagram 2.4 on page 24.

Such a bar chart is often called a compound or component bar chart, since it illustrates the components that go to make a total. Sometimes we may be more interested in expressing our information in the form of percentages. It may be important to our argument that tax on North Sea Oil is 54·4% of total selling price rather than that it is 6.8 dollars. There is nothing to stop us from constructing a component bar chart the length of which represents 100% subdivided into sections to show the percentage that each component item forms of the total. In the case of tax, then, the section of the bar representing tax paid would be just over one half the length of the bar.

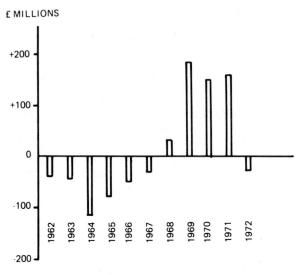

Source: Bank of England
           Quarterly June 1973

U.K. net invisible earnings from non-sterling areas

Diagram 2.3

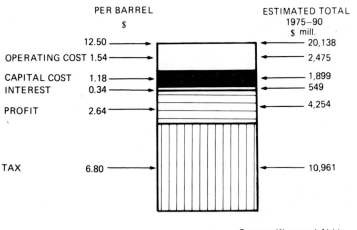

Source: Kitcat and Aitkin
           Report on North Sea Oil

Costs of North Sea oil

Diagram 2.4

Such a diagram, for obvious reasons, is called a percentage component bar chart.

As a final example of the use of the bar chart we will try to show how it can be used to derive information which is not immediately obvious. With Britain's entry into E.E.C. a burning question is the efficiency of European agriculture. But how can efficiency be measured? It is fair to say that if 30% of the total labour force is engaged in agriculture but the agrarian output is only 10% of the Gross National Product, that country's agriculture is inefficient compared with a country for which the figures are 10% and 12% respectively, and this will be the criterion we will use.

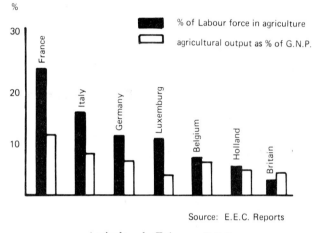

Source: E.E.C. Reports

Agricultural efficiency – E.E.C.

Diagram 2.5

We think you will agree that, using our criterion of efficiency, of the seven countries shown, only three – Holland, Belgium and Britain – can be said to be efficient producers in the agricultural sector, and this may well be a factor in the problems facing the common agricultural policy of the E.E.C.

2. *The Pie (or Circular) Diagram*

The circular, or pie diagram is a device beloved of those who present statistical data for the general public. It is a rare report, and a still rarer copy of the *Economist* magazine which does not contain several such diagrams. In fact, we firmly believe that the extent to which this technique is used grossly exaggerates its utility.

This diagram has only one real use – to show the relative size of the component parts of a total. A complete circle represents the total, and this circle is divided into segments the size of which represents the relative importance of each constituent of the total. Thus, if we were trying to show the nature of road accidents in a particular area, we might find that of 300 accidents occurring last year, 57 involved motor-cycles. We now have to mark off a segment of the circle corresponding in size to the proportion of accidents involving motor-cycles, that is, 57/300 or 19/100. Since there are 360 degrees in a circle the appropriate segment must subtend an angle of $19/100 \times 360$ degrees at the centre, i.e. an angle of 68.4 degrees. Our complete pie diagram will appear something like this:

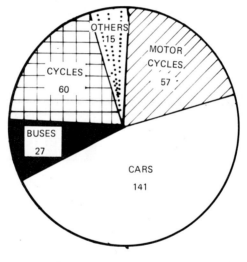

Source: Figures are illustrative

Analysis of road accidents 1975

Diagram 2.6

Even with this single simple example you should find it easy to spot the weaknesses of the pie diagram:

(a) It involves cumbersome calculations.
(b) It is more difficult to compare segments of a circle in a pie diagram than to compare heights in a bar diagram.

(c) It gives no information as to absolute magnitude unless figures are inserted in each segment, whereas the bar diagram is scaled against a single axis.

Our own advice is not to use this method of presentation unless it is forced upon you.

3. *Plotting the Frequency Distribution – the Histogram*

You will remember that the frequency distribution examines the frequency of occurrence of different values of a variable at a given point in time, and that the values of the variable are combined together into classes of a predetermined size. It is this type of distribution that the histogram presents. The histogram is so similar to a bar chart that students often assume that they are one and the same thing. There is, however, a major difference between them. In a bar chart we are interested in only one factor, say output, the magnitude of which can be represented by the height of a bar. It does not matter how wide the bar is; we look only at the height. In a histogram, however, we are interested in two factors – the width of the classes represented by the width of the bar, and the frequency with which items within each class are found, represented by the height of the bar. In these circumstances it is the area of the bar which really interests us. Now, admittedly, in many of the cases you will deal with this distinction makes little difference. The class intervals are the same throughout the frequency distribution, so the width of the bars is the same and the relative heights of the bars will indicate directly the relative frequencies. Often, however, class intervals at the top and bottom of the distribution are left 'open', or are different from the class intervals in the main body of the table.

Suppose, for example, that the last group is twice as wide as every other class in the distribution. We will have to double the width of the bar to represent this doubling of the class interval. Remember though, it is the area of the bar that we are interested in, and so, having doubled the width, we will have to halve the height. This is not as confusing as most students believe if you think about what we are doing. In doubling the class intervals we are combining into one wider group items that belong to two of the narrower groups. To be consistent, then, we have to make an arbitrary assumption that the frequency of the wider class is divided equally between each of the narrower classes. Suppose that throughout our table the width of the class is £5, but that the width of the last class is increased to £10. It appears as '£80 and under £90'. In this class appear items which we would have expected to appear in the two classes '£80 and under £85' and '£85 and under £90'. Doubling the width of the bar indicates that we are combining these two classes into one, and to illustrate the frequency we assume that each of these two 'narrow' classes contains half the number of items in the 'wider' class. That is, we halve the height of the wider bar. Be careful, however, not to draw a line down the middle of the wider bar to try to indicate this. We are only making an assumption – if you do draw such a line you are saying that if we plotted the two 'narrow' groups separately each would have exactly the same frequency, and this we cannot know.

Bearing this in mind, let us plot the histogram of the frequency distribution of weekly earnings that we obtained in the last chapter.

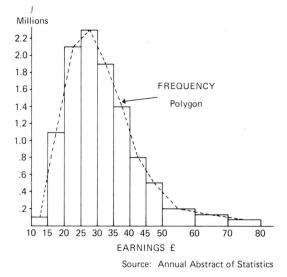

Source: Annual Abstract of Statistics

Weekly earnings of full-time adults 1971

Diagram 2.7

Note especially the last three groups where the class interval rises from £5 to £10 and the height of the bars is halved.

A similar picture of the distribution is given by the frequency polygon which converts the histogram into a simple graph. Notice that we form the graph by joining the mid-points of the top of the bars. You will find that this convention of using the central value of the group to represent the group as a whole is a very common technique in statistical analysis. Here we are joining the mid-points by straight lines to give us the polygon, but sometimes you will be asked to construct a frequency curve and will join the mid-points of the top of the bars by a smooth curve instead of straight lines. Frequency curves of this type are very common when we wish to illustrate particular types of frequency distribution, and one such distribution, the 'Normal Distribution', you will hear a great deal about in later chapters.

Finally, it is often useful to present the distribution in a different way altogether. Instead of tabulating the frequency of each class we would like to know the frequency with which the variable falls *below* a particular value. The Chancellor who wishes to help the more poorly paid in society might well propose to introduce a tax exemption bill applying to all those earning less than £35 a week. Naturally, he will wish to know firstly how many people this bill will affect, and, secondly, how many more wage earners than before will now be free of the burden of income tax.

It is, of course, simple to add up the frequencies of the first five classes of our frequency distribution, but there is more than this. For many purposes it is easier to read off directly the frequency we require, and there are measures we will introduce you to in later chapters which are far, far easier to obtain graphically than to calculate.

To obtain information of this nature the statistician has devised the Ogive or Cumulative Frequency graph. This diagram plots, on the horizontal axis, certain values of the variable, usually the upper value of each group; on the vertical axis it shows the frequency of the items with a value less than this. Thus, in constructing the ogive, we first construct a cumulative frequency table from our frequency distribution in this way:

Wage (£)	Cumulative Frequency (millions)
Under 15	0.1
20	1.2 (i.e. 0.1 + 1.1)
25	3.3 (i.e. 0.1 + 1.1 + 2.1)
30	5.6
and so on until we reach the final group	
Under 80	11.0

It is this table that we plot as the ogive, see Diagram 2.8 on page 30.

The first thing you will notice is that we have joined the points on the ogive by straight lines rather than the smooth curve that you are probably more used to. The reason for this is that we do not know how the items in any group are scattered between the upper

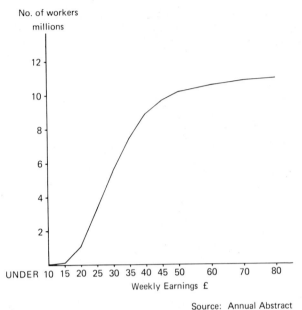

No. of workers
millions

Source: Annual Abstract

Earnings of full-time adults April 1971

Diagram 2.8

and lower limits; so we make the only reasonable assumption that we can – that the items in any group are distributed evenly across the group. It may be a false assumption. We may find, in the group £25 and under £30, that all the 2.3 million members get a wage of £29.50; but it is not likely. So long as there is a reasonable number of members within the group, we are fairly safe in assuming an even distribution. We know that it will not materially affect our results.

4. *Plotting the Time Series*

You will remember from the last chapter that much data is given in the form of a time series, in which we take a variable and show how its magnitude has varied over a period of time. We have obtained from the United Kingdom Annual Abstract of Statistics the following table showing how consumer expenditure at constant prices varied during the period of time when prices in the United Kingdom were rising at an alarming rate, 1964 to 1974.

Consumer Expenditure at Constant Prices
(£ million)

1964	28330	1970	31472
1965	28760	1971	32397
1966	29301	1972	34318
1967	29869	1973	35962
1968	30598	1974	35741
1969	30715		

Source: Annual Abstract of Statistics

Perhaps you will agree that these figures, involving thousands of millions of pounds, mean very little; if we are honest probably very few of you even read the figures in detail.

But suppose we now draw a graph of these figures!

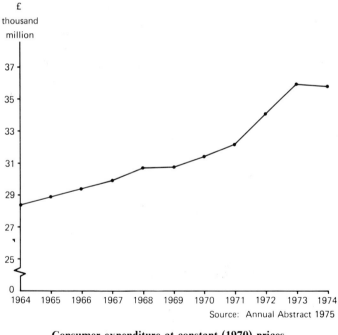

Source: Annual Abstract 1975

Consumer expenditure at constant (1970) prices

Diagram 2.9

We are sure that even a quick glance at this graph will leave you with a permanent impression of the way in which consumer expenditure has been rising – slowly and steadily from 1964 to 1970, then much more rapidly, reaching a peak in 1973. Since we have plotted expenditure at constant prices, this represents a rising consumpton of goods, i.e. a rising standard of living (it may of course be at the expense of past saving).

You will have noticed the break in the graph on the vertical axis and the sudden jump from 0 to 25. This is a device used by statisticians when every figure is high and we do not want to crush our graph into a small space at the top of the graph paper. Remember too that we could have left you with a very different impression of the behaviour of consumer expenditure by adjusting the scales on the axis. Try it for yourself by doubling the scale on the vertical axis and halving the horizontal scale; or halving the vertical scale and doubling the horizontal. We have altered the scales in diagrams 2.10 and 2.11. After looking at these three graphs of consumer expenditure can you really draw any conclusions as to the rate at which consumer expenditure has been rising? We know it has gone up – and that is about all.

Now, this is all very well, but our friends, the economists, will immediately want to know what we have been spending more on. Are we buying more food and clothes, buying more houses, or wasting our resources in riotous living? For their sakes, and for yours, we add below the way in which consumption of four sub-categories of our expenditure have been behaving in the same period. Whenever we wish to compare the way in which several variables have been behaving over a period of time, it is perfectly permissible to draw as many as four or five time series on the same axes, as long as we clearly distinguish the different graphs and the diagram is not too difficult to interpret.

	Expenditure on			
	Food	Drink	Clothing	Housing
		(£ thousand million)		
1964	6080	1866	2366	3481
1965	6081	1849	2426	3597
1966	6170	1922	2425	3695
1967	6228	2001	2450	3836
1968	6260	2108	2568	3973
1969	6264	2149	2596	4106
1970	6365	2296	2693	4181
1971	6362	2463	2726	4287
1972	6320	2641	2910	4377
1973	6388	2988	3060	4483
1974	6418	3081	3039	4460

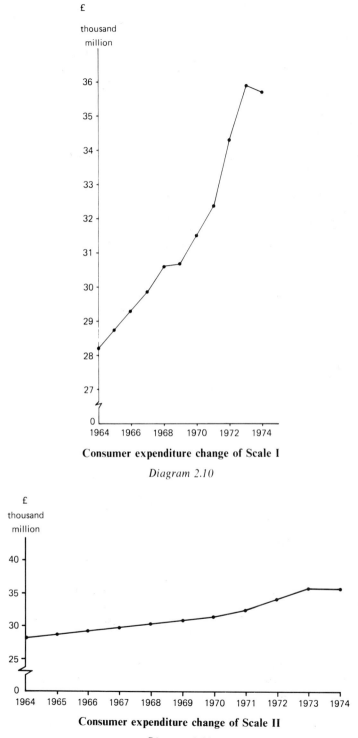

Consumer expenditure change of Scale I

Diagram 2.10

Consumer expenditure change of Scale II

Diagram 2.11

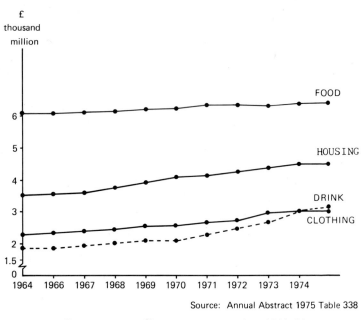

Source: Annual Abstract 1975 Table 338

Consumer expenditure at constant prices 1964–74

Diagram 2.12

You can see from the graphs we have drawn how the pattern of expenditure is changing. Although total consumption was rising fairly rapidly over this period, expenditure on food seems to have risen very slowly indeed – the slope of the graph is almost non-existent. Far different is the case of drink. Particularly from 1969 expenditure on drink rose at an alarming rate. Remember that this expenditure is listed at constant (1970) prices, so the rise of the graph represents increasing real consumption. Economists and sociologists would find this an interesting comment on human behaviour, and, in looking at this diagram, use your knowledge of other subjects to interpret what has been happening.

Do you remember when we discussed the bar chart we showed how it could be used to illustrate the constituents of a given total? Now, there are times when we want to illustrate how these constituents have varied over time. It may be, for example, that over the course of years road accidents involving bicycles have been forming a smaller and smaller part of total road accidents, while accidents involving motor-cars have been gradually forming an increasing proportion of total accidents. There is nothing to stop us from drawing three or four different time series, one for each type of vehicle showing the number of accidents involving that type of vehicle. We could even draw a number of graphs showing the percentage of accidents involving each type of vehicle, and we have no doubt that the diagrams would bring out the changing pattern. For this type of analysis it is far better to use a special type of diagram, the *Strata Graph*, or, if you are dealing in percentages, the *Percentage Strata Graph*. We must, however, keep the number of constituents reasonably few since otherwise the diagram may become difficult to interpret. The great advantage of this type of presentation is, as you will see, that the lines showing the magnitude of each constituent can never cross. Diagram 2.13 is a typical strata graph, showing the constitution of road accidents over a period of time in a large city. In order to stress the points that we would like to bring out, the figures are purely imaginary, so do not think that your own town is abnormal if the pattern of accidents is different from the one we have represented.

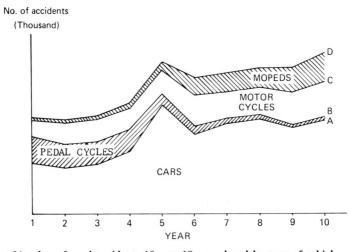

Number of road accidents 19... to 19... analysed by type of vehicle

Diagram 2.13

The principle of the strata graph is that our totals are successively cumulated. Thus the height of line A represents the number of accidents involving motor-cars each year. When we consider those accidents involving bicycles we add together for each year those accidents involving motor-cars and those involving bicycles to produce line B, the height of which for any year tells us the number of accidents involving (motor-cars + bicycles). In the same way line C is the graph of the number of accidents involving (motor-cars + bicycles + motor-cycles). Finally when we add to these figures those accidents involving mopeds, we arrive at line D, which is the total number of accidents for all vehicles. You will have realised already that the distance between each line represents those accidents involving a particular vehicle. Thus the gap between A and B shows us accidents involving bicycles and the gap between B and C those involving motor-cycles. It is, of course, desirable to distinguish each type of vehicle by distinctive shading to give the diagram clarity, but we think you will agree that such a diagram is relatively easy to interpret. Even a cursory glance tells us that the total number of road accidents has been on the increase, but within this total three distinct trends are apparent. Bicycle accidents, which were quite numerous in the early years, have dwindled away and are now very few: conversely, moped accidents, which were very few in the early years, probably because there were few moped owners, are now becoming quite an important constituent of total accidents: car accidents have increased, and although it is difficult to judge, probably remain much the same proportion of an increased total. Motor-cycle accidents, it is apparent, have remained fairly constant over the years.

If we wish to draw a percentage strata graph, it is just as easy, although the initial calculations, converting our figures into percentages, are very cumbersome. Can you see that the line D in such a graph would be a horizontal straight line at 100%?

5. *Logarithmic Graphs*

As we have seen, one of the problems with ordinary graphs is that they tend to give a false impression of the way in which figures are changing. Using a vertical scale of 1 inch = 100 units, a change from 100 to 200 units is represented by the same upward movement as a change from 1000 to 1100 units, even though it is 100% change as compared with a 10% change. The slope of the graph is the same – yet the rate of change is very different. Now, in most cases this does not matter. We may be interested only in the swings of the absolute figures; or the range of the figures may be such that the difference in the rates of change is negligible. If this is the case, we can get all we need from the graphs we have drawn. However, if we are considering inflation, for example, it is the rate at which prices are rising which is important, rather than the actual price increases.

Fortunately, if we plot the logarithms of our figures rather than the figures themselves, we can produce a graph the slope of which represents the real rate of change. Why should this be so?

Consider a case in which prices are rising by 20% a year. We can easily construct a table to show what happens to prices.

Period	Price	Log of Price	Difference of Logs
1	100	2.0000	
2	120	2.0792	0.0792
3	144	2.1584	0.0792
4	172.8	2.2375	0.0792
5	207.36	2.3167	0.0792

Don't you find it rather frightening that an inflation rate less than that of Britain in the 1970's will more than double prices in five years?

As you can see, the log of each price rises by 0.0792 irrespective of the magnitude of the price change, and hence we obtain a straight-line graph if we plot the logarithms. This of course tells us that the rate of change of prices is constant. It does not tell us what the rate of change is, but merely enables us to compare rates of change over time.

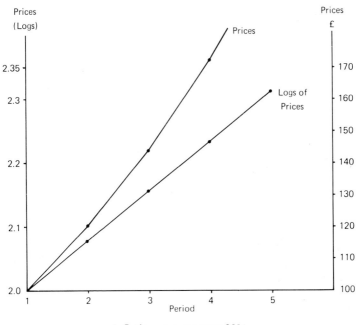

Inflation at a constant 20%

Diagram 2.14

Strictly such a graph is known as a *semi-logarithmic* graph, as we plot logarithms only on the vertical axis. On the horizontal axis we do not plot the logarithms of the time periods. Later in this book, however, you will meet examples of graphs in which we plot logarithms along both axes, to give us a fully logarithmic graph.

As you can see from the diagram, if we plot the prices themselves the slope of the curve gets steeper and the fact that the rate of change is the same is completely hidden.

Often a logarithmic graph can be used also when the figures with which we are concerned range so widely that it is inconvenient to use a normal graph. Such a situation would occur if we tried to plot German price movements during the great inflation of the 1920's when prices were increasing by hundreds of times each month.

Now, although few students find difficulty in mastering the principles involved in the construction of semi-logarithmic graphs, this is such a common question in all statistics examinations at this level that we would strongly recommend you to work through the following example with us, making sure that you understand each step. It was set at a recent Ordinary National Certificate examination, though it might well have appeared in any of the many first-year professional examinations.

EXAMPLE

Sales of Two Companies

Sales (£000)

Year	Company A	Company B
1961	2240	980
1962	2460	1082
1963	2680	1205
1964	2915	1289
1965	3136	1382
1966	3362	1476
1967	3590	1580
1968	3821	1687
1969	4049	1787
1970	4280	1891

(a) Plot the time series on (i) an arithmetic scale graph,
                             (ii) a semi-logarithmic graph.
(b) Interpret the results.

Well, the first part of this question will cause you no difficulty at all. As you well know, an arithmetic scale graph is a normal graph, in which we let a given distance (usually a centimetre) represent a given change in the magnitude of the variable on both the horizontal and the vertical axes. We then plot the figures given in the question according to the scale we have used. Thus, in diagram 2.14a, on the horizontal axis we have let two centimetres represent one year, while on the vertical axis it represents £500,000 sales. We have plotted the graphs showing the variation in the sales of the two companies in the normal way.

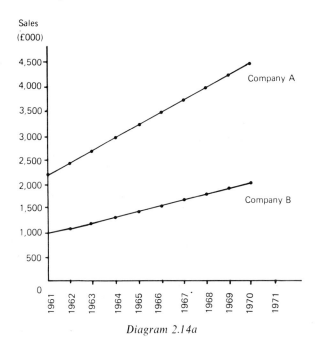

Diagram 2.14a

When we now come to consider the semi-logarithmic graphs, we have to be careful. Some examining boards will issue you only with the normal graph paper we have used so far; others will issue you with graph paper already designed for semi-logarithmic use. Let us suppose firstly that you have been issued only with the normal arithmetic scale graph paper. In this case, as you know, we will plot the years along the horizontal axis as normally, but along the vertical axis you will have to plot the logarithms of the sales figure for each year. Our first step then must be to obtain these logarithms. We strongly advise you to do this as a part of the answer and not on a piece of scrap paper. It is easy to make a mistake, and if you do examiners are far more inclined to be generous if they can trace easily where the mistake has arisen. So we proceed as follows:

	Company A		Company B	
Year	Sales	Log	Sales	Log
1961	2240	3.3502	980	2.9912
1962	2460	3.3909	1082	3.0342
1963	2680	3.4281	1205	3.0810
1964	2915	3.4646	1289	3.1103
1965	3136	3.4964	1382	3.1405
1966	3362	3.5266	1476	3.1691
1967	3590	3.5551	1580	3.1987
1968	3821	3.5822	1687	3.2271
1969	4049	3.6073	1787	3.2521
1970	4280	3.6314	1891	3.2767

Although this seems to be a cumbersome process, almost any of the small pocket calculators you are normally allowed to use will give you the logarithms you require in a matter of seconds. All you have to do now is to scale the vertical axis to accommodate the logarithms you have obtained, and draw the graphs. We have done this in diagram 2.14b, but you will notice that we have also inserted on the vertical axis on the right some of the absolute values of the sales. While modern management is well aware of the use of semi-logarithmic graphs they also wish to be able to see at a glance the value of the sales turnover without having to refer to a book of log tables.

Even a quick glance at diagrams 2.14a and 2.14b brings out the advantages of the semi-logarithmic graph. The graphs of the sales figures on arithmetic scale imply that the two companies increased their sales at a steady rate throughout the whole period. But as you are aware, such graphs show absolute changes, not *rates* of change, and equal absolute increases imply a declining *rate* of increase. This is well brought out in the semi-logarithmic graphs, where a close look at company A shows a marked tendency of the rate of change to fall.

More important, the two graphs give completely different impressions of the relative performance of the two companies. The arithmetic scale graph implies that company A is expanding more rapidly than company B because the slope of the graph of the former's sales is steeper. But again the use of absolute figures is deceptive. The semi-logarithmic graphs show that company B's performance is at least as good as that of company A in that it is expanding at the same

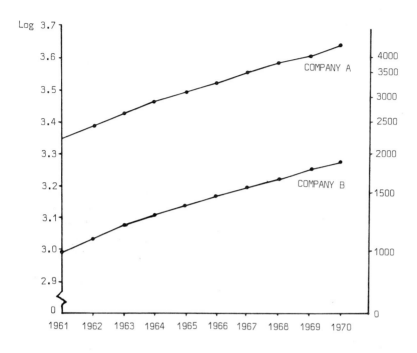

Diagram 2.14b

rate, while on a very close examination we find that the rate of growth over the whole period is marginally better than that of company A, and from 1964 onwards growth certainly seems to be steadier and more sustained than that of company A. Thus, we may come to the conclusion that, although both companies have grown substantially in the period, company B, although smaller, appears to have done marginally the better.

Now this is all very well, but suppose you are issued with semi-logarithmic graph paper already ruled. The great advantage of this paper is that you can insert the absolute figures of sales on the graph without first having to look up the logarithms. Probably, however, few of you have had the opportunity yet of seeing semi-logarithmic graph paper, so let us explain the principles on which it is ruled. One axis is ruled normally, in centimetres and millimetres (after all, it is *semi*-logarithmic). But the other axis is quite differently ruled. It is drawn on the basis that equal distances represent equal percentage changes rather than equal absolute changes. Thus, if one centimetre represents a change from 10 to 100 (an increase of 10 times), the next centimetre will represent a change from 100 to 1000 (also an increase of 10 times).

There is more to it than this, however. No-one would expect you to calculate the percentage change for each figure that you have to plot on the graph. We have merely stated the obvious – that one axis of the semi-logarithmic graph paper is scaled logarithmically. Let us take it further. If we take the first centimetre on the vertical scale to represent an increase of 1 unit (from 1 to 2), the next centimetre would represent an increase from 2 to 4. We could have obtained exactly the same effect by plotting logarithms. The log of 1 is 0, so you will realise that the logarithmic graph can range upwards only from an absolute value of 1 (not 0 as can the arithmetic scale graph). Now the logarithm of 2 is 0.30103, and the logarithm of 4 is 0.60206. Similarly the logarithm of 8 is 0.90309. Can you see that, in allowing each centimetre to represent the same proportional increase in the absolute figures, we are scaling according to the logarithms of the numbers? In this case one centimetre represents an increase in the logarithm of .30103; and when we add .30103 to a logarithm, we are in fact multiplying the previous number by two. So each successive centimetre represents an increasing change in the absolute figures – 2, 4, 8, 16 and so on.

But the logarithmic scale is not drawn in centimetres as is the arithmetic axis. Suppose once again that we take the first vertical division on the graph paper to be one centimetre long (whether it is or not depends on the graph paper with which you are issued). We can let this centimetre represent any absolute magnitude that we wish. Let us again assume that it represents an increase from 1 to 2. The next main division on our graph paper will also represent an absolute increase of one unit, from 2 to 3, but this division will not be a centimetre deep. We have already said that the second centimetre represents an increase in absolute values from 2 to 4, so you would naturally expect the second division representing an increase from 2 to 3 to be less than a centimetre deep. It will in fact be about .585 centimetres deep only. Thus each successive unit increase on the logarithmic axis will entail a smaller and smaller vertical rise, and the vertical scaling will look something like the diagram at top of page 43.

In practice, of course, the graph paper you will be given will have each main division subdivided as normal graph paper is into ten subsections to enable you to plot the intermediate figures. If you have not seen such graph paper before, we strongly recommend that you immediately study carefully diagram 2.14c, where we have drawn the two graphs we are concerned with on semi-logarithmic paper, and, most important, obtain a stock of such paper of your own and prac-

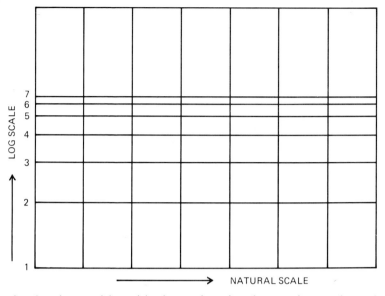

tice drawing semi-logarithmic graphs using the exercises at the end
of this chapter.

6. *The Lorenz Curve*

If you look at statistics of income one of the first things that strikes
you is the inequality in the distribution of incomes in most countries.
Not only is the range of incomes wide, from under £1000 a year to
£20,000 a year and more in the United Kingdom, but we also find
that a very small percentage of the income recipients at the top of
the scale receive a disproportionately large share of total income.
Equally, the very large percentage of low income earners receive in
total a very small percentage of the total income. You must, at some
time in your life, have met such statements as 'the top 5% of income
recipients receive over 70% of total income'.

Now any economist will tell you that one purpose of our taxation
system, or any taxation system which is progressive, is to reduce the
inequality of incomes, and naturally we would all like to know how
far the system is succeeding in this objective. Statisticians have derived a diagram, the Lorenz curve, which enables us to show graphically the extent of inequality, not only of incomes, but also of many
other things.

In this diagram, considering income distribution, we measure on

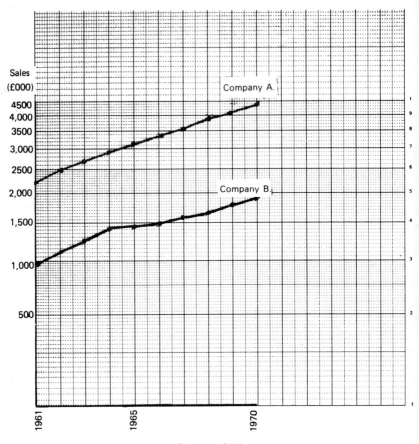

Diagram 2.14c

the horizontal axis the percentage of population, and on the vertical axis the percentage of income, see diagram on page 45.

Now, obviously, if incomes are distributed equally, the bottom 10% of income earners will receive 10% of total income, the bottom 20% of income earners will receive 20% of total income and so on. The graph representing such a distribution of income will be the straight line OR passing through the origin and at 45 degrees (provided, that is, that the horizontal and vertical scales are the same), and any divergence from this line will indicate some degree of inequality. The point A for example would be interpreted as 'the bottom $x\%$ of income earners receive $y\%$ of total income', and, since x is

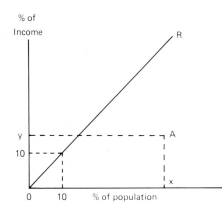

greater than *y*, would be derived from a situation such as 'the bottom 65% of income earners receive only 32% of total incomes'.

Let us illustrate the use of Lorenz curves by applying them to the following income statistics of the United Kingdom.

Income Class	No. of Incomes		Pre-tax Income		Post-tax Income	
£	(000)	%	£m	%	£m	%
50–249	5070	18.6	991	4.9	990	5.5
250–499	6570	24.2	2590	12.8	2486	13.8
500–749	6155	22.6	4143	20.5	3844	21.4
750–999	4830	17.8	4580	22.6	4168	23.2
1000–1999	4145	15.2	5849	28.9	5113	28.5
2000–3999	353	1.3	1305	6.4	940	5.2
4000–5999	59	0.2	469	2.3	281	1.6
6000 and over	18	0.1	330	1.6	129	0.8
	27200		20257		17951	

Source: National Income and Expenditure

The first step in the construction of our diagram is to calculate the percentages appropriate to each group and each column. Thus the 5,070,000 individuals in the income class £50–£249 comprise 18.6% of all income recipients and they received 4.9% of all pre-tax income. We have inserted the relevant percentages in the body of the table, although in an examination you would have to calculate each of them from the original figures given to you.

The next step is to cumulate the percentages you have calculated in this way:

Income Earners (%)		Pre-tax Income (%)	Post-tax Income (%)
18.6	receive	4.9	5.5
42.8		17.7	19.3
65.4		38.2	40.7
83.2		60.8	63.9
98.4		89.7	92.4
99.7		96.1	97.6
99.9		98.4	99.2
100.0		100.0	100.0

It is now easy to draw the Lorenz curves relating to pre-tax and post-tax income:

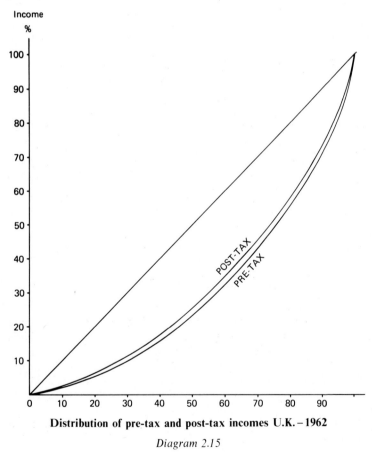

Distribution of pre-tax and post-tax incomes U.K. – 1962

Diagram 2.15

Now any divergence from our straight line of equal distribution of income indicates that there is inequality in the distribution of incomes, and the further the Lorenz curve is from this line of reference, the greater is the degree of inequality. It is worth noting that if the Lorenz curve is below the straight line the inequality is in favour of the upper income groups in that a high percentage of low income earners receive a small percentage of income. If, on the other hand, the Lorenz curve is above the straight line, it implies that a given percentage of the bottom income earners receive a higher percentage of total income; the inequality, that is, works in favour of the poor.

Looking at our diagram, it is apparent that at this time there was a great deal of inequality in the income structure of the United Kingdom. Although the taxation system did reduce it, the reduction seems to have been minimal. We have not, however, asked what was done with the tax revenue. Much of it was returned to the lower income groups in the form of social benefits – family allowances, supplementary benefits, subsidised housing and so on. It may well be that when we allow for this transfer of income, the effects of taxation would appear very different.

7. *The Z Chart*

A diagram which is often used in industry and commerce, although it seems to be less popular among statisticians, is the Z Chart, so called because the completed diagram takes the form of the letter Z. This is merely a device to enable management to show concisely three different aspects of a time series plotted on the one graph. On the bottom bar of the Z we plot the time series of monthly (or weekly)

	Output – ABC Limited		Cumulative Total	Moving Annual Total
	Last Year	Current Year		
January	9	11	11	146
February	8	14	25	152
March	9	12	37	155
April	13	15	52	157
May	14	16	68	159
June	18	19	87	160
July	16	18	105	162
August	15	14	119	161
September	12	14	133	163
October	10	13	146	166
November	9	11	157	168
December	11	15	172	172

sales, or output, or whatever variable we are considering. On the diagonal bar of the Z we plot the cumulative total to date, that is, the total sales or output we have achieved since the beginning of the year. Finally as the top bar of the Z we plot the total sales achieved in the last year: the first or January figure is the total sales achieved during the period 1st February last to 31st January this year; the February figure is the total from last March until the end of February this year, and so on.

We will illustrate by plotting the figures of output for a firm ABC Ltd. The figures are simplified to enable you to follow the calculations more easily. Obviously, although we are plotting figures for the current

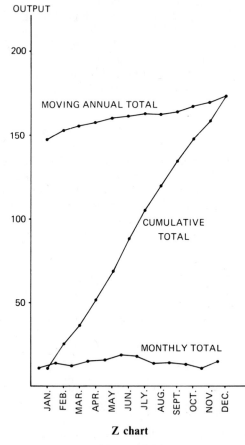

Z chart

Diagram 2.16

year only, if we are to obtain a running total of sales over the last twelve months we will need the figures for two years.

If you look carefully at the graph, the first thing that you will notice is that while the moving annual total and the cumulative total figures are plotted on the vertical lines representing each month, the monthly total is plotted in the middle of each month. The reason for this is easy to see. The monthly figures show performance during the whole of the month, and, as you are aware, the way to show this is by plotting points in the middle of the period. The other totals, however, represent performance over a period of time ending on a specific date, and are intended to show achievement up to and including that date. Thus these figures are more correctly plotted at the end of the months. You will see too what a vast amount of information is given by this simple diagram. The cumulative total tells us performance to date, and it is a simple matter to superimpose on the diagram a line showing planned or expected performance. Thus we can see at a glance whether our plans are being realised or whether we are falling behind. The moving annual total enables us to compare performance this year with that at a comparable time last year. If this chart is rising it means that figures in that month are higher than they were in the same month last year. Thus we have the means of making a direct comparison with last year. Finally the monthly total enables us to keep a direct check on what is happening now; and if we are falling behind our plan we can usually spot a month with low figures which has caused this and so discover why. Is it any wonder, with this wealth of information to be had, that the Z chart is so popular in industry?

8. *The Scatter Diagram*

The final diagram we will introduce you to is not a graph at all. It looks at first glance rather like a series of dots placed haphazardly on a sheet of graph paper. But it is anything but haphazard as we will see. The basic aim underlying the scatter diagram is to try to ascertain if there is a relationship between two factors, such that when one is high the other is high, when one is low the other is low. Or perhaps the relationship is inverse – when one variable is low, the other is high and vice versa. Suppose we were examining the relationship between the level of employment and the level of industrial investment, see diagrams on next page.

Firstly we will have figures over a considerable period of time giving us the level of industrial investment and the percentage employment rate associated with that level of investment. Let us just

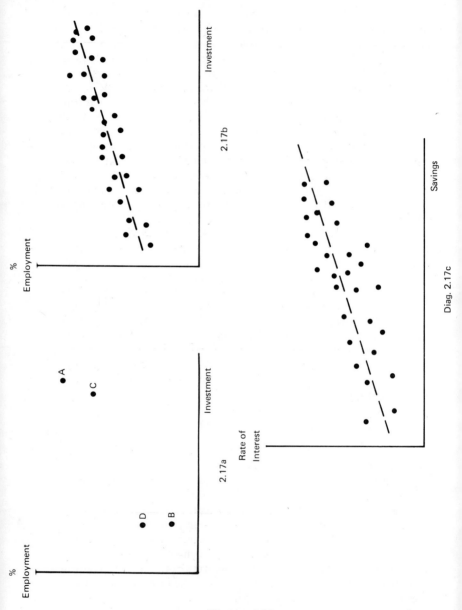

Diagram 2.17

take four of those pairs of figures. The first pair tells us that the level of investment is high and associated with it was a high level of employment. This position is indicated by point A in diagram 2.17a. Another pair of figures tells us that when investment was slightly lower employment was considerably lower – point C. Still a third pair of figures tells us that at a time when investment was low employment was also low. This is indicated by point B. If we examine the last figures we find that although investment was the same as before, the level of employment was, in fact, very much higher – point D. If we plot sufficient pairs of figures we may well get a series of crosses such as those on diagram 2.17b which show a pattern. Generally the higher the level of investment the higher the level of employment, and this we have indicated by inserting freehand a dotted line rising upwards from left to right. The same sort of pattern is seen when we examine savings and the rate of interest in diagram 2.17c. Of course, as you can see from the scatter of the crosses the relationship is not perfect. We cannot forecast the exact level of employment from the level of investment. It would be fine if we could do this, but at the moment all we are interested in is the general tendency. We will show you later how to calculate the degree of relationship mathematically, and how to fit the dotted line we have drawn more precisely than we have done in this diagram. Before you leave the scatter diagram, experiment for yourself. Draw a scatter diagram showing the relationship between investment and *un*employment. You should get an inverse relationship – the crosses *falling* from left to right. And finally, try to draw a scatter diagram in which there is no clear relationship shown between two variables.

Some Pitfalls to be Avoided

We must not leave the subject of graphs and diagrams without giving you some advice on what not to do. Unfortunately you will find examples every day of diagrams which illustrate what we are about to say should not happen.

A device beloved of advertisers today is to represent their information in the form of little pictures or ideograms. The sales of a particular brand of beer may be represented by the size of a foaming tankard, the amount of washing-up liquid you get for a penny by the height of liquid in a test-tube. Now, many advertisers using this technique are merely doing their job to the best of their ability; but some advertisements we have seen seem designed to mislead the reader, see diagram on next page.

Look at diagram 2.18 which represents the sales of 'Whizz' by varying the size of the packet.

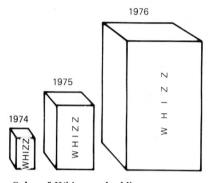

Sales of Whiz are doubling every year

Diagram 2.18

There is nothing wrong with this technique – it can put over the idea of increasing sales forcibly and effectively. But look at the size of the packets. Doubling the dimensions of a packet does not indicate, of course, that sales have doubled. The volume of the second packet is in fact eight times that of the first, and the volume of the last packet is, believe it or not, sixty-four times that of the first. Thus, in spite of the writing saying that sales are doubling every year, the reader is left with a completely false impression of the rate at which they are rising.

Even more unpardonable, in our opinion, is the situation shown in diagram 2.19, see facing page.

You know that before you draw any graph, you should clearly mark the scales on the axis. Before you indignantly retort that this is an obvious point and will never be forgotten, you must realise that many people do quite deliberately omit the scales, intending to mislead. You must have seen this situation in television commercials. A mysterious line runs across the screen – showing absolutely nothing, but still leaving the impression that sales are skyrocketing and that we are missing the chance of a lifetime by not buying the product. Couple this with the statement that this is the housewives' choice and we are caught. No-one likes to be out of step with one's friends and neighbours.

Equally bad, if not worse, is the invention of units that do not exist. The scales should tell us something; they should use units that are real and that can be understood. But look at diagram 2.20, see facing page.

Imagine this graph on your television screen, and the smooth voice of the announcer 'proving' by pointing to the graph that daily brush-

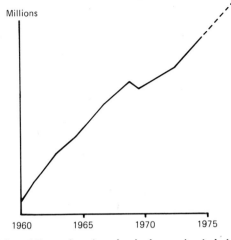

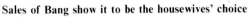

Sales of Bang show it to be the housewives' choice

Diagram 2.19

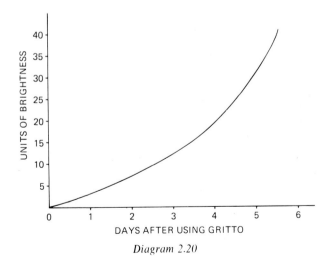

Diagram 2.20

ing with Gritto is bound to make our teeth whiter. But what is a unit of brightness? We are afraid that we do not know, and we very much suspect that the advertising agencies do not know either.

Students often ask us which is the best diagram to use, for a particular purpose. There is no real answer to this and we suggest that you do not waste time looking for one. Any diagram should present the salient features of the data simply and vividly. Equally, if the reader has to spend a great deal of time 'sorting out' what a diagram means, it is a bad diagram.

But do not let it stop here. Certain features of the data should be obvious from the diagram. Now ask questions. Why has the variable behaved in this manner? Why has A behaved differently from B? Is there a relationship between C and D, and, if so, what is this relationship? Only by asking questions such as these will you get full value from your diagrams.

The rest of this book takes the data we have illustrated in this chapter (and other data), and analyses it mathematically so as to answer questions such as these, and to extract as much information as possible from the data we have. This is not an automatic process. We will not do this or the other merely because questions may be asked in an examination paper, but rather because figures always leave unanswered questions about relationships and behaviour. Take a genuine interest in the raw material you have, and it will amply repay study – bolstering up your knowledge of economics, sociology, and of life generally.

EXERCISES TO CHAPTER TWO

2.1   (i) Write short notes on the construction and use of

   (a) bar charts,
   (b) pie charts,
   (c) line graphs,

illustrating your answer by using examples from a business environment.

   (ii) What are the advantages and disadvantages of using these diagrammatic methods when presenting reports?   O.N.C.

2.2   Write brief notes on the following:

   (a) The pie chart,
   (b) Scatter diagram,
   (c) Histogram,
   (d) Band or strata chart.   O.N.C.

2.3 Indicate the more important uses of any two of the following graphs and charts, supporting your answers with appropriate diagrammatic examples:

(i) Histogram,
(ii) Zee chart,
(iii) Cumulative frequency curve.   I.C.S.A.

2.4 Indicate the more important uses of any two of the following charts and graphs, and provide diagrammatic examples to support your answers:

(a) Cumulative frequency curve,
(b) Z (or Zee) chart,
(c) Ratio scale chart,
(d) Ideograph (pictogram).   I.C.S.A.

2.5 (a) Statistical information is sometimes shown in the form of ideographs (pictograms). For example, pictures of sacks of different sizes or alternatively pictures of different numbers of sacks of the same size may be used to show the production of flour in different countries. Comment on the advantages and disadvantages of these pictorial forms.

(b) Describe the purpose and construction of a pie chart, illustrating your answer with a simple example of your own invention.
     Scot. A.S.C.

2.6 Explain the use and method of construction of three of the following ways of representing data, illustrating your remarks with an example in each case:

(a) Bar charts,
(b) Pie charts,
(c) Lorenz curve,
(d) Pictogram.   O.N.C.

2.7 (a) What are the advantages of using charts and graphs in statistical investigations?

(b) Describe clearly the methods to be employed in constructing:

(i) a pie chart,
(ii) a histogram.

(c) State the kind of diagram you consider most suitable to illustrate:

(i) daily hours of sunshine for a period of one month,
(ii) the number of workers, male and female, employed in a factory at each of three dates,

(iii) monthly sales, cumulative sales and a curve showing trend.

Briefly give your reasons for your choice in each case.

O.N.C.

2.8   Discuss the suitability of a compound bar chart, a pie chart, and a pictogram for the presentation of data to:

(a) top management,
(b) lower management,
(c) the public.

Give examples of data which could be satisfactorily presented by each of these charts. (Do not draw the charts.)   O.N.C.

2.9   A daily count of the number of rejects from the assembly line of a local manufacturer has yielded the following data:

138	164	150	132	144	125	149	157
146	158	140	147	136	148	152	144
168	126	138	176	163	119	154	165
146	173	142	147	135	153	140	135
161	145	135	142	150	156	145	128

(a) Using the data, construct a frequency distribution table and from that sketch the corresponding frequency curve.

(b) Comment on the shape of the frequency curve you have obtained and compare it with the sketched shapes of two others with which you are familiar.   O.N.C.

2.10   The set of figures below shows the ages at which 50 employees were appointed to a certain grade.

28	27	30	27	28	28	26	27	28	28
26	28	29	31	27	28	27	29	27	29
28	27	31	27	27	29	30	27	28	28
28	29	28	29	27	30	27	28	27	29
28	27	28	29	29	28	28	28	28	27

Write the data in the form of a frequency table and draw the frequency curve; by observing the shape of this curve, comment on the skewness of the distribution.

Draw also the cumulative relative frequency curve.   O.N.C.

2.11   Estimates of Gross Domestic Product (GDP) in current prices from 1951 to 1972 in £m are given at top of facing page.

	£m		£m
1951	12,639	1962	25,279
2	13,790	3	26,878
3	14,877	4	29,187
4	15,726	5	31,156
5	16,867	6	33,057
6	18,264	7	34,835
7	19,369	8	37,263
8	20,196	9	39,667
9	21,248	1970	43,303
1960	22,633	1	48,675
1	24,213	2	53,940

Source: National Income and Expenditure, 1973.

(a) Construct a frequency distribution and a histogram of these figures and comment.
(b) Indicate how these current price estimates can be converted to real (i.e. constant price) estimates of GDP.   C.I.P.F.A.

2.12   The following is a record of marks scored by candidates in an examination:

77	59	84	73	51	43	50	81	61	53	69
37	58	63	67	61	90	61	50	60	84	56
77	57	42	43	41	49	37	21	24	35	34
50	11	52	30	16	33	67	87	64	47	59
37	92	88	30	38	22	22	49	46	50	64
23	73	73	48	26	36	51	85	71	57	45

(a) Tabulate the marks in the form of a frequency distribution, grouping by suitable intervals.
(b) Construct a histogram from your frequency distribution.
(c) Explain the essential differences between a histogram and a bar chart.   Scot. A.S.C.

2.13   *Stocks of Coal – Great Britain, July 1972 to June 1973*
(*thousand tons*)

	Total	Opencast Sites and Central Stocking Grounds	Collieries
1972			
July	8,839	3,419	5,420
August	9,282	3,530	5,752
September	9,764	3,528	6,236
October	10,030	3,473	6,557
November	10,471	3,458	7,013
December	10,934	3,376	7,558
1973			
January	11,130	3,201	7,929
February	11,455	3,224	8,231
March	11,972	3,244	8,728

	Total	Opencast Sites and Central Stocking Grounds	Collieries
April	12,470	3,268	9,202
May	12,925	3,332	9,593
June	13,292	3,417	9,875

Source: Department of Trade and Industry.

(a) Write a short report stressing the main features of the data given above and include any derived statistics which may be appropriate.

(b) Prepare a suitable diagram or graph which will illustrate your report. O.N.C.

2.14   *Household Expenditure in 1971*

	£	Per Cent of Total
Housing	3.98	12.8
Fuel, light and power	1.85	6.0
Food	8.02	25.9
Alcoholic drink	1.46	4.7
Tobacco	1.30	4.2
Clothing and footwear	2.81	9.0
Durable household goods	2.01	6.5
Other goods	2.32	7.5
Transport and vehicles	4.26	13.7
Services	2.90	9.4
Miscellaneous	0.09	0.3
Total weekly household expenditure	30.99	100.0

Draw carefully and neatly a chart, graph or diagram to represent in visual form the household expenditure in units of actual money spent. Draw carefully and neatly a second chart, graph or diagram to represent in visual form the household expenditure in percentage terms. State the reasons for your choice. O.N.C.

2.15 *Unemployed in Great Britain Receiving Unemployment Benefit*
(*thousands*)

	Total	Unemployment Benefit Only	Unemployment Benefit and Supplementary Allowance
1970			
February	332	260	72
May	303	238	65
August	286	226	60
November	305	245	60

	Total	Unemployment Benefit Only	Unemployment Benefit and Supplementary Allowance
1971			
February	401	312	89
May	406	310	96
August	427	321	106
November	494	379	115
1972			
February	514	391	123
May	451	339	112
August	385	291	94
November	344	261	83

Source: Department of Employment.

(a) Prepare a suitable graph or chart to represent the data given above.
(b) Write a short report on the main features revealed by the table and your graph or chart using derived figures where appropriate.   O.N.C.

2.16   *National Insurance – Great Britain: New Claims – Weekly Averages*
(*thousands*)

Year	Sickness and Invalidity Benefits	Injury Benefit	Unemployment Benefit
1966	206.1	18.5	50.6
1967	193.2	18.8	63.0
1968	204.0	18.0	58.8
1969	219.4	17.9	59.6
1970	204.5	15.8	60.7
1971	169.3	14.0	68.7

Source: Department of Health and Social Security.

Prepare a suitable graph or chart to show the data given above relating to National Insurance claims in Great Britain. Write a short report on the main points revealed by your graph, using derived figures where appropriate. Explain carefully what is meant by 'Weekly Averages' and why this term is used rather than that relating to any other time period.   O.N.C.

2.17   *Subjects studied at Britannia College of Commerce 1972*

Subject	Number of Students
Professional:	
Management	240
Banking	120
Accountancy	980

Subject	Number of Students
Languages:	
Spanish	20
French	220
German	100
General:	
G.C.E.	350
O.N.C.	225
H.N.C.	115

(a) Depict the data given above in the form of:

   (i) a simple bar chart,
   (ii) a component bar chart (actuals),
   (iii) a percentage component bar chart,
   (iv) a pie chart.

(b) Comment on the effectiveness of using the pie chart and the component bar chart as a means of illustrating data classification.   O.N.C.

2.18   A sales department of a firm might plot a Z chart to check or monitor the annual performance of its sales staff. Describe such a chart with an example and explain how it is used.   A.C.A.

2.19   The production figures for a company were as follows:

	Jan.	Feb.	Mar.	Apr.	May	June
1973	60,746	57,071	63,621	66,014	71,736	80,213
1974	68,123	58,983	60,693	61,247	67,778	76,567

	July	Aug.	Sept.	Oct.	Nov.	Dec.
1973	91,780	92,314	76,770	67,123	71,512	87,490
1974	92,124	99,632	104,210	99,634	88,241	107,870

(a) Round the above production figures to the nearest thousand.
(b) Use the rounded figures to produce a Z chart for 1974.
(c) Comment on your chart.   Scot. A.S.C.

2.20

Imported Softwood Deliveries (monthly averages)
(thousand cubic metres)

Month	1972	1973
January	532	882
February	667	527
March	731	828
April	629	654
May	791	940
June	746	838
July	828	870

Month	1972	1973
August	553	851
September	800	833
October	919	1004
November	900	806
December	576	535

Source: Department of Industry.

From the information given, construct a Z chart for 1973. Explain when you might find such charts used and comment briefly on the advantages of representing data in this way.

O.N.C.

2.21   *Tonnage and Service Speed of Passenger Liners of the X-Y Company*

Gross Tonnage	Service Speed (knots)
26,000	25.0
21,700	24.0
26,000	25.0
21,630	24.0
20,300	19.4
15,020	21.6
15,010	21.6
20,100	20.0
26,300	24.6
21,660	20.5
10,470	19.4
20,450	22.2
11,730	20.1
12,150	19.9
16,990	19.6
19,930	19.4
14,440	19.0
9,420	19.3

(a) What is the purpose of analysing data by means of a scatter diagram?
(b) Draw a scatter diagram to illustrate the above figures.
(c) Comment on what the diagram reveals.   O.N.C.

2.22   *Transport: Great Britain 1973*

	Number of New Registrations of Road Vehicles	Index of Vehicle Distances Travelled (av. 1963 = 100)
January	206,295	153
February	198,531	142
March	223,353	177
April	192,364	180
May	194,446	184

	Number of New Registrations of Road Vehicles	Index of Vehicle Distances Travelled (av. 1963 = 100)
June	186,845	197
July	172,407	214
August	254,438	212
September	159,388	197

Source: Department of the Environment.

(a) The table of transport in Great Britain given above contains two sets of data expressed in different terms. By means of a ratio-scale graph show how these two sets of data may be compared. Use natural scale paper.

(b) Comment on the situation revealed by your graph.

O.N.C.

2.23 (i) Describe four diagrammatic methods of presenting numerical data.

(ii) Explain how semi-logarithmic paper differs from arithmetic (or difference) graph paper and give an example of a situation in which semi-logarithmic graph paper would normally be used.

(iii) The following hypothetical data shows the state of weather in London on ten consecutive days.

Day	1	2	3	4	5	6	7	8	9	10
Noon temp. (°C)	19	18	17	20	21	19	18	20	22	19
	C	W	W	S	S	C	W	S	S	C

(C – cloudy, W – wet and S – sunny)

By using appropriate diagrammatic methods, illustrate:

(a) the proportion of days which were cloudy, wet and sunny;
(b) how the noon temperature varied from day to day.

O.N.C.

2.24 (a) What advantages has semi-logarithmic graph over a natural scale graph?

(b) Plot the following two series on the same diagram using semi-logarithmic graph paper to show their relative movements and comment on the results.

How could a similar comparison be achieved without using semi-logarithmic paper?

Growth of a Company

	1970	1971	1972	1973	1974
Turnover (£)	70,000	400,000	1,200,000	1,800,000	4,100,000
Cost of materials (£)	30,000	160,000	500,000	750,000	1,400,000

O.N.C.

2.25 (a) For what reasons do we use semi-logarithmic or ratio-scale graph paper rather than the more usual arithmetic scale paper?
(b) Plot the data given below, on semi-logarithmic paper.
(c) Comment briefly on what your graph shows.

Consumer's expenditure in the United Kingdom in £m at current prices from 1960 to 1970

Item / Year	1960	1964	1968	1970
Total consumer expenditure	16,900	21,500	27,200	31,300
Food	4,200	4,900	5,700	6,400
Housing	1,660	2,340	3,290	3,900
Running costs of vehicles	450	780	1,400	1,700

Source: Annual Abstract of Statistics.

O.N.C.

2.26 The following table shows the sales of natural gas in the United States, and the natural gas sales of the Metropolitan Gas Corporation, for the period from 1956 to 1968:

Year	United States Natural Gas Sales Cubic Feet (billions)	Metropolitan Gas Corporation Natural Gas Sales Cubic Feet (billions)
1956	7,500	850
1957	8,013	1,030
1958	8,502	1,090
1959	8,750	1,150
1960	9,501	1,250
1961	10,095	1,275
1962	10,700	1,300
1963	11,030	1,350
1964	12,050	1,350
1965	12,800	1,280
1966	13,250	1,302
1967	13,900	1,390
1968	15,500	1,500

(a) Graph this data on a semi-logarithmic scale.
(b) State what the graph indicates about the comparative natural gas sales of the Metropolitan Gas Corporation and the industry as a whole, and explain the advantage of using a semi-logarithmic scale.   A.C.A.

2.27 Using a slide rule or a table of logarithms you are required to construct semi-log graphs and plot on them the following data:

	In Great Britain			
Year	Total expenditure on highways (£ million)	Total number of cars licensed (thousands)	Total number of goods vehicles licensed (thousands)	Total casualties in road accidents (thousands)
1959	228.0	4,972	1,378	333
1960	238.0	5,532	1,448	348
1961	270.7	5,983	1,503	350
1962	301.2	6,560	1,522	342
1963	342.4	7,380	1,582	356
1964	405.8	8,252	1,633	385
1965	421.2	8,922	1,661	397
1966	457.4	9,522	1,639	392
1967	528.2	10,312	1,692	370
1968	580.9	10,825	1,640	349

Source: Annual Abstract of Statistics.

Interpret the graphs you have drawn and give the advantages, if any, of this type of presentation.   I.C.M.A.

2.28   (a) Plot the following data using arithmetic scale graph paper.

Period	1	2	3	4	5	6	7	8
Data	200	320	640	1180	2080	4050	6480	9030

(b) Describe two methods of drafting a semi-logarithmic curve when no semi-logarithmic graph paper is available. Using one of those methods plot the data and state the advantages and disadvantages of using the semi-log scale over the more usual arithmetic scale.
                                                                        I.C.M.A.

2.29   *Stoppages of Work due to Industrial Disputes*

	Number of Stoppages beginning in 1973	Aggregate Number of Working Days Lost in these Stoppages (to nearest thousand)
Under 250 days	1200	125
250 and under 500	453	161
500 and under 1000	402	282
1000 and under 5000	592	1250
5000 and under 25,000	180	1844
25,000 and under 50,000	24	859
50,000 days and over	22	2625

Illustrate the above data by means of a Lorenz curve. Why is this form of graph the most suitable for displaying the above information?   O.N.C.

2.30 (a) Construct a Lorenz curve in respect of the following data concerning the net output of manufacturing industry X:

Manufacturing Industry X

Average Number of Employees	Number of Firms	Net Output (£ million)
25 and under 100	205	16
100 and under 300	200	60
300 and under 500	35	18
500 and under 750	30	26
750 and under 1,000	20	26
1,000 and under 1,500	10	54

(b) Explain the purpose of presenting information in the form of the Lorenz curve, and comment on your answer to (a) above.

A.C.A.

2.31 The following table gives incomes before and after tax for the United Kingdom:

Income Class (£)	No. of Incomes (thousands)	Income before tax for the class (£ million)	Income after tax for the class (£ million)
50– 249	5,070	991	990
250– 499	6,570	2,590	2,486
500– 749	6,155	4,143	3,844
750– 999	4,830	4,580	4,168
1,000–1,999	4,145	5,849	5,113
2,000–3,999	353	1,305	940
4,000–5,999	59	469	281
6,000 and over	18	330	129
Total	27,200	20,257	17,951

Source: National Income and Expenditure.

Plot the Lorenz curves for income before and after tax and comment on your findings. C.I.P.F.A.

2.32 Industrial relations have been deteriorating in the Wessex factory of JK Limited and personnel management has established that a contributory factor is the inequalities of earnings of operators paid on the basis of an incentive scheme. Operators work an eight-hour day and bonus is paid progressively after measured work equivalent to 360 standard minutes has been produced. Table A, below, shows the position for the month of June 1975 in respect of operator production. Improvements are made in working conditions in the areas where poor performances were recorded and subsequently in October 1975 the results in table B, below, were measured.

(a) Present the data in tables A and B in the form of a Lorenz curve;
(b) Comment on the results.

Standard Minutes Produced per Operator per Day	Table A June 1975 Number of Operators	Table B October 1975 Number of Operators
300	10	4
320	32	11
340	20	11
360	18	9
380	2	10
400	5	12
420	5	12
440	5	11
460	3	10
480		5
500		5

C.I.P.F.A.

Chapter Three

Approximation and Error

Does it surprise you that in a course on Statistics we should devote a whole chapter to the subject of error? Surely the aim of a course such as this should rather be to teach you about accuracy, not about errors. You may believe, in fact, that we should devote our time to teaching you how to avoid error.

This apparently strange chapter becomes less strange if we consider what we mean by error. To the majority of people trained in answering mathematical problems, the very idea of error implies that we have made a mistake. Certainly, if we say that $4 + 3 - 2 = 6$, we have made an error in our calculations, and our answer is wrong. It would be futile to pretend that this sort of thing does not happen in statistical work. No-one is perfect, and even writers of textbooks sometimes make mistakes that would cause a first-year student to feel ashamed.

Even if our calculations are accurate, our answers may still be wrong because of deficiencies in our raw material. We doubt very much if even the Census of Population taken, in the United Kingdom, every ten years, can claim to be completely accurate. The investigator might not ask the right questions; the respondent may tick the wrong answer; the statistician might analyse the data wrongly, or he might misread his figures, writing 796 instead of 769 when constructing his frequency distributions. There are so many possible mistakes that can be made that one sometimes wonders whether any statistician can ever guarantee one hundred per cent accuracy.

When, however, we talk of statistical error, it is not in this sense that we are using the word. Often it is inconvenient, or impossible, to give figures which are correct to the last unit. When we say that 1.7 million children die every year in a particular area, we obviously do not mean that exactly 1,700,000 children die every year. What we are saying is that approximately 1.7 million children die, and a note at the head of our table will tell us the extent of our approximation. It is very likely that a figure such as this would be accurate to the nearest 0.1 of a million. The annual number of deaths, that is, could be anything between 1,650,000 and 1,750,000. In quoting 1.7 million, we could be as far as 50,000 different from the absolutely accurate figure. It is this difference between the approximate figure and the true figure that the statistician calls 'error'. It is, then, a very different concept from that of a mistake. When we make a mistake we do not know the amount by which our results are wrong; when we speak of error we are qualifying the degree of accuracy of our result. Then, too, a mistake is usually involuntary and something to be avoided; approximations are made to improve the presentation of our figures and in this sense the creation of statistical error is deliberate. So useful is the idea of approximation that you will find very few statistical tabulations which give figures with absolute accuracy, and this is understandable. Which of the following statements do you think that you could remember most easily? 'The output of steel was 110 million tons' or 'The output of steel was 109,764,397 tons.' The widespread use of approximations, however, means that any conclusions drawn from our figures are themselves subject to error, and we must look very carefully at the effects of approximating our figures.

Approximation

Suppose we come across a table telling us the number of cattle in our country at a particular date. We might find the heading of the column in which we are interested reads, 'No. of Cattle (million)'. What does this mean precisely? The fact that we have 'million' in brackets tells us that the person who has constructed the table has approximated his figures to the nearest million. Thus, if he tells us that the number of cattle in the country was 25 millions, we know that the true figure must lie between 24,500,000 and 25,500,000. If it were any less than 24,500,000 the approximated figure would be 24 millions, if it were any more than 25,500,000 the approximated figure would be 26 millions. A problem of course arises if the true figure were exactly 24.5 or exactly 25.5 millions. Do we raise or lower the figure in order to approximate? A good general rule is to look at the number of millions, and if it is an odd number raise it, if it is an even number lower it. If we were approximating to the nearest thousand we would naturally look to see whether we had an even or odd number of thousands, and so on.

In tabular work it is often enough to put the degree of approximation in brackets like this: (millions). For other purposes it may be much more convenient to give the approximated figure and append to it the maximum amount of the possible error. Thus we could express exactly the same information as before in the form:

No. of cattle = 25 million ± 500,000

Occasionally too it is convenient to express the error in percentage form, and we could say:

No. of cattle = 25 million ± 2%

Each of these three statements says exactly the same thing. It makes little difference which way you put it. What is important is that whenever you approximate you should indicate clearly the basis of your approximation.

If you are approximating a number of figures and then totalling them, a peculiar result may arise. It is possible that when you add the approximated figures you do not get the same result as when you approximate the exact total. For example:

	Actual Output (tons)	Output (million tons)
Firm A	102,428,621	102
Firm B	204,364,147	204
Firm C	673,424,961	673
	980,217,729	980 NOT 979

You can see that, because of the approximations, the addition of the approximated totals is only 979. But the total output to the nearest million tons is 980 million. This is the figure that goes in the total of the approximated figures and you must *never* adjust it merely to make your additions seem to be right.

Biassed and Unbiassed Errors

When we are dealing with a number of figures that we are totalling, the amount of error in our total depends to a very large extent on the way in which we are approximating. If we are approximating to the *nearest* hundred (or thousand, or million), some of our approximated figures will be too high, others will be too low. But the excesses and the deficits will tend to cancel each other out and the aggregate error will probably be very small. In fact, the greater the number of items we consider, the smaller is the total error likely to be relative to the actual total. Such an error is said to be unbiassed, because it is not consistently in the same direction. Suppose we are approximating the following figures.

Actual Figures	To nearest thousand	Error
81,171	81	−171
316	0	−316
3,521	4	+479
2,638	3	+362
34,451	34	−451
5,467	5	−467
95,711	96	+289
90,501	91	+499
842	1	+158
Total 314,618	315	+382

As you can see, the error in the approximated total is only +382 in a total of 315,000, an error of only 0.12%; it is equally apparent that the reason for such a small error is that the positive and negative errors offset each other.

But suppose we were to approximate to the nearest thousand above, or to the nearest thousand below. Here the picture is very different. Far from offsetting each other, the errors are all in the same direction and the aggregate error is cumulative. We can see what a tremendous difference it makes to the error in our total if we use the same figures as above, but approximate them differently.

Approximation to the nearest thousand

	Above	Below
	82	81
	1	0
	4	3
	3	2
	35	34
	6	5
	96	95
	91	90
	1	0
	319	310
Error	+4382	−4618
Percentage error	+1.39%	−1.46%

This type of error is known as a biassed error – for obvious reasons, and, as you can see, the aggregate error is dramatically larger than the aggregate unbiassed error. Why, then, should we ever concern ourselves with biassed errors? Often, when we are collecting statistics, an element of error may creep into every figure we collect. Many people argue, for example, that if we are collecting ages every woman will tend to understate her age. Whether this is correct or not, it is certainly true that if we are recording temperature or atmospheric pressure on an instrument which is recording wrongly, we will consistently overstate or understate the true reading. The error that results in any of these cases will be a biassed error, and we must learn to be aware of it.

Absolute and Relative Error

You will have noticed that in the last section we said that the unbiassed error in the figures we were discussing was $+382$ or $+0.12\%$. When we state it as $+382$ we are measuring the arithmetic difference between the actual total and the approximated total, and this we call the *absolute* error. Unfortunately, the size of the absolute error does not give us any indication of the importance of the error involved. An error of 5 in a total of 50 is of much greater importance relatively than an error of 500 in a total of 50,000. To enable us to compare the extent of the error when widely differing totals are involved, the *relative* error is used. This is merely the absolute error expressed as a percentage of the approximated total.

Calculations Involving Error

In both theory and practice we often have to make calculations in which error is present. We might wish to know the number of children likely to be born next year in our local town in order to plan maternity services. But the population statistics may well be available only to the nearest thousand, and the birth rate only accurate to one place of decimals. Similarly if we are planning the building of schools two or three years ahead, we need to know the number of children likely to be born in the relevant years, and also the number of these who will die before reaching school age. We will also want to know the number of children who will move out of the area with their parents, and the number who will move into the area. All these figures are usually available, but every one of them is approximate, and the potential amount of error involved in any calculation can be very large.

Fortunately, provided we know the amount of error involved in each of our figures, it is simple to calculate the probable degree of error arising in the final result. Let us look first at the simple processes of addition and subtraction. Suppose we are adding together

50,000 correct to the nearest 1000 and 3600 correct to the nearest 100

that is, $(50,000 \pm 500) + (3600 \pm 50)$

The maximum result we could possibly obtain would be when we added together the two largest figures, i.e. $50,500 + 3650 = 54,150$. The smallest result we could get is when we add together the two smallest numbers, i.e. $49,500 + 3,550 = 53,050$. Thus, our result would lie between 53,050 and 54,150 which we may state as $53,600 \pm 550$.

Let us now subtract 727 ± 15 from 926 ± 20. Here the maximum result is obtained when we subtract the smallest total from the largest: $946 - 712 = 234$. The minimum result is obtained when we subtract the largest figure that 727 could reach from the smallest figure that 926 could reach: $906 - 742 = 164$. Our result lies between 234 and 164, and again we can express this as 199 ± 35.

We will now put these two results together and look at them carefully.

$$(50,000 \pm 500) + (3,600 \pm 50) = 53,600 \pm 550$$
$$(926 \pm 20) - (727 \pm 15) = 199 \pm 35$$

It is apparent that when we are adding or subtracting we perform the normal arithmetic process ignoring the fact that the figures are approximated, and that the maximum possible error to which this total is subject is plus or minus the sum of the individual *absolute* errors. Be careful when performing this calculation. You will often find that one or more errors are given as relative errors, but the rule applies only to the sum of the absolute errors.

This result could be of importance to any manufacturer, especially during a time when his costs are likely to vary. Suppose that a garment manufacturer wishes to know what price he should quote for cotton shirts to be delivered in six months' time. He knows that his average fixed cost will be 35 pence per shirt but that his supplies of cotton may cost up to 20% more or 20% less than the current cost of 85 pence per shirt. Similarly, his wage cost will be $£1.20 \pm 5$ pence per shirt depending on changes in productivity and wage rates. His total cost per shirt would be:

$$[35 + (85 \pm 20\%) + (120 \pm 5)] \text{ pence or } [35 + (85 \pm 17) + (120 \pm 5)] \text{ pence}$$

and this equals $£2.40 \pm .22$.

He could not then be sure of making a profit unless he sold his shirts at a price greater than £2.62 each. Of course, if all went extremely well he might be able to break even if he sold at a price as low as £2.18, but he cannot be sure of this. You will notice that in this calculation, in the case in which a percentage error was given we immediately changed it into the absolute error.

When we come to multiplication and division we find that the assessment of error in the answer is not quite so simple as this. We find that the error that arises in one direction is different, and often very different, from that arising in the other. Suppose we are multiplying $40 \pm 10\%$ by $20 \pm 5\%$. The result is 800 plus and minus an error. The largest figure we could get is $44 \times 21 = 924$, an error of $+124$ or $+15.5\%$. To our surprise, however, when we calculate the smallest figure it is $36 \times 19 = 684$, an error of only -116 or -14.5%.

When multiplying two approximate values, it is customary to state the *largest* error that could occur, so the result above would be given as $800 \pm 15.5\%$. The same thing is true when we are dividing. If we are dividing 1000 ± 50 by 100 ± 10 the quotient is 10. The largest error that could occur is when the result of our division is a maximum, and this occurs when we divide the largest dividend by the smallest possible divisor, i.e. $1050 \div 90 = 11.667$. Thus the largest error could be $+1.667$ or $+16.67\%$, and our result is stated as

$$(1000 \pm 50) \div (100 \pm 10) = 10 \pm 16.67\%$$

You should not try to remember the formulae for these operations devised by some earlier writers. Remember the basic principle – the maximum error is always possible and it is this, therefore, that should be quoted. Remember too that no amount of juggling with figures can increase accuracy when you are dealing with approximated figures. The accuracy of your result can never be better than, and can seldom be even as good as, the least accurate of the figures used in your calculation.

Let us conclude this chapter by looking at an exercise set by the Institute of Statisticians.

A motorist whose car has a broken mileage recorder and who measures distance travelled by map reading, wishes to assess his petrol consumption in miles per gallon, on a continental trip. His petrol gauge indicates his fuel consumption in litres with an error of $\pm 10\%$. He also uses approximate conversion figures of 1 gallon = 4.5 litres and 1 mile = 1.6 kilometres instead of the more accurate 1 gallon = 4.55 litres and 1 mile = 1.61 kilometres.

Estimate his total fuel consumption in miles per gallon if he claims to be getting 31 miles per gallon after a trip of exactly 615 miles.

Notice that here only the amount of petrol consumed is subject to error in the sense in which we have been discussing it. The remaining errors are errors in converting litres into gallons and kilometres into miles. So firstly let us eliminate the errors made when converting European into English measurement.

When our motorist says that he has travelled 615 miles, he is in fact saying that he has travelled $615 \times 1.6 = 984$ kilometres. But, of course, this is not really 615 miles since he used the wrong conversion factor. The distance travelled in miles is really $984 \div 1.61 = 611.18$.

Now a motorist who says he is getting a petrol consumption of 31 miles per gallon on a trip of 615 miles, is saying that he has used $615 \div 31 = 19.84$ gallons of petrol, or, as his gauge reads in litres, 19.84×4.5 litres of petrol, or 89.28 litres. We know, however, that this reading is subject to a 10% error, so the true petrol consumption lies somewhere between $89.28 + 8.928$ litres, and $89.28 - 8.928$, between 98.208 and 80.352 litres. In gallons then his petrol consumption for the journey of 611.18 miles lay somewhere between $98.208 \div 4.55$ and $80.352 \div 4.55$ gallons, between 21.584 and 17.66 gallons.

We now have the motorist's true mileage and the true limits of his petrol consumption. Thus his fuel consumption lies between $611.18 \div 21.584$ and $611.18 \div 17.66$ miles per gallon, or between *28.32 and 34.61 miles per gallon.*

This seems to be quite a wide range and is possibly not a very satisfactory answer to our problem. What you must remember is that when we say between 28.32 and 34.61 we are quoting extreme limits. It does not seem half as bad if we put the solution as 31.465 ± 3.145 miles per gallon. Here the implication given is that the motorist will get about $31\frac{1}{2}$ miles to the gallon subject to a small error of about 3 miles per gallon either way. The concentration is switched from extreme figures and quite a wide range to a central figure with only about 10% error.

Enough has been said in this chapter to warn you against reading too much into published statistics. In all but a few cases, figures are quoted approximately and hence are subject to error. You can imagine the size of the error in your conclusions if you begin to calculate using figures approximated to the nearest hundred million. Fortunately, as you will see, most calculations of error in statistics do not involve magnitudes as great as this, and the calculation of the probable error in our results can indeed be extremely useful.

EXERCISES TO CHAPTER THREE

3.1   Write an essay on the importance of accuracy and approximation when using statistics.   O.N.C.

3.2   (a) Explain what is meant by the term 'error' in statistics and the circumstances in which it may arise.
   (b) 2.91; 3.473; 8.2; 4.005.

  (i) Add the above rounded figures and state the answer as
      accurately as possible, showing the limits of error.
 (ii) Calculate the percentage relative error in (i).

(c) (i) The death rate of the population of a certain town was
      stated to be 15.5 per thousand when the population was
      known to be 22,000 expressed to the nearest thousand.
      Calculate, as accurately as possible, the number of deaths
      during the year.
 (ii) Calculate the percentage relative error in (i).   O.N.C.

3.3   An inventor plans to set up a business to manufacture and market a product which incorporates his recently patented device. He
considers the product will sell for £10 and that in the first year 120,000
plus or minus 20% will be sold. The cost of the material in the product
is estimated at £4, a figure which is considered to be correct to within
10%, similarly, the labour cost is estimated at £1.50 but it is thought
this could increase by 20%. The first year's fixed costs are expected
to be £100,000 plus or minus 5%. You are required to calculate for
the first year,

  (a) the estimated profit,
  (b) the minimum expected profit, and
  (c) the maximum expected profit.   A.I.A.

3.4   Explain what is meant by the statistical terms:

   (i) unbiassed error,
  (ii) biassed error,
 (iii) absolute error,
  (iv) relative error.

A builder has a plot of land on which he can build 350 houses.
His costs are estimated as follows:

	£
Land	2,000,000
Materials	750,000 to the nearest £10,000
Labour	1,000,000 ± 2%
Overheads	600,000 ± 5%

He intends to sell the houses at £14,000 ± £250 each. Assuming he
sells all the houses, estimate his profit from the contract (express
the answer in the form of £x ± error).   O.N.C.

3.5   Statistical data is frequently rounded in some way before calculations begin or schedules compiled.

  (a) What advantages are obtained from rounding?
  (b) Explain what is meant by the terms:

(i) unbiassed error,
(ii) biassed error,
(iii) absolute error,
(iv) relative error,

and illustrate with the calculation of each by using the following actual figures:

56,321	998
1,465	15,431
43,501	9,702
2,786	11,100
12,157	7,009

I.C.M.A.

3.6 (a) Discuss the various types of error in statistics.
     (b) *Return of twelve American banks at 31st December 1964*

Total advances	\$2,830 million
Ratio of advances to deposits	25.8%
Ratio of cash to deposits	12.4%

Given that the above figures are correct to three significant figures, estimate (a) the amount of deposits and (b) the amount of cash. State the limits of error in each case.   O.N.C.

3.7 Calculate the answers required in each of the following cases. Give the limits of error. The degree of approximation is given.

  (a) (i) $(283 \pm 3\%) + (146 \pm 1\%)$,
       (ii) $(490 \pm 3\%) - (230 \pm 1\%)$.
  (b) Total bank advances £984m.
      Ratio of advances to deposits 15.5%.
      Both figures are correct to 3 significant figures.
      Estimate the amount of deposits.
  (c) Acreage sown 3,982,000 to the nearest 1000 acres.
      Yield per acre 21 cwt correct to the nearest cwt.
      Estimate the total yield in tons.   O.N.C.

3.8 (a) If $A = 5600$ to the nearest hundred and $B = 120$ to the nearest ten calculate
       (i) $A + B$
       (ii) $A - B$, giving the absolute and relative errors in both cases.
     (b) Using logarithms or a slide rule calculate the value of each of the following correct to 3 significant figures.
       (i) $\dfrac{11 \times 136 - 3 \times 5}{\sqrt{[(11 \times 167 - 3^2)(11 \times 148 - 5^2)]}}$
       (ii) $\sqrt[4]{(268 \times 343 \times 496 \times 534)}$ O.N.C.

3.9   *Imports of Motor-cars and Motor-cycles into a Country in 1966*

	Unit	No. of Units Imported	Total Value (£m)
Motor-cars	thousands	10.3	8.6
Motor-cycles	thousands	42.6	2.8

Each entry is correct to the number of figures given in the table.

   (a) Calculate the average import price per vehicle of each type and state the limits of error.
   (b) What is meant by the term 'error' in Statistics?   O.N.C.

3.10   (a) What are the advantages of using approximate amounts?
   (b) The total output of 86 businesses amounted to 3,829,000 tons. Estimate the possible error in this figure if, in arriving at the total,
       (i) the output of each business had been rounded off to the nearest thousand tons,
       (ii) the output of each business has been rounded off to the nearest thousand tons above the actual figure.
   (c) (i) Factory A produced 28 million tons in 1973. The number of workers was 206,000. Calculate the average output per worker and indicate the possible absolute error of your answer if it is suspected that both of the values have been rounded off.
       (ii) Factory B produces 1250 (to the nearest ten) tins of pink powder per batch and 2700 (to the nearest ten) tins of white powder per batch.

          Each tin contains between 80 and 100 ounces of powder. Calculate the total pounds' weight of powder in a consignment of two batches of pink powder and one batch of white powder sent to a customer. Show the relative error of your total.   O.N.C.

3.11   *Value of United Kingdom exports of chemicals during 1971*

	£ thousand
Chemical elements and compounds	19,295
Dyeing, tanning and colouring materials	7,385
Medicinal and pharmaceutical products	14,036
Essential oils and perfume materials	6,021
Explosive and pyrotechnic products	1,001
Plastic materials and artificial resins	13,326
All other	12,601
Total	73,665

Source: Department of Trade and Industry.

(a) Explain the terms (i) *absolute error* and (ii) *relative error.*
(b) Approximate the above data to

    (i) the nearest million £.
    (ii) the nearest hundred thousand £.

(c) Estimate the absolute and percentage relative errors of the totals obtained in (b).
(d) Using (c) state the answers in (b) as accurately as possible showing the limits of error.   O.N.C.

3.12   A firm's estimated sales for 1967 are 83,000 units at a price of £5 each. These figures are liable to errors of 1% and 5% respectively. The estimated costs are:

Wages £72,500 ± 2%,
Materials £125,000 ± 4%,
Other expenses £41,500 ± 3%.

(a) Calculate the approximate net profit for the year giving the limits of possible error.
(b) Calculate the relative errors in the estimate of net profit.
        O.N.C.

3.13

Personal Incomes U.K. 1966

	£000m	%
Consumer expenditure		
Food	5.3	17
Other	18.8	60
Income taxes	3.7	11
National Insurance		
contributions	1.8	6
Savings	1.9	6
Total Personal Income	31.5	100

Source: National Income and Expenditure 1967.

The data given in the table are rounded to the nearest £100m, i.e. to 1%. Calculate, giving the error in each case:

(a) Consumer expenditure.
(b) Income after tax.
(c) The aggregate amount saved given total personal incomes and % savings.
(d) % savings given aggregated savings and total personal incomes.   C.I.P.F.A.

3.14 (a) What do you understand by the terms

     (i) biassed rounding off,
     (ii) unbiassed rounding off,
     (iii) compensatory error,
     (iv) cumulative error?

(b) The following figures, taken from the annual abstract of statistics, show the value of U.K. exports in 1970 (in £ millions) to E.F.T.A. and E.E.C. countries.

E.F.T.A. countries	£ millions
Finland	128.9
Sweden	364.1
Norway	173.8
Denmark	221.2
Switzerland	209.3
Portugal	88.6
Austria	90.7

E.E.C. countries	
Western Germany	502.9
Netherlands	377.8
Belgium and Luxembourg	294.3
France	339.2
Italy	239.7

   (i) Obtain totals for both E.E.C. and E.F.T.A. countries.
   (ii) Round off each figure in an unbiassed sense to the nearest £10 millions and again obtain the totals.
   (iii) Calculate the relative error in the total resulting from your rounding for E.F.T.A. countries.
   (iv) If you wish to take the difference between exports to E.F.T.A. and E.E.C. countries, how would you round your totals if you wished your rounding errors at that stage to be compensatory?
                                              O.N.C.

3.15 A company is marketing a new product to sell at £5. The sales for the first year are expected to be $50,000 \pm 10\%$. The costs are calculated to be:

Fixed overheads $£40,000 \pm 5\%$,
Variable costs £3 per unit sold.

Calculate:

(a) The net profit which can be obtained, giving the limits.
(b) The rate of net profit to sales and the limits.
(c) What would be the net profit if there were no variation?
                                              O.N.C.

3.16   (a) Define the terms

    (i) absolute error,
    (ii) relative error,
    (iii) compensating error.

  (b) A firm works a nominal 40-hour week but with overtime and short time its actual working week varies by as much as $\frac{1}{2}$ hour from the nominal figure. The firm produces (50 ± 1) articles per hour. If the production costs and selling prices are £2.00 and £3.00 respectively per unit rounded off to the nearest 10 pence, estimate

    (i) the weekly profit,
    (ii) the percentage profit, based on cost price, per unit sold (to the nearest 0.5%).   O.N.C.

3.17   (a) Use logarithms or a slide rule to calculate the value of each of the following, correct to 3 significant figures.

    (i) $\sqrt{468} + (24.3)^2$

    (ii) $1 - \dfrac{6 \times 728}{16(16^2 - 1)}$

    (iii) $37.5 + \dfrac{117 - 89}{83} \times 4$

  (b) If $x = 90.8956$, write the value of x correct to

    (i) 4 significant figures,
    (ii) 3 decimal places,
    (iii) the nearest integer,
    (iv) the nearest tenth.   O.N.C.

Chapter Four

Measures of Central Tendency

If you think carefully about it, you will realise that statisticians spend a great deal of their time making comparisons, and the conclusions they reach are often of fundamental importance to every one of us. Comparing income today with income ten years ago is an indicator of how our living standards have changed. Comparing incomes between regions helps the government in its regional policies. Comparing how our prices are changing over time in relation to price changes abroad indicates how competitive our industries are, and comparing our balance of payments over time indicates our ability to pay our way in the world.

Many of the comparisons made present no problems, as we are comparing a single figure value. For example, we can state that I.C.I. earned a certain profit in 1975, and compare this with the profit earned in 1976. Any problems involved in this comparison will be concerned with the calculation of the profit and the rate of inflation, and no-one will dispute that it is legitimate to compare profit in 1975 with profit in 1976 as long as inflation is taken into account. In some cases, however, the things we are trying to compare vary in themselves. Suppose, for example, we attempt to compare incomes on Merseyside with incomes in London: not only is there a variation within the regions, but also a variation within each region. In the second chapter you saw that we could put raw data into a frequency distribution, and present it in the form of a histogram etc. No doubt we could draw histograms, showing the distribution of incomes in London and Merseyside, and this would enable us to state that incomes earned in London exceeded incomes earned on Merseyside. But is this good enough?

You can probably identify two problems in the statement above. Firstly, do we mean that *all* incomes in London exceed *all* incomes on Merseyside? Obviously not! Many people on Merseyside will earn much more than, say, a porter on the Underground. Secondly, given that incomes earned in London exceed incomes earned on Merseyside, we would wish to know by how much. In other words, we wish to *quantify* the differences in income, and we certainly will

not be able to do this by just looking at a frequency distribution
or a histogram. What we need is some figure that is *representative*
of income in London. We can then obtain a representative figure
for Merseyside incomes, compare them, and draw some conclusions
as to the size of the difference in incomes.

How are we going to obtain this representative figure? Probably
you have guessed already, especially in the current economic climate
with our preoccupation with income levels. The TV newscaster does
not state that incomes have risen by 10% over the last twelve months:
he states that *average* incomes have risen. We are given information
on *average* hourly rates of pay, *average* rainfall levels, batting and
bowling *averages*, the *average* amount we spend on drink – and so
on. The advertising men are very fond of telling us what the *average
man* buys, where he goes for his holidays, and what he does with
his leisure.

Three conclusions can be drawn from this last paragraph. Firstly,
an average is obviously meant to tell us something about the matter
under consideration, and unless it is representative of the data, it
obviously cannot do this efficiently. Secondly, the word 'average' is
one that we meet daily in our conversation, and is a word that is
used in a very loose manner. How many times have you heard people
use such remarks as 'I *think* that on average I use *about* five gallons
of petrol per week'? Here the idea of an average and an *estimate*
are shading into each other. We must avoid this at all costs. An
average is capable of being calculated from data, and so it is precise.
Thirdly, averages are used to describe a wide variety of data, and
we must be really sure that we know what an average is. In fact there
are many types of average, and we must be sure to select the right
one for the right job. If we don't do this, then there is a great danger
that the average we quote will not be representative of the data.

The Arithmetic Mean

Most people will tell you to calculate an average something like this:
total all the numbers in the group and divide by how many numbers
there are in the group. So the average of 5, 7, 9, and 10 is

$$\frac{5+7+9+10}{4}=7.75$$

In fact, it is easier to demonstrate how to calculate an average than
it is to explain how to calculate it. Now mathematicians have developed two useful symbols to overcome this problem. Suppose we
put this group of figures we wish to average in a column, and give

this column a heading x. The group we considered above would look like this:

$$x$$
$$5$$
$$7$$
$$9$$
$$10$$

If we wish to total these figures, the statistician would state Σx – meaning take the sum of the column headed x. (Σ is a Greek capital letter pronounced *sigma*.) Also, we state that there are n figures in the column (in this case $n=4$). So the expression

$$\frac{\Sigma x}{n}$$

tells us precisely how to calculate the average. We stated earlier that there are many forms of average, and the average we have just calculated is called the *arithmetic mean*. Statisticians use the symbol $\bar{x}$ (pronounce it 'x-bar') to stand for the arithmetic mean, so we can write

$$\bar{x} = \frac{\Sigma x}{n}$$

The arithmetic mean is certainly the most widely used average, both by statisticians and laymen. It will be useful, then, to examine in what sense it is representative. Returning to our example, we have

$$x = 5, 7, 9, 10 \quad \bar{x} = 7.75$$

Notice that the arithmetic mean represents not one single item in the group, so it cannot be representative in the sense that it is typical. It follows, then, that 'representative' means something other than typical. If we subtract the mean from each of the items in the group, we have

$$-2.75, \ -0.75, \ +1.25, \ +2.25$$

We call each of these differences a *deviation* from the arithmetic mean. Notice that the sum of these deviations is zero. Using the sigma notation we have

$$\Sigma(x - \bar{x}) = 0$$

So the arithmetic mean tells us the point about which the values in the group cluster ('mean' in fact means centre, and statisticians call averages measures of central tendency – hence the title of this

chapter). This is what we imply when we state that the mean is representative. So we now have a definition of the arithmetic mean – a
measure chosen such that the sum of the deviations from it is zero.

For the moment, we shall postpone judging whether this meaning
of representative is valid, and concentrate on this important definf-
tion of the mean. In fact, the definition enables us in many cases to
simplify our calculations of the arithmetic mean. Suppose we guess
a value for the arithmetic mean (call this guess x_0). Now if our guess
is correct, then the sum of the deviations from x_0 would be zero.
If it isn't, then our guess was wrong, and we can adjust our guess
to give the true value of the mean. Suppose, for example, we wish
to find the arithmetic mean of the group

$$100.1, \ 100.2, \ 100.4, \ 100.8$$

If we guess the mean to be 100, then the deviations are

$$+0.1, \ +0.2, \ +0.4, \ +0.8, \quad \text{sum} = 1.5$$

Clearly, our guess was too low, and we must adjust our guess by

$$\frac{+1.5}{4} = +0.375$$

so the true value of the mean is

$$100 + 0.375 = 100.375$$

(You should check this value by calculating the mean directly.) We
can again use the sigma sign to show precisely how to use this method
to calculate the arithmetic mean.

$$\bar{x} = x_0 + \frac{\Sigma(x - x_0)}{n}$$

In other words, the arithmetic mean is the assumed mean plus a
correction factor.

Now let us examine another factor of the arithmetic mean which
will simplify calculations. We can multiply or divide the group of
numbers we wish to average, and find the average of this adjusted
group. We can then adjust the average we have calculated to the
true value. Suppose, for example, we want to find the arithmetic mean
of the group

$$0.0002, \ 0.0005, \ 0.0012, \ 0.0015$$

Multiplying this group by 10,000 we have

$$2, \ 5, \ 12, \ 15$$

which has a mean of 8.5. To obtain a true value for the mean, we now divide by 10,000, giving

$$\bar{x} = 0.00085$$

Of course, in many cases you would not bother to use either of the simplifications mentioned – especially if you have access to a calculating machine. Later, though, we shall meet cases where they speed up our calculations considerably, and also lessen the risk of arithmetic error.

The Arithmetic Mean of a Frequency Distribution

In the first chapter we recommended that you put raw data into frequency distributions wherever possible, so we must now examine how to find their arithmetic mean. If we consult the General Household Survey, we would learn that 1000 couples married in 1965 would be expected to have the following number of children in 1973.

Number of children	0	1	2	3	4
Number of families	364	362	226	44	4

We require to know the mean number of children per family. First, we will write the data into two columns, one headed x (the number of children – this is our variable) and the other headed f (frequency). If we multiply the columns together (fx) this will give the total number of children for each family size. So, for example, we see that there are a total of 132 children from 3 children families.

x	f	fx
0	364	0
1	362	362
2	226	452
3	44	132
4	4	16
	1000	962

Adding up the fx column, there are a total of 962 children in the 1000 families, which gives an average of $\frac{962}{1000} = 0.962$ children per family. Now we know that Σf means total the column headed f (this gives the total number of families) and Σfx means total the column headed fx (which gives the total number of children). So we now know how to find the arithmetic mean of a discrete frequency distribution.

$$\bar{x} = \frac{\Sigma fx}{\Sigma f}$$

Now this is all very well, but much economic data is in the form of grouped, continuous frequency distributions. Suppose we wished to find the average age of the male labour force. We could obtain the data we require from the Annual Abstract of Statistics. We will find the average age in 1971, and in an exercise at the end of this chapter you will be asked to calculate the average for a later year. You will then be able to compare the two years.

Age	Number in employment (millions)	Age	Number in employment (millions)
15, but under 20	1.1	45–	1.5
20–	1.7	50–	1.3
25–	1.5	55–	1.4
30–	1.3	60–	1.1
35–	1.3	65 but under 70	0.4
40–	1.4		14.0

Now we have a problem here: look at the age group 20 to 25 years. Within this group there are 1.7 million men, but we have no idea what their *actual* ages are. So we are going to have to make some assumption about their ages. Probably the most sensible assumption to make is that the 1.7 million men in this group have an average age of 22.5 years – the mid-point of the group. If we do this for all groups, then we can use the formula we obtained earlier to calculate the arithmetic mean.

Mid-point x	Frequency f	fx
17.5	1.1	19.25
22.5	1.7	38.25
27.5	1.5	41.25
32.5	1.3	42.25
37.5	1.3	48.75
42.5	1.4	59.50
47.5	1.5	71.25
52.5	1.3	68.25
57.5	1.4	80.50
62.5	1.1	68.75
67.5	0.4	27.00
	14.0	565.00

$$\bar{x} = \frac{\Sigma fx}{\Sigma f} = \frac{565}{14} = 40.36$$

So the average age of working males in 1971 was 40.36 years.

Now let us see if we can simplify the arithmetic involved in these calculations. Well, the first thing we can do is to multiply all the frequencies by 10: this will remove the decimal fractions and not make any difference to our answer. We can take an assumed mean (in this case we will take 42.5) and calculate the deviations of the items x from 42.5. Notice that all the deviations are divisible by 5, and if we do this we obtain a column that we head d.

x	$(x-42.5)$	d	f	fd
17.5	-25	-5	11	-55
22.5	-20	-4	17	-68
27.5	-15	-3	15	-45
32.5	-10	-2	13	-26
37.5	-5	-1	13	-13
42.5	0	0	14	0
47.5	5	1	15	15
52.5	10	2	13	26
57.5	15	3	14	42
62.5	20	4	11	44
67.5	25	5	4	20
			140	-60

So the average deviation from the mean is $-\frac{60}{140} = -\frac{3}{7}$. But as we divided the deviations by 5, we must multiply the average deviation by 5 to give $-\frac{15}{7}$. In other words, our value for the assumed mean is $\frac{15}{7}$ greater than the true value of the mean. So the true value of the mean is

$$42.5 - \tfrac{15}{7} = 40.36 \text{ years}$$

which agrees with the value we obtained earlier.

Now if we say that d is the deviation from the assumed mean divided by a constant c then we can write a formula for our simplified method like this:

$$\bar{x} = x_0 + \frac{c\,\Sigma fd}{\Sigma f}$$

Notice that the constant c is normally equal to the class width, though you can choose any value for c which is convenient.

It will be interesting to examine the accuracy of the two means we have calculated. Considering first the mean number of children per family, the distribution gave us the exact number of children in each of the 1000 families. So our calculation of the mean number of children gave us the exact value for the mean: the same result would have been obtained if we had used the frequency distribution or the raw data. However, this is not so with the mean age of the male working population as we did not know the exact age of any of the individuals. In fact, for the members in each class we found it necessary to make an assumption about their ages, so we cannot guarantee the accuracy of the mean. You should realise that although it is much more convenient to consider grouped frequency distributions than raw data, the price we pay for this convenience is the loss of accuracy. In most cases, however, the loss in accuracy is not too serious – later you will be asked to verify this fact.

So far we have considered frequency distributions with constant class widths. Now let us look at a case where the class width is uneven.

Distribution of Earnings of Weekly Paid Adults aged 21 and over, April 1971

	Frequency (millions)	Mid-point (x)
£10, but under £16	0.2	14
£16–	0.4	17
£18–	0.6	19
£20–	0.7	21
£22–	0.9	23
£24–	1.0	25
£26–	0.9	27
£28–	0.9	29
£30–	1.9	32.5
£35–	1.4	37.5
£40–	0.8	42.5
£45–	0.5	47.5
£50–	0.4	55
£60–	0.3	65
£70, but under £100	0.1	85

Source: Annual Abstract of Statistics.

It will certainly be worthwhile multiplying the frequencies by 10, and probably taking an assumed mean (in this case we have chosen

£30). However, there is no suitable constant for simplifying the deviations. So we have:

x	$(x-30)$	f	$f(x-30)$
14	-16	2	-32
17	-13	4	-52
19	-11	6	-66
21	-9	7	-63
23	-7	9	-63
25	-5	10	-50
27	-3	9	-27
29	-1	9	-9
32.5	2.5	19	47.5
37.5	7.5	14	105
42.5	12.5	8	100
47.5	17.5	5	87.5
55	25	4	100
65	35	3	105
85	55	1	55
		110	238

$$\bar{x} = 30 + \tfrac{238}{110}$$
$$= £32.16 \text{ per week}$$

So sometimes it is not practical to use the simplified method, and you should always weigh up carefully whether it is worth the labour involved. Better still, buy an electronic calculator (they are very reasonably priced these days) and it will always be worthwhile using the first method.

Limitations on the Use of the Arithmetic Mean

Earlier, we postponed judgement on just how representative was the arithmetic mean. We simply stated that 'representative' certainly doesn't mean typical. The time has now come to put the arithmetic mean through a series of tests, and see how it performs.

If you examine sources of published statistics, you will be surprised how often frequency distributions have 'open-ended' classes. We reproduce below a frequency distribution showing the estimated wealth of individuals in Great Britain in 1968.

Wealth	% of Total
Not over £5000	78.38
£5000–£15,000	16.17
£15,000–£25,000	2.52
£25,000–£50,000	1.88
£50,000–£100,000	0.70
£100,000–£200,000	0.23
£200,000–	0.11

Source: Annual Abstract of Statistics.

When we calculated the mean from a frequency distribution, we had to make assumptions about the values of the items in each class. We took the mid-point as the representative value of each class. But what assumptions can we make about the average wealth of individuals in the final class? It would be a brave man indeed who would estimate the upper limit for this group. Likewise, what would be a reasonable lower limit to put on the first class? Unless we have adequate information about the first and last groups, we cannot calculate the mean for this type of distribution. To obtain a mean, we must refer to the raw data (and this just is not available for government published statistics). Clearly, we need a measure that does not depend upon adequate knowledge of extreme values of the distribution. This problem of open-ended statistics is one you will meet continually in analysis of published statistics – in fact we had quite a job finding distributions that were not open-ended! Before we leave this point, however, it should be stated that if you *must* estimate the missing limit for open-ended distributions, make sure that the frequencies in the open-ended classes are small in relation to other frequencies. Any inaccuracies due to estimates shouldn't, then, be too serious.

The second point about the arithmetic mean is that it often produces results that are not suitable from a communication viewpoint. Earlier, we found that the average number of children per family was 0.962. Most people would consider this to be a ridiculous statement. In situations like this, people expect an integer (i.e. a whole number) to be representative of the number of children per family. If we are going to ensure that all averages are integers, then we must change our idea of an average.

The third point is perhaps the most important of all: the mean is highly sensitive to extreme values. Consider the case of Fred, who at an interview for a job is told that the average income of salesmen in the company is £8000 per year. He accepts the job as he considers the firm to be very progressive with excellent prospects for himself. Although his starting salary is only £2000 a year, his salary will obviously climb very quickly. You could imagine how cheated Fred felt when he found that the sales force consisted of just five men: the sales director on £30,000 a year and four salesmen on £2500 a year! The extreme value (in this case the sales director's salary) has caused the arithmetic mean to be most unrepresentative. To examine this point further, let us return again to the distribution of weekly incomes of males over the age of 21. The cumulative frequency distribution would look like this:

	Cumulative Frequency (millions)
Under £16	0.2
Under £18	0.6
Under £20	1.2
Under £22	1.9
Under £24	2.8
Under £26	3.8
Under £28	4.7
Under £30	5.6
Under £35	7.5
Under £40	8.9
Under £45	9.7
Under £50	10.2
Under £60	10.6
Under £70	10.9
Under £100	11.0

Consulting the ogive for this distribution (Fig. 4.1), we see that 6.45 million people earn less than the average wage of £32.16, which represents nearly 60% of all workers in this category. On this basis, many would claim that the mean is not representative of this data. Had we taken *all* incomes rather than weekly incomes only, then the average would have been much higher (and hence even more unrepresentative). This is the reason that so many people scoff at the average income figures that are quoted from time to time.

Before we search for an alternative to the arithmetic mean, we must say something in its defence. The main redeeming feature of the arithmetic mean is that its calculation involves the use of *all* the data. We will see later that this is not a characteristic of alternatives to the arithmetic mean. In other words, the weaknesses of the arithmetic mean are also its strengths. Because all the data is used, and because the arithmetic mean is capable of precise calculation, most statisticians still prefer it to other measures. In fact the arithmetic mean

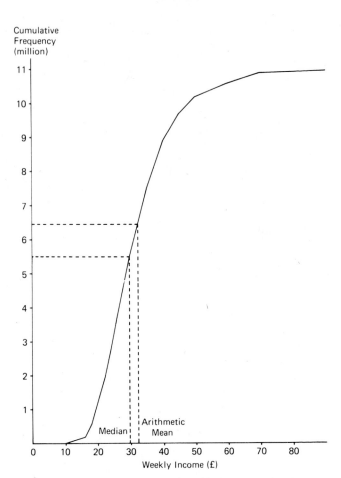

Cumulative frequency distribution of weekly incomes of males over 21 years old 1971

Figure 4.1

is capable of, and is the basis for, advanced analysis. Any alternative to the arithmetic mean cannot be used for advanced analysis, so their uses are descriptive rather than analytical.

The Median

Suppose we arranged a group of numbers in ascending order, then the median would be the value of the item in the middle. So the median of the group 3, 4, 7, 9, 11 is 7. Notice that the median is quite unaffected by extremities at either end of the group. Take the case of the sales force considered earlier: the incomes are

£2500, £2500, £2500, £2500, £30,000

and the median income is £2500. The actual size of the director's income makes no difference whatsoever to the median: if the director's salary was doubled or halved then the median would still remain £2500. So the median is quite insensitive to extreme values in the group or distribution, and certainly overcomes the major objections to the arithmetic mean. If you arrange a group of n items in ascending order, then the value of the $\left(\frac{n+1}{2}\right)$th item is the value of the median. If we had an even number of items, then there will be *two* middle items. Conventionally, we take the median to be the arithmetic mean of the two middle items. So the median of 4, 9, 13, 17, 30, 32 is $\frac{13+17}{2} = 15$. Now if n is large, the difference between $\left(\frac{n+1}{2}\right)$ and $\frac{n}{2}$ is negligible – so take $\frac{n}{2}$ in such cases. Finally, then, we can see that half the items in a distribution will be more than the median, and half the items less than it.

Look again at the cumulative frequency distribution of weekly incomes. There are 11 million workers, so if we wish to find the median income, this will involve finding the income of the 5.5 millionth worker. Reading off the income of this worker from the ogive, we find that the median income is £29.8, compared with a mean income of £32.16. You would probably find that most people would accept the median as being more representative than the arithmetic mean.

It is often quite difficult to read off the value of the median from the ogive, and to overcome this problem it is useful to magnify that part of the ogive containing the median. From the cumulative frequency distribution, we can see that 5.6 million people earn less than £30 per week, and 4.7 million earn less than £28 per week. So the median lies somewhere between £28 and £30 per week. We can plot these points on a graph and join them with a straight line. Reading off from Fig. 4.2, we see that the median income is £29.78.

If you look carefully at Fig. 4.2, you will realise that it is possible to calculate rather than read off the value of the median. Do you remember the similar triangle theorems? If you do, then you will realise that

$$\frac{AB}{AC} = \frac{ED}{AE}$$

$$\text{so} \quad ED = \frac{AB \times AE}{AC}$$

Statistics

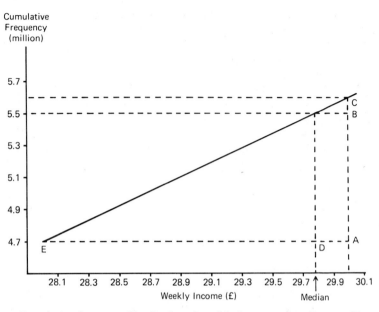

Cumulative frequency distribution of weekly incomes of males over 21 years old 1971

Figure 4.2

Now we can see that *ED* is the amount by which the median exceeds 28, so the median is

$$28 + \frac{AB \times AE}{AC}$$

$$28 + \frac{0.8 \times 2}{0.9}$$

$$= 29.78$$

It might be useful to see how we could obtain these figures directly from the cumulative frequency distribution. The relevant parts of this distribution are:

	Cumulative Frequency
Under £28	4.7
Under £30	5.6

so we see that the median is in the group £28–£30, and the median is:

$$28 + \frac{0.8 \times 2}{0.9}$$

Clearly, 28 represents the lower class boundary (LCB) of the median group, and AE represents the class interval of this group. The quantity AC is the frequency of the median group (5.6–4.7) and the quantity AB is the median item minus cumulative frequency up to the median group (5.5–4.7). So we can calculate the median like this:

$$LCB + \frac{\text{class interval} \times ([\frac{n+1}{2}] - \text{cum. frequency to median group})}{\text{frequency of median group}}$$

Now let us see if we can calculate the median directly, i.e. without reference to graphs.

Size of Companies Acquired 1969

Cost	Frequency	Cumulative Frequency
Not more than £100 thousand	279	279
£100 thou. but under £200 thou.	157	436
£200 thou. but under £500 thou.	166	602
£500 thou. but under £1 mill.	117	719
£1 mill. but under £2 mill.	58	777
£2 mill. but under £5 mill.	66	843
£5 mill. but under £10 mill.	30	873
£10 mill. but under £20 mill.	12	885
£20 mill. but under £50 mill.	5	890
Over £50 million	1	891

Source: *Board of Trade Journal*

We wish to find the median cost of companies acquired, i.e. the cost of the $\frac{891+1}{2} = 446$th company. The median company is in the group £200 thou.–£500 thou., which contains 166 companies. Hence the median is

$$£200,000 + \frac{300,000 \times (446 - 436)}{166}$$

$$= £218,072$$

Notice how difficult it would be to calculate the arithmetic mean of this distribution. It would be extremely difficult to put a lower limit on the first group, or an upper limit on the last group. The median, then, has decided advantages over the arithmetic mean: it can cope with open-ended distributions and is unaffected by extremities at either end of the distribution. Its disadvantage is that it ignores the bulk of the data presented to us, and this disadvantage really is critical! We would like to emphasise again that you should always attempt to use the mean rather than the median, especially if there is not much difference between them. In fact, the difference between them depends on the skewness of the distribution (this is illustrated in Fig. 4.3). The median splits the area under the frequency curve

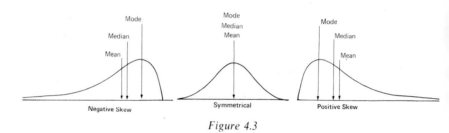

Figure 4.3

into two halves. If the distribution is symmetrical, then the mean and median will coincide. With a negatively skewed distribution the median exceeds the mean, and with a positively skewed distribution the mean exceeds the median. The more pronounced is the skew, the greater will be the difference between the mean and median. Let us now attempt to summarise this into a simple rule: if you require a representative measure and the distribution is markedly skew, use the median – otherwise use the mean.

One final problem concerned with the median is that we cannot pool two medians to find an overall median. If we know that a factory employs 100 women at a median wage of £32 per week and 200 men at a median wage of £43 per week, we cannot calculate the median wage for all workers without consulting the raw data. But this is not the case with the arithmetic mean. Suppose the data referred to mean rather than median wages, then the total wages earned by women would be £32 × 100 = £3200, and the total wages earned by men would be £43 × 200 = £8600. So the labour force of 300 earns £11,800 per week, which gives an average wage of $\frac{11,800}{300}$ = £39.33 per week. This pooling of arithmetic means is extremely useful: a feature we will meet again later.

The Mode

The mode is the value or attribute that occurs most often, so is an extremely simple concept. Look again at the incomes of the sales force described earlier and you will realise that the modal income is £2500. Straight away, though, we can see a snag with the mode: if all the numbers in the group are different, then we cannot have a modal value.

With a frequency distribution, the mode is the value with the greatest frequency. Let us examine again the distribution of the number of children of 1000 young married couples.

Number of children	0	1	2	3	4
Number of families	364	362	226	44	4

The mean number of children per family we calculated to be 0.962, and the median number of children is one (i.e. the number of children in the 500th family). But the modal number of children is zero, because more families are childless than have any other number of children.

Finding the mode of a grouped frequency distribution will not be quite so easy. Consider again the distribution of weekly paid adults: the class width is not constant so the modal class cannot be obtained by inspection. Probably the best way to deal with this is to draw

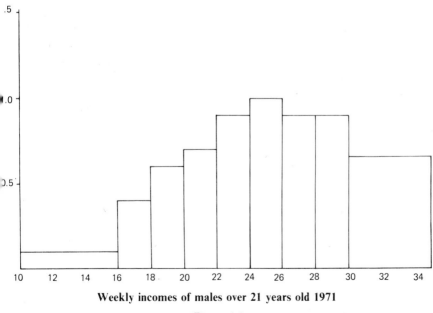

Weekly incomes of males over 21 years old 1971

Figure 4.4

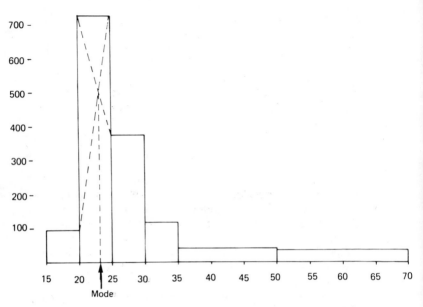

Age distribution of drug addicts known to the Home Office, 1972 (Source: Home Office)

Figure 4.5

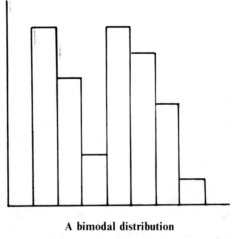

A bimodal distribution

Figure 4.6

the histogram of the distribution. If you examine the distribution carefully, you will see that incomes in excess of £35 are falling off rapidly, so we will concentrate our attention on incomes less than this figure. Consulting Fig. 4.4 we can see that the modal class is £24–£26 per week, and as the adjacent classes have the same frequency, we might be justified in saying the modal income was £25 per week, see diagram on previous page.

Suppose the adjacent classes do not have the same frequencies; then we would estimate the mode by splitting the modal class in the ratio of the frequencies of the adjacent classes. This is often done geometrically as illustrated in Fig. 4.5, see diagram on opposite page.

The mode has the same weaknesses as the median: it ignores the bulk of the data and is not capable of being pooled. We have also seen that in certain groups of numbers, a mode might not be present. Also, in some distributions it is possible to have more than one mode – a distribution like the one in Fig. 4.6 is called bimodal. To quote two modes is just clouding the issue. The strength of the mode is that it is extremely easy both as a concept and as a measure of calculation. It is particularly useful to describe attributes – when we state that the average family cleans their teeth with 'Gritto', we mean that more families use Gritto than any other toothpaste. You can readily understand why the mode is so popular with market researchers! See diagram on opposite page.

Before we conclude measures of central tendency, there is one final point we should consider. Why did we call the mean the *arithmetic* mean? This surely implies that there are other means we could consider. This is indeed the case, and if we calculate a mean, we must be absolutely certain that we are using the right one! Let us, therefore, consider some alternative means (called minor means) and discuss their appropriate usage.

The Harmonic Mean

Suppose a motorist told you that he travelled from Liverpool to Manchester at an average speed of 40 kph, and returned at an average speed of 50 kph. If he then claimed that his overall average speed was 45 kph, you would probably agree with him, wouldn't you? However, you would be quite wrong. Let us examine the problem in more detail. The distance from Liverpool to Manchester is 55 km, so the time taken at 40 kph is $\frac{55}{40} = \frac{11}{8}$ hours, and the time taken at 50 kph is $\frac{55}{50} = \frac{11}{10}$ hours. The time taken for both journeys is

$$\frac{11}{8} + \frac{11}{10} = \frac{99}{40} \text{ hours}$$

and the total distance travelled is 110 km. Now we know that average speed is distance divided by time, so the average speed for the round journey is

$$110 \times \frac{40}{99} = 44\tfrac{4}{9} \, \text{kph}$$

So you see that averaging the two speeds simply by adding them and dividing by two gives us the wrong answer. Why is the arithmetic mean not appropriate here? Well the reason is that the different speeds are maintained for the same *distance* and not the same *time*. If they were maintained for the same time then the arithmetic mean would have been appropriate. What we should have used here is the *harmonic mean*, which is used for averaging rates and prices. We calculate the harmonic mean as follows

$$\text{H.M.} = \frac{n}{\sum \left(\dfrac{1}{x}\right)}$$

or using our example

Average speed
$$= \frac{2}{\frac{1}{40} + \frac{1}{50}}$$
$$= \frac{2 \times 200}{9}$$
$$= 44\tfrac{4}{9} \, \text{kph}$$

Now let us examine an example using prices. Suppose we made a mixture using four ingredients costing £1, £2, £3 and £4 per kilogram respectively, and spent an equal amount on each ingredient, then the price per kilogram of the mix is

$$\frac{4}{1 + \frac{1}{2} + \frac{1}{3} + \frac{1}{4}} = £1.92 \text{ per kilo}$$

However, had we mixed equal quantities *worth* of ingredients, then the price would have been £2.50 per kilo. You should check these conclusions by direct calculation.

The Geometric Mean

Let us suppose we invest £100 at 10% per annum compound interest. At the end of the first year we would have £100 + £10 = £110 invested. At the end of the second year we would have £110 + 10% of £110 = £121 invested. Now we can continue in this fashion and calculate the sum available at the end of each year for 10 years. The graph of the sum available against time is shown in Fig. 4.7.

The sum available at the end of the 10th year is £259.37. Now suppose we knew the sum available after 10 years, could we use the

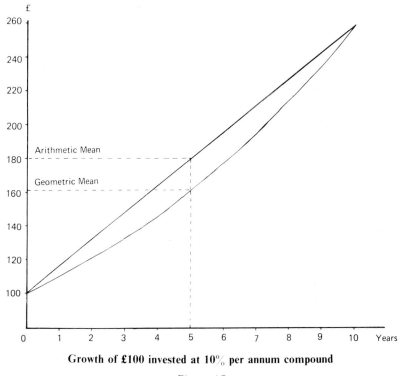

Growth of £100 invested at 10% per annum compound

Figure 4.7

arithmetic mean to estimate the sum available after 5 years? The arithmetic mean would be

$$\frac{100 + 259.37}{2} = £179.69$$

which, as you can see from the graph, is a rotten estimate. Once again, we have used the wrong mean. The arithmetic mean would have given a good estimate had the sum invested earned a constant *amount*. In other words, it would have worked if the sum invested had earned simple interest – the graph would have been a straight line. In this case, however, the sum invested increases by a constant *proportion*, and a much better estimate is achieved if we use the *geometric mean*.

$$G.M. = \sqrt[n]{x_1 \times x_2 \times \ldots \times x_n}$$

which simply states that we multiply the n numbers together, and then take the nth root. So our estimate of the sum available after 5 years is

$$\sqrt{100 \times 259.37}$$
$$= £161.05$$

which agrees exactly with the value obtained from the graph.

This method of estimating a 'mid-point' value by using an average is called *interpolation*. To attempt to clarify which mean should be used, consider this problem: suppose you started work earning £1500 per year, and you were told what your salary would be in 10 years' time. You want to estimate your salary after 5 years. If your salary rises by constant annual increments, then the arithmetic mean would be appropriate, but if it rises by a constant percentage of the previous year's salary, you would have to use the geometric mean. Again, a census is taken every 10 years, and it would be useful to use these figures to estimate the population on the 5-year intervals. As populations do not grow by constant amounts, the geometric mean would give a better estimate. But even using a geometric mean might not give a good estimate: can you think why this might be so?

Now a word or two in conclusion. We have seen that there are many forms of 'average', and it is vitally important that you choose the right one for the job. We must state, though, that the arithmetic mean is by far the most important and is most commonly used in preference to the other alternatives. As you work through this book, you will meet the arithmetic mean over and over again (from now on we shall refer to it simply as the mean) – but always bear in mind that it does have limitations!

EXERCISES TO CHAPTER 4

4.1 Explain why it is frequently necessary to summarise masses of data by using representative or typical values. Describe two such measures and their methods of calculation.　　　　A.C.A.

4.2 If we examine the batting average table for Coalshire we find that Fred Sloggin has an average of 51 runs, and D. E. M. Bones has an average of 39 runs. Would you conclude that Sloggin was the more effective batsman?

Sloggin's average of 51 runs has been obtained in 39 innings. The next innings will be his last of the season. How many runs must he score in the last innings if his final average is to be at least 55 runs?

4.3   Given that $\Sigma(x-\bar{x})=0$, show that $\bar{x}=\dfrac{\Sigma x}{n}$

4.4   *No. of children per 1000 families in which couples were married in 1960–4*

No. of children	0	1	2	3	4	5	6+
Frequency (%)	5.3	5.2	55.4	11.4	18.9	1.5	2.3

Source: General Household Survey.

Calculate the median.

Calculate the mean number of children per family for the above data, given that the average size of a family with 6 or more children is 6.5.

4.5   A company employing 60 people found that the number of sick days taken by its employees last year were as follows:

10	5	12	0	2	35	11	12	4	9
12	17	3	7	8	8	8	10	11	29
44	4	9	3	6	6	7	13	18	4
15	25	5	2	7	20	9	16	10	9
5	2	31	6	0	7	10	9	22	1
3	1	23	9	12	18	6	9	31	0

Group the above figures into intervals of five days. Calculate the mean. Draw the cumulative frequency curve of the distribution and comment on the distribution.   O.N.C.

4.6   *Orders Received*

Value of Order (£00)	Number of Orders Received
0 and under 5	20
5 and under 10	51
10 and under 15	139
15 and under 20	116
20 and under 25	31
25 and under 30	14
30 and over	5
	376

(a) From the above table of orders received calculate the mean value of orders received.

(b) Comment briefly on your results for (a)

(c) Suppose the value of the median to be less than the mean. What
would this indicate?   O.N.C.

4.7   The rateable values of 120 houses were found and the results
are shown below.

Rateable Value (£)	Number of Houses
70– 79.99	3
80– 89.99	15
90– 99.99	30
100–109.99	36
110–119.99	18
120–129.99	12
130–139.99	6

Calculate the mean of the distribution.   O.N.C.

4.8   The table below gives the age distribution of the management
of a large company.

Age	Frequency
Under 20	2
20–29	12
30–39	31
40–49	39
50–59	26
Over 60	10

Calculate the mean of the distribution. List the assumptions you
made in carrying out the calculation and explain why you think you
were justified in making them.   O.N.C.

4.9   *Age Distribution of the Members of a Golf Club*

Age (in completed years)	No. of Members
10–19	185
20–29	263
30–39	325
40–49	442
50–59	368
60–69	134
70 and over	83

(a) Calculate the arithmetic mean age for the data. (Use mid-value
of Group 40–49 as a working origin.)
(b) Define and distinguish between discrete and continuous variables.   O.N.C.

4.10   The frequency table gives the age distribution of the estimated
male population of Northern Ireland on 30th June 1971.

(a) Draw a histogram of this data.
(b) Calculate the arithmetic mean for this distribution.

Age	Number (000's)
0– 9	164
10–19	141
20–29	108
30–39	83
40–49	83
50–59	77
60–69	59
70 and over	41

O.N.C.

4.11   Distinguish between discrete and continuous data. The data below shows the number of local telephone calls made by 75 subscribers during a certain interval of time.

No. of Calls Made	No. of Subscribers
1–10	9
11–15	12
16–20	24
21–25	16
26–40	14
	75

(a) Draw a histogram to illustrate the data.
(b) Calculate the average number of calls made per subscriber.
(c) Calculate the maximum error in your average due to grouping in the data given.   O.N.C.

4.12   *Mileages Recorded by 60 Commercial Travellers in the Course of One Week*

515	611	530	557	586	528
533	516	519	560	572	509
520	543	556	532	512	605
559	549	539	609	589	537
524	521	513	541	581	618
544	545	535	568	583	521
555	552	579	581	558	539
562	578	563	598	594	560
595	507	562	532	590	578
526	533	574	531	584	543

(a) From this data tabulate directly a grouped frequency distribution using equal class intervals and starting with '500–under 520'.
(b) Construct the histogram of this distribution.

(c) What is the direction of skew of this distribution?
(d) Calculate the arithmetic mean of the grouped frequency distribution.
(e) Explain why the arithmetic mean of the ungrouped data would be different from the mean obtained in (d).　　　　O.N.C.

4.13　Values of orders taken by representatives employed by a wholesale firm during 1967. The values are rounded off to the nearest £1.

Value of Order (£)	No. of Orders
5– 9	85
10–19	120
20–29	225
30–49	135
50–99	105
100 and over	20

(a) Illustrate the data by means of a histogram.
(b) Calculate the median and mark it on your histogram.
　　　　O.N.C.

4.14　The following table shows the age distribution of employees in two factories A and B. Estimate the median age in each factory using an appropriate graph and check the results by calculation.

Age of Employees	Number of Employees	
	A	B
15–19	79	5
20–24	98	23
25–29	128	58
30–34	83	104
35–39	39	141
40–44	19	98
45–49	11	43
50–54	7	19
55–59	3	6

　　　　O.N.C.

4.15　Explain the difference between a continuous variable and a discrete variable.

The table below gives the earnings (to the nearest £) of 150 employees in a large factory

Income	Frequency	Income	Frequency
£5000–£5499	1	£2500–£2999	8
£4500–£4999	0	£2000–£2499	34
£4000–£4499	1	£1500–£1999	38
£3500–£3999	2	£1000–£1499	42
£3000–£3499	4	£500– £999	20

(a) What are the class boundaries of the class with frequency 8?
(b) Draw a cumulative frequency curve of the distribution.
(c) What percentage of the group earn less than £2200?
(d) Calculate the median income as accurately as you can.
(e) Under what conditions is the median a better measure of central tendency than the arithmetic mean?   O.N.C.

4.16   The income distribution of a sample of about 7000 households is given as follows:

Household Weekly Income in the U.K. in 1969

Income (£ per week)	% of Households
under 8	7.1
8 and under 10	4.4
10 and under 15	9.0
15 and under 20	8.2
20 and under 25	10.8
25 and under 30	12.0
30 and under 35	11.9
35 and under 40	9.7
40 and under 50	12.7
50 and under 60	6.7
60 and over	7.5
Total:	100.0

Source: Family Expenditure Survey, Report for 1969.

(a) Obtain the cumulative frequencies and plot the cumulative frequency curve.
(b) A firm proposes to market a household product in two qualities – standard and de luxe – which it expects to sell in the income brackets £24–£36 and £32–£48 per week respectively.

If each 1% of the sample can be taken to represent 180,000 households in the population at large, estimate the market size for each quality separately and for the two grades together.   O.N.C.

4.17   *Distribution of Personal Incomes before Tax in the U.K. 1969–70*

Income Range (£)	Number of Incomes (00,000's)
below 400	7
400 and under 600	26
600 and under 800	27
800 and under 1000	26
1000 and under 1250	32
1250 and under 1500	30
1500 and under 2000	42
2000 and under 3000	19
3000 and over	8
Total	217

Source: Social Trends, 1971 modified.

(a) Obtain the cumulative frequencies.

(b) By calculation or graphically, obtain the median.

(c) Would you expect the arithmetic mean of the distribution to be greater than, equal to, or less than the median? Explain your answer. (Do not carry out any further calculations.)   O.N.C.

4.18 (a) Define the median, mean, and mode listing the advantages and disadvantages attributable to each.

  (b) (i) Calculate the median, mean and mode for the following:

Wage Groups (hourly rate in pence)	Number of Employees
50 and under 60	5
60 and under 70	25
70 and under 80	134
80 and under 90	85
90 and under 100	69
100 and under 110	43
110 and under 120	34

  (ii) Illustrate a use for each of the three statistics calculated.
                                                                I.C.M.A.

4.19 The marks scored by students in an examination are shown below. (Marking is in whole marks only.)

Marks Scored	10–19	20–29	30–39	40–49	50–59	60–69	70–79	80–89	90–99
No. of Students	4	12	23	37	43	32	19	8	2

(a) Draw a histogram to illustrate the above distribution.

(b) What are the class boundaries of the modal class?

(c) Estimate by calculation the median mark.

(d) If $16\frac{2}{3}\%$ of the pupils are to be given a pass with distinction, what mark will be necessary to achieve this?

(e) What proportion would fail if the pass mark were 48?
                                                                O.N.C.

4.20 The following figures give the age at 1st June 1974 of a sample of 100 students taking O.N.C. in Business Studies examinations in 1974. The ages are rounded to the next lowest complete month.

Years	Months	Years	Months	Years	Months	Years	Months	Years	Months
17	7	18	4	17	0	16	5	18	8
18	2	18	3	17	11	18	8	18	7
17	9	17	3	17	10	18	9	17	3
16	5	17	1	18	9	17	2	17	10
19	2	18	9	19	5	16	10	18	1

Years	Months	Years	Months	Years	Months	Years	Months	Years	Months
17	9	17	8	17	3	17	3	18	4
17	3	18	11	17	4	16	9	17	11
16	11	19	0	18	0	16	8	18	0
18	5	19	8	17	9	17	1	18	3
18	4	16	4	17	11	18	4	18	1
17	11	16	10	16	10	19	0	16	10
17	10	18	1	17	2	18	11	16	11
18	3	17	8	17	2	17	11	17	2
16	9	17	7	17	1	18	0	17	3
17	2	16	11	17	7	17	10	17	8
18	0	17	3	16	10	17	3	17	11
17	0	18	2	18	3	16	9	18	2
17	8	18	11	17	2	16	6	17	10
17	9	17	5	17	3	17	5	17	10
18	1	18	5	17	9	17	8	18	3

(a) From these figures compile a frequency distribution table. You are advised to work in half-yearly class intervals, paying particular attention to the way you select these intervals and their class boundaries.
(b) Draw a histogram to represent the frequency distribution.
(c) From the histogram find a value for the modal age.

O.N.C.

4.21 A random sample of the accounts of 50 construction companies gave the following frequency distribution of profit for 1973–4.

Profit (£ million)	Number of Companies
−10 and under −5	2
−5 and under 0	0
0 and under 5	2
5 and under 10	4
10 and under 15	8
15 and under 20	11
20 and under 25	13
25 and under 30	6
30 and under 35	4

Required: Construct an ogive of the cumulative frequency distribution and use it to estimate:

(1) the median profit,
(2) the profit exceeded by 75% of companies,
(3) the number of companies out of 500 similar ones whose profit for that year was between 8 and 18 million pounds.

A.C.A.

4.22 (a) Required: Place the arithmetic mean, median and mode in order of merit as averages for the following frequency distributions, and briefly explain your rankings in each case.

(1) Incomes, taken from a wages survey.
(2) Ladies' shoe sizes, based on sales data.
(3) Percentage of defective products, based on batches examined.

(b) The following table shows the number of hours of sunshine recorded during July at Bournpool for the years 1965–73:

Hours of Sunshine	Number of Days
0 and under 1	1
1 and under 2	2
2 and under 3	4
3 and under 4	11
4 and under 5	24
5 and under 6	35
6 and under 7	43
7 and under 8	49
8 and under 9	54
9 and under 10	31
10 and under 11	15
11 and under 12	10
	279

Required: Calculate:

(1) the mean number of hours of sunshine,
(2) the median number of hours of sunshine.   A.C.A.

4.23 The table below gives the distribution of marks of a group of candidates taking a statistics examination.

Examination Results 1973

Mark	Number of Candidates
30 and under 40	2
40 and under 50	5
50 and under 60	7
60 and under 70	13
70 and under 80	15
80 and under 90	5
90 and under 100	3

You are required to:

(a) calculate the mean and the median marks, and
(b) explain what the values calculated in your answer to (a) indicate about the distribution of examination results, particularly with reference to the difference between the mean and median values.   A.C.A.

4.24 In a survey of the value of orders received, a manufacturing company obtained the following grouped frequency table:

Value of Orders (£)	Number of Orders
100 and up to but less than 200	169
200 and up to but less than 300	176
300 and up to but less than 400	75
400 and up to but less than 500	32
500 and up to but less than 600	8

Draw the histogram for this distribution and from this, or by other means, find the value of the modal order, to the nearer £1. Calculate the mean value of orders, and thus estimate the total value of all the orders.   I.C.S.A.

4.25 By taking random samples over a period information has been collected giving the following age distribution of young persons attending a sport and recreation centre:

Age in Years	Number of Young Persons
12 and under 13	3
13 and under 14	11
14 and under 15	29
15 and under 16	99
16 and under 17	203
17 and under 18	258
18 and under 19	247

(a) Calculate to the nearest month the arithmetic mean age and the median age of young persons attending the centre.
(b) Find the modal age to the nearest month of young persons attending the centre.

Discuss the relative merits and possible uses of these three measures of central position.   O.N.C.

4.26   *Personal Incomes before tax 1967–8 U.K.*

Income Range	Number (thousands)	Income for Class (£ millions)
less than £350	903	283
£350– £450	1346	539
£450– £600	2388	1251
£600– £800	3058	2140
£800–£1000	3134	2821
£1000–£1200	2953	3239
£1200–£1400	2510	3255
£1400–£1750	2874	4471
£1750–£3000	2007	4247
over £3000	558	3026
Total	21731	25272

Source: Abstract of Regional Statistics 1970.

Find the mean, median and modal incomes. Which, in your opinion, is the best indicator of the average income?

Portray the data in the above table either by a suitable histogram or by means of a Lorenz curve. Which do you think is the best method of visual presentation? C.I.P.F.A.

4.27 (a) Discuss the importance of averages in statistical analysis, and describe the characteristics and methods of calculation of two *commonly* used averages.

(b) Using the geometric mean, calculate the average annual ratio of change in family income from the data in the following table

Year	Family Income as a Ratio of Preceding Year's Income
1967	1.05
1968	1.17
1969	1.33
1970	1.25

(c) Explain the use of the geometric mean as an average and what your answer indicates about the change in family income over the period. A.C.A.

4.28 Given that the population of the United Kingdom in 1962 was 53,266,000 and in 1972 was 55,933,000; estimate the population in 1967. Comment on your estimate given that the population in 1967 was 54,746,000.

4.29 Suppose we decided to make a general-purpose fertiliser by mixing together in equal values 5 ingredients costing £1, £5, £6, £9, and £11 per kilo. Find the cost per kilo of the mixture.

4.30 Prove that the sum of squares of the deviations of the items from the arithmetic mean is a minimum (you will need a knowledge of differential calculus to be able to show this).

Chapter Five

Index Numbers

In the last chapter, we explored at some depth the meaning of the word average, and we were at pains to point out that an average is not necessarily representative of the data it describes. In this chapter, we are going to concern ourselves with averages at work – especially in an economic context. Make no mistake about it, averages do play a very important part in our lives – especially those that try to describe economic data. Now statisticians have constructed a device which attempts to measure the magnitude of economic changes over time – a device called an *index number*. This device is also used for international comparisons of economic data. Almost certainly, the Index of Retail Prices is the most widely quoted of all index numbers. Let us now examine just how important this index is to all of us.

You will realise that the Index of Retail Prices attempts to measure the change in the price of a whole range of goods and services that we regularly buy. So you can see that it is attempting to measure the cost of living – something that vitally concerns us all. In these times of inflation, the retail price index is probably more important than at any other time in its existence. The United Kingdom government has introduced measures in an attempt to reduce our rate of inflation to single figures, and this index will be used as a yardstick of its success. However, its importance does not stop here. Increases in the cost of living have been accepted as justification for an increase in pay, and the Index of Retail Prices has often been used as a basis for wage negotiations. In fact, a few years ago many million workers obtained an automatic 40p rise per week for each one-point rise in the cost of living index – the so-called threshold payments. Due to government pressure, it is no longer fashionable to link wage rates to the cost of living directly, but any incomes policy that ignores the index altogether seems doomed to failure. As further examples of the importance of this index we could note that the government have introduced an index-linked issue of savings certificates (provided they are redeemed after retirement), the value of which will rise with the cost of living. Also, it is government policy to make pensions index-linked. If we are willing to accept index linking as desirable, we should be sure that we know what an index is, how it is calculated and what its limitations are.

Without doubt, an index is an extremely fashionable statistical tool. Open any copy of the Annual Abstract of Statistics and you are sure to be impressed by the number of indexes (or indices, if you prefer this form of the plural) that are calculated by the government statisticians. In fact, no self-respecting government department would fail to produce at least one index! We do not wish you to get the impression that all index numbers are generated by government departments – the Financial Times Ordinary Share Index, and the Economist's Key Indicators are notable indexes generated by the private sector. With the great number of indexes available, and the fact that they are used as a basis for taking decisions of national importance, it is worrying to be told that some statisticians doubt their validity. Moroney,[1] for example, thinks their compilation is a pure waste of time and effort. Now we cannot subscribe to this view. Index numbers are an invaluable tool in the decision-taking process – provided that they are treated with caution!

What is an Index Number?

One of the commodities which is subject to frequent price fluctuations is gold. The following prices for gold on the London Bullion Market were extracted from the *Financial Times* (prices are approximate as we had to extract them from a graph that was not very easy to read).

End of	$ per fine ounce
Aug. 1975	155
Sept.	143
Oct.	144
Nov.	139
Dec.	140
Jan. 1976	131

We notice that the trend in gold prices has been steadily downwards. The price at the end of September was $\frac{143}{155} \times 100 = 92.3\%$ of the previous month's price and the price at the end of October was 92.9% of the price at the end of August. If we call the price at the end of August 100% we can calculate percentages for each of the other months like this:

[1] Moroney: *Facts from Figures* (Pelican).

End of	Price as % of Aug. 1975	
Aug. 1975		100
Sept.	$\frac{143}{155} \times 100$	92.3
Oct.	$\frac{144}{155} \times 100$	92.9
Nov.	$\frac{139}{155} \times 100$	89.7
Dec.	$\frac{140}{155} \times 100$	90.3
Jan.	$\frac{131}{155} \times 100$	84.5

The percentages we have calculated in the final column are index numbers (it is usual to drop the percentage sign). We first decide on a *base* (in this case, August 1975), and calculate the relative change in price for the following periods. In other words, if we call the price in the base period P_0, and the price in any following period P_n, then the index for that period is

$$\frac{P_n}{P_0} \times 100$$

If this is all that is involved in index numbers you might well wonder what all the controversy surrounding them could possibly be about! Well, for a start, this is a very simple series of index numbers, and we will soon be examining more complicated ones (and hence more controversial ones). But even with an index as simple as this one, there is a problem involved: the choice of a suitable base period. We wish really to choose a base when the price is as 'normal' as possible, i.e. when the price is not unduly high or unduly low. Otherwise, the index will move away from the base figure too quickly and show very large deviations from it. Suppose, for example, the price of a particular stock at certain periods of time was

April	125p	(takeover rumour)
July	69p	(takeover unsuccessful, poor dividends announced)
Dec.	95p	(quite good dividends forecast)

then the price index for this particular stock could be

April = 100		July = 100	Dec. = 100
April	100	181.2	131.6
July	55.2	100	72.6
Dec.	76	137.7	100

The best base to choose is probably December, because this minimises the greatest deviation from the base (31.6). Does this matter? Well, there is evidence to show that people are more likely to understand and appreciate smaller percentage changes than larger ones. This is one of the reasons that statisticians tend to update the bases that they use. Another reason is that bases in the not-too-distant past tend to be much more meaningful to the users of the index. It would be much more reasonable to compare prices now with prices in (say) 1970 than it would be to compare them with prices in 1949.

This problem of choosing a suitable base can also be illustrated if we are constructing an index to measure the volume of production. Suppose we wish to measure the increase in motor-vehicle production. If we take as our base a month in which there is a major strike, then the index in the following months would be bound to show a substantial increase and give a misleading impression of the prosperity of the motor industry. If we were constructing an index of motor-car sales, which do you think would be the *worst* month to choose as a base?

A Simple Aggregate Index

So far, we have concerned ourselves with measuring the price changes for a single commodity – but suppose we want to measure changes in the cost of living. Our monthly spending is made up of a whole range of goods, and in measuring cost of living changes we will want to take this into account. We could, of course, construct a separate index for each of the goods we buy, but this would be very cumbersome. What we require is a single index that will efficiently measure changes in the cost of living for us. Suppose we wish to construct a price index for gardeners. Typical items that they might buy would be

| | Price in | |
	1975	1976
Seeds (per packet)	8p	10p
Onion sets (per lb)	20p	24p
Seed compost (per kilo)	65p	85p
Fertiliser (per kilo)	75p	£1.25
	£1.68p	£2.44

So we can see that a bundle of gardening goods costing £1.68 in 1975 would cost £2.44 in 1976. If we take 1975 as our base year, then the price index for 1976 could be calculated like this:

$$\frac{2.44}{1.68} \times 100 = 145.2, \quad 1975 = 100$$

An index constructed like this is called a *simple aggregate index*, and from it we can conclude that the cost of gardening has risen 45.2% between 1975 and 1976. Or can we? Suppose we had quoted the price of fertiliser in 5 kilo units, then the prices would be:

	1975	1976
Seeds (per packet)	8p	10p
Onion sets (per lb)	20p	24p
Seed compost (per kilo)	65p	85p
Fertiliser (per 5 kilo)	£3.75p	£6.25
	£4.68	£7.44

Again taking 1975 as our base, the price index for 1976 is

$$\frac{7.44}{4.68} \times 100 = 158.9$$

which gives a very different result from the previous one! The trouble with simple aggregate indexes is that the result you get depends on the quantities you choose. If we had quoted the price of onion sets in 3-lb units the result would have been different again. Try it for yourself and see. The problem here is to decide what quantities are appropriate, and for this reason few people would take such indexes seriously (though they are still used). What we require is an index independent of the quantities bought.

Suppose that for each good we divide the 1976 price by the 1975 price. This gives us the *price relatives* with 1975 as base.

	1975	1976	Price Relative
Seeds (per packet)	8p	10p	1.25
Onion sets (per lb)	20p	24p	1.20
Seed compost (per kilo)	65p	85p	1.31
Fertiliser (per kilo)	75p	£1.25	1.66
			5.42

So the price relative shows the percentage change in price for each of the goods (seeds, for example, cost 25% more in 1976 than in 1975). If we find the arithmetic mean of the price relatives, and multiply by 100, we have the price index for 1976.

$$\frac{5.42}{4} \times 100 = 135.5$$

Suppose we call the price in the base year P_0, and the price in the nth year P_n, then an index of the arithmetic mean of the price relatives can be calculated like this:

$$\frac{\sum \dfrac{P_n}{P_0}}{x} \times 100$$

where x is the number of goods we are considering.

The great advantage of this index over the simple aggregate index is that it is independent of the quantities used (the price relative for fertiliser is 1.66 whether we measure in kilos or in 5 kilos). In this respect, it is a better index than the simple aggregate index. However, it does have its faults, as it takes no account of the quantities bought. Would it be true to say that a 25% increase in the price of seeds has less significance than a 31% increase in the price of seed compost? On a percentage basis, the answer must without doubt be 'yes', but in fact the significance of price changes depends on the actual price (a 50% increase in petrol prices is more significant than a 50% increase in the price of matches). Also, the significance of a price increase depends on the quantities bought (a 50% increase in the price of tobacco has no significance to the non-smoker). We shall now turn our attention to devising an index that attempts to overcome these problems.

Weighted Averages

Returning to our friend the gardener, suppose we asked him to supply us with details of the quantities of materials he bought in 1975. Suppose he bought the following quantities:

> 20 packets of seeds
> 2 lb of onion sets
> 1 kilo of seed compost
> 3 kilos of fertiliser

Multiplying these quantities by their prices, we can calculate how much he spent on these goods in 1975. Also, we know the prices of these goods in 1976, so we can calculate how much the 1975 quantities would cost if they were bought in 1976.

1975 Quantities (q_0)	1975 Prices (p_0)	1976 Prices (p_n)	$p_0 q_0$	$p_n q_0$
20	8	10	160	200
2	20	24	40	48
1	65	85	65	85
3	75	125	225	375
			490	708

So we can see that the batch of gardening goods bought in 1975 cost £4.90, and if we had bought the same batch in 1976 it would have cost £7.08. So if we say that the goods cost 100 in 1975, their cost in 1976 would be –

$$\frac{708}{490} \times 100 = 144.5$$

that is, a 44.5% increase in price.

Notice that we call the base year quantities q_0, the base year prices p_0, and the prices of the same goods in the nth year p_n. So we can calculate this index by taking

$$\frac{\Sigma\, p_n q_0}{\Sigma p_0 q_0} \times 100$$

It shows what the cost of goods in the nth year would be, assuming that we bought the same quantities as in the base year, and assuming that we called the base year price 100. An index calculated in this way is called a *Laspeyre index*, and without doubt it is a considerable improvement on the previous two indexes.

Before we judge how efficient is the Laspeyre index, we should note that in practice it is not usually calculated in the way we have done – it is more usual to use price relatives and weights. To understand what is meant by weights, let us examine the total outlay on each good in 1975.

Outlay	Price Relative
£1.60 on seeds	1.25
£0.40 on onion sets	1.20
£0.65 on seed compost	1.31
£2.25 on fertiliser	1.66
£4.90	

The total outlay on each good measures the relative size of each good in our purchases, and we can see that a doubling in the price of, say, fertiliser is more significant than a doubling in the price of onion sets. Alongside the outlays we have written the price relatives. Notice that seed compost has increased in price by a greater percentage than seeds, but as seeds involve a greater total outlay, the increase in the price of seeds is probably more significant. If we multiply price relative by total outlay, then we will be taking into account the fact that expenditure on some items is more significant than expenditure on others. We will be *weighting* the price relatives, and using the expenditures in 1975 as weights. Notice that our suspicions are confirmed: the increase in price of seeds is more significant than the in-

Weights (w)	Price Relatives (PR)	$w \times PR$
1.60	1.25	2.0000
0.40	1.20	0.4800
0.65	1.31	0.8515
2.25	1.66	3.7350
4.90		7.0665

crease in price of seed compost. An index for 1976 is now obtained like this:

$$\frac{7.0665}{4.90} \times 100 = 144.2, \quad \text{i.e.}$$

$$\frac{\Sigma\,(\text{price relative} \times \text{weight})}{\Sigma\,(\text{weights})} \times 100$$

This gives an identical index to the expression for the Laspeyre index (the difference of 0.3 is due to rounding off the price relatives).

More usually, the weights are made to total some convenient figure. Often this figure is one; in the case of the Index of Retail Prices it is 1000. So in the case of seeds, for example, the weights could be expressed as

$$\frac{1.6}{4.9} = 0.3265, \quad \text{in which case the weights would total one}$$

or $1.6 \times \dfrac{1000}{4.9} = 326.5, \quad$ in which case the weights would total 1000.

Whichever way is used, we are considering weights as the outlay on each item relative to total outlay, and the index obtained would be identical to using *actual* outlay on each item. Try it for yourself and see. The reason for using relative outlay is that it is easier to divide by one or a thousand than it is to divide by (say) 4.9 (remember we will be calculating an index for each year). Also, relative outlay makes comparison between items easier than actual outlay.

Both methods that we have used are weighted averages. In the first case, we used prices and quantities – in fact the quantities were acting as weights. So if we wish to use base year quantities as weights, then we must use actual prices to calculate our price index. However, if we use base year expenditures as weights, then we use price relatives to calculate the index. Most statisticians prefer to use expenditure rather than quantities as weights. The reason is quite simply that it is easier to obtain data on expenditure (the cost of living data is obtained by the Survey of Household Expenditure – that is by sampling). Also, we can consider occasions when 'quantities' wouldn't make sense – how can one define 'quantities' of public transport? However, it would be quite possible to obtain details of personal expenditure on public transport.

We have considered weighted averages without considering the problems involved in weighting. Take the example of our gardener: we have included seeds, onion sets, seed compost and fertiliser on his annual shopping list. Clearly, this list cannot be exhaustive: many other items should be included on the list. This is a basic problem of constructing a price index – what should be included and what should be left out. We have not included gardening tools on the assumption that he already has them, but tools wear out and will need replacing. Hence changes in the price of tools will ultimately affect our gardener, and should be included in our index. If we are going to use quantities as weights, then we must take into account the life of tools. It would be much easier to weight tools in our index by taking the money outlay on tools by a number of representative gardeners.

It might be useful to list at this point the items included in the General Index of Retail Prices.

Commodity	Weight[1]
Food	228
Alcoholic drink	81
Tobacco	46
Housing	112
Fuel and light	56
Durable household goods	75
Clothing and footwear	84
Transport and vehicles	140
Miscellaneous goods	74
Services	57
Meals bought and consumed outside the home	47
	1000

[1] Weights are for 1976.

Durable goods includes such items as television sets, washing machines, etc.

Let us summarise what we have done so far. We have calculated an index called a Laspeyre index, which tells us what we would have paid in year n for a collection of goods assuming we bought base year quantities. This description is true whether we use expenditure or quantities as weights. The point is that the Laspeyre index uses base year statistics as weights. Now many statisticians doubt the validity of taking base year weights, as it implies that the quantities we buy do not vary over time. In many cases this will not be true. Suppose we have a cost of living index based on 1970, and one of the items included is potatoes. The index for 1976 would assume that we bought the same quantity of potatoes as in 1970. But the period 1975–6 saw a dramatic increase in the price of potatoes, and one consequence of this was a fall in demand. Without doubt, people consumed considerably less potatoes and turned to substitutes, so because of this fall in quantity purchased the Laspeyre index tends to *overstate* increases in price. Another problem is that tastes tend to change fairly markedly over time, so weights that were appropriate for 1970 will not be appropriate for 1976. For example, few colour television sets were bought in 1970 in preference to monochrome, but in 1976 this situation was completely reversed.

In an attempt to overcome these problems, many statisticians have suggested that current year quantities should be used as weights. Our index now becomes

$$\frac{\Sigma\, p_n q_n}{\Sigma\, p_0 q_n} \times 100$$

and such an index is called a *Paasche* index. The approach here is quite different: we ask what would be the total outlay in the base year if we bought current year quantities, and compare this with current year outlay. This certainly overcomes the main objections to the Laspeyre index, but does tend to raise problems of its own. Firstly, the Paasche index is not a pure price index as it also takes into account changes in quantities bought. Just, then, as the Laspeyre index tends to *overstate* the effect of rising prices, the Paasche index tends to *understate* the effects. Secondly, it can be a long and expensive job calculating the values for the weights with a Paasche index. This must be done for every period, while with a Laspeyre index this is done for the base year only. The current cost of living index is a compromise between the two: the index is published monthly and the weights are adjusted annually by the Survey of Consumer Expenditure.

Chain Base Index Numbers

Earlier, we suggested why the base period should not be in the too distant past. An alternative is to use a chain base index, where the base used is the previous period. This method has found particular favour in the United States. Let us return to the example of gold prices considered earlier, and calculate chain based index numbers for this data.

Time Period	Price ($)	Price Index, previous month $= 100$	Price Index Aug. $= 100$
August	155	100	100
September	143	$\frac{143}{155} \times 100 = 92.3$	92.3
October	144	$\frac{144}{143} \times 100 = 100.7$	92.9
November	139	$\frac{139}{144} \times 100 = 96.5$	89.7
December	140	$\frac{140}{139} \times 100 = 100.7$	90.3
January	131	$\frac{131}{140} \times 100 = 93.6$	84.5

So we can see that in (say) January the price of gold bullion was 6.4% lower than in the previous month. We can apply this method to the weighted indexes we considered earlier. The Laspeyre index would become

$$\frac{\Sigma\, p_n q_0}{\Sigma p_{n-1} q_0} \times 100$$

i.e. using base period weights, current and previous year's prices. The Paasche index becomes

$$\frac{\Sigma\, p_n q_n}{\Sigma\, p_{n-1} q_n} \times 100.$$

Chain based index numbers are particularly suited for period by period comparisons, but if we are to compare the movement of prices over time then the fixed based indexes are much easier to interpret.

Volume Indexes

So far, we have concerned ourselves with finding a price index. We have considered changes in price and used quantities as weights. In many cases, however, we use exactly the opposite procedure – consider changes in quantities and use prices as weights. This gives what we call a *volume* index, and the Index of Industrial Production is an example.[1]

Suppose we compare the expenditure on two collections of goods at different periods of time. If we keep the quantities the same, then any variation in outlay is due to changes in price, so we can calculate

[1] In fact, the Index of Industrial Production uses volume of net output as weights.

a price index. If however, we keep the prices the same, then any variation in outlay must be due to changes in quantity, so we can calculate a quantity index. If then, we use quantities as weights we obtain a price index, but if we use prices as weights we obtain a volume index. Again we have the choice between current year and base year weighting, so we have

$$\text{Laspeyre volume index} = \frac{\Sigma\, p_0 q_n}{\Sigma\, p_0 q_0} \times 100$$

$$\text{Paasche volume index} = \frac{\Sigma\, p_n q_n}{\Sigma\, p_n q_0} \times 100$$

In an attempt to clarify the difference between a price and a volume index, let us examine a question set for the Scottish National Certificate in Business Studies.

Imports through Certain U.K. Ports

	Declared Value (£ million)	Value at 1950 Prices (£ million)
1950	522	522
1951	430	533
1952	351	469

The question asks us to distinguish between declared value and value at 1950 prices, and to construct index numbers for price and volume with 1950 as base year.

Let us take the figures for 1952 as an example. The declared value for 1952 is the 1952 quantities imported valued at 1952 prices, so if we call 1952 year n, the £351m represents $\Sigma\, p_n q_n$. The other figure for 1952 takes the quantities imported, but values them at 1950 prices, and as 1950 is our base year the £469 represents $\Sigma\, p_0 q_n$.

In fact, the column headed 'value at 1950 prices' enables us to calculate a volume index quite easily. The first figure (£522m) is base year quantities at base year prices ($\Sigma\, p_0 q_0$) and the remaining figures represent current year quantities at base year prices ($\Sigma\, p_0 q_n$). So we have all the information to calculate a Laspeyre volume index.

$$\text{Volume index for } 1951 = \frac{533}{522} \times 100 = 102.1$$

$$\text{Volume index for } 1952 = \frac{469}{522} \times 100 = 89.8$$

To find the price index, we notice that for each year we have current year quantities at current year prices ($\Sigma\, p_n q_n$), and current year quantities at base year prices ($\Sigma\, p_0 q_n$). So we have all the information to calculate a Paasche price index.

$$\text{Price index for } 1951 = \frac{430}{533} \times 100 = 80.7$$

$$\text{Price index for } 1952 = \frac{351}{469} \times 100 = 74.8$$

So we can conclude that the fall in the value of imports in 1951 was entirely due to the fall in import prices (the quantity imported actually increased). The fall in value of imports in 1952 was partly due to import prices and partly due to the fall in the quantity imported.

Using an Index for 'Deflating' a Series

It is a well-known fact that wages have risen dramatically since 1960, and standards of living have risen too. However, as we all know, price rises can erode increases in earnings, and economists have coined the phrase 'real wages' which shows how incomes have changed, taking price changes into account. Let us examine the relevant statistics.

Year	Average Weekly Earnings of Manual Workers in Manufacturing Industries (£)	Retail Price Index
1960	15.16	114.5
1961	15.89	117.5
1962	16.34	100
1963	17.29	103.6
1964	18.66	107.0
1965	20.16	112.1
1966	20.78	116.5
1967	21.89	119.4
1968	23.62	125.0
1969	25.54	131.8
1970	28.91	140.2
1971	31.37	153.4
1972	36.20	164.3
1973	41.52	179.4
1974	49.12	191.8

Source: Annual Abstract of Statistics.

The first problem that we notice is that the price index has undergone a change of base. Earlier figures have 1956 as base, while later figures have 1962 as base. We will need to obtain a price index related to a single base, and it is usual to take the most recent base as the base for the entire series. So we will want to recalculate price indexes for 1960 and 1961 with 1962 as base. Now when a base changes, it is usual to calculate a price index for a few periods using both the new and the old base. Consulting the Annual Abstract, we see that for 1962 the price index using the old base was 119.3, so we have:

$$\text{Price index for } 1960 = 114.5 \times \frac{100}{119.3} = 95.98$$

$$\text{Price index for } 1961 = 117.5 \times \frac{100}{119.3} = 98.49$$

We can now use the retail price index to deflate actual earnings and obtain real wages (taking into account price rises since 1962). For example, average wage for 1970 at 1962 prices is

$$\frac{28.91}{140.2} \times 100 = £20.62$$

So actual and real wages over the period would look like this:

Year	Average Weekly Earnings (£)	Real Income
1960	£15.16	£15.79
1961	£15.89	£16.13
1962	£16.34	£16.34
1963	£17.29	£16.69
1964	£18.66	£17.44
1965	£20.16	£17.98
1966	£20.78	£17.84
1967	£21.89	£18.33
1968	£23.62	£18.90
1969	£25.54	£19.38
1970	£28.91	£20.62
1971	£31.37	£20.45
1972	£36.20	£22.03
1973	£41.52	£23.14
1974	£49.12	£25.61

When actual weekly earnings are deflated, a very different picture emerges; though without doubt living standards have risen. Notice that in all years except 1971 wages were rising faster than prices. We could if we wish calculate an index of real wages with 1962 (or any other year for that matter) as base by dividing current year real wages by 16.34 and multiplying by 100. So the index for 1970 would be:

$$\frac{20.62}{16.34} \times 100 = 126.2$$

Standardised Death Rates

Before we finish this chapter, we should note that there are many other types of weighted average in addition to the ones mentioned here. We shall now examine one such average *not* in index form. Interest in death is not just confined to people like Vincent Price and undertakers – statisticians are interested in *death rates* because they help to make population predictions. If we consult the Registrar General's Statistical Review of England and Wales (Medical) we can find all the information on births and deaths that we could use. The book is rather like the *Guinness Book of Records* – once you start reading it you can't put it down! Did you know, for example, that not one single person died of Rat-bite Fever in the last decade? This information must come as a great relief to you!

In any case, consulting the tables for 1971, we can extract the following information

	Estimated Population (thousands)	Number of Deaths
Merseyside Conurbation	1,263.0	15,514
East Anglia	1,680.9	18,900

We obtain the crude death rate by calculating the number of deaths per thousand of population. So we have

Crude death rate for Merseyside is

$$\frac{15,514}{1,263} = 12.28 \text{ per thousand}$$

and for East Anglia is

$$\frac{18,900}{1,680.9} = 11.24 \text{ per thousand}$$

Surprisingly, perhaps, there is little difference between the crude death rates – one is normally induced to believe that it is healthier to live in rural areas than it is to live in conurbations. However, crude death rates are not really suited to comparisons because they are influenced by different age structures. Suppose, for example, that East Anglia has a high proportion of babies under one year and a high proportion of old people. These age groups have high mortality rates and will tend to push the crude death rate upwards. Let us calculate the death rates for different age groups in both regions.

Age	Merseyside Conurbation			East Anglia		
	Population ('000's)	Number of Deaths	Deaths per thou.	Population ('000's)	Number of Deaths	Deaths per thou.
Under 1 year	21.1	437	20.71	26.1	406	15.56
1– 4	80.0	75	0.94	107.3	59	0.55
5–14	225.6	87	0.39	259.9	89	0.34
15–24	195.6	109	0.56	247.0	166	0.67
25–34	142.8	126	0.88	214.8	159	0.74
35–44	144.4	330	2.29	195.8	316	1.61
45–54	150.7	1,063	7.05	196.6	926	4.71
55–64	147.8	2,660	18.00	195.3	2,416	12.37
65–74	101.6	4,231	41.64	151.9	5,047	33.23
75 and over	53.4	6,396	119.78	86.2	9,316	108.07
	1,263.0	15,514		1,680.9	18,900	

We notice that the death rate on Merseyside is higher at all age groups except the group 15–24 (can you suggest reasons why this group should be the odd-one-out?). Notice that Merseyside has a significantly higher mortality rate for its infants and very old people. But what we really require to calculate is a mortality rate that does not depend upon the age structure of the region. What we shall do is to take a standard population (usually the population of England and Wales is chosen) and calculate the expected number of deaths if East Anglian and Merseyside death rates were experienced. We can then calculate what we call a standardised death rate – the number of deaths per thousand which would occur in the standard population if the regional death rate applies to this population. Thus, the standardised death rate depends only on the region's mortality rates and not on its age structure.

Age Group	Population of England and Wales ('000's)	Merseyside Death Rates	Expected No. of Deaths	Anglian Death Rates	Expected No. of Deaths
Under 1 year	781.6	20.71	16,187	15.56	12,162
1– 4	3,138.3	0.94	2,950	0.55	1,726
5–14	7,756.6	0.39	3,025	0.34	2,637
15–24	7,082.7	0.56	3,966	0.67	4,745
25–34	6,143.8	0.88	5,407	0.74	4,546
35–44	5,721.0	2.29	13,101	1.61	9,211
45–54	6,012.8	7.05	42,390	4.71	28,320
55–64	5,780.8	18.00	104,054	12.37	71,508
65–74	4,150.3	41.64	172,818	33.23	137,914
75 and over	2,247.1	119.78	269,158	108.07	242,844
	48,815		633,056		515,613

The standardised death rate for Merseyside is $\frac{633,056}{48,815} = 12.97$ per thousand, and for East Anglia is $\frac{515,613}{48,815} = 10.56$ per thousand. So standardising increases the Merseyside death rate but reduces the Anglian death rate.

EXERCISES TO CHAPTER 5

5.1   What considerations must be borne in mind when an index number is compiled? You should illustrate your answer by reference to any index number with which you are familiar.   O.N.C.

5.2   What is the purpose of an index number? Describe the main methods for constructing index numbers, indicating the advantages and disadvantages of each. Illustrate one of the methods by reference to any index number in current use.   C.I.P.F.A.

5.3   Why are weights used in the construction of index numbers? What is meant by:

(a) base weighting;
(b) current weighting;

and what are the advantages and disadvantages of each?
          I.C.M.A.

5.4   Define the following kinds of index numbers:

(a) fixed base;
(b) chain base;
(c) base weighted;
(d) current weighted.

   Give an example of any published index with which you are familiar, briefly indicating how it is compiled and what the information it gives is intended to show.   O.N.C.

5.5   A company has reached an agreement with representatives of its employees that wages and salaries will in future be tied to a local cost of living index which the company will compile. Advise the company how they should gather information and compile this local cost of living index. What are the problems the company will encounter in completing this exercise?   O.N.C.

5.6 (a) Explain briefly the principles of index number construction.

(b) A certain company uses approximately 6, 2, 5, 3 thousand units of raw materials, A, B, C, D respectively. The average price (£) per unit of the raw materials in 1970 and 1973 is given in the following table:

	Average Price in 1970	Average Price in 1973
Raw material A	10	15
B	21	39
C	2	3
D	46	101

Calculate the Simple Aggregative Index for the year 1973 with 1970 as base year. Calculate also a Weighted Aggregative Index for the period 1970–3 and explain why this may be considered preferable to the Simple Aggregative Index.   O.N.C.

5.7   The average prices of four commodities for the years 1969, 1970 and 1971 are shown in the following table:

Commodity	Average Price per Unit (£)		
	1969	1970	1971
A	8	15	14
B	54	70	72
C	15	22	29
D	75	84	78

(i) Calculate the *Simple Aggregative Index* for each of the years 1970 and 1971 with 1969 as base year.
(ii) Write down *two* main disadvantages in the use of the Simple Aggregative Index.
(iii) The number of units used annually by a certain company is approximately 5000, 1000, 3000 and 8000 for commodities A, B, C and D respectively. Calculate a Weighted Aggregative Index for the period 1969–71 and explain to what extent this Index overcomes the disadvantages you mentioned in part (ii) of this question.   O.N.C.

5.8

Index Numbers of Wholesale and Retail Prices

Food Manufacturing Industries Price Indices		Food Index of Retail Prices $(16/1/62 = 100)$
Materials and Fuel Used $(1970 = 100)$	Output $(1970 = 100)$	
1972		
January	111.4	112.2	163.9
February	110.1	111.8	165.1
March	110.3	112.0	166.0
April	108.9	111.4	164.6
May	109.8	111.9	166.3
June	109.4	112.5	169.2
July	110.1	113.2	169.2
August	113.0	115.4	172.3
September	113.1	115.9	172.4
October	114.8	116.8	172.8
November	118.6	117.6	174.3
December	125.4	118.5	176.9

Source: Monthly Digest of Statistics.

(a) Explain what is meant by (i) *index number* and (ii) *base year*.
(b) Using January 1972 as the base period reduce the above figures to a comparable basis.
(c) Comment briefly on the results in (b).   O.N.C.

5.9 (a) Describe the main features of the Index of Industrial Production.

(b) The following table shows the U.S. consumption (millions of pounds) and price (dollars per pound) of vegetable oil products.

Type of Oil	1963		1964		1965	
	Quantity	Price	Quantity	Price	Quantity	Price
Soybean	322	0.13	368	0.12	367	0.13
Cotton seed	96	0.15	114	0.14	123	0.14
Linseed	32	0.13	31	0.13	19	0.12

Required: Taking 1963 as the base year, calculate Laspeyre's base weighted index numbers for the general level of prices of these products for 1964 and 1965.   A.C.A.

5.10 (a) In relation to index numbers, explain what is meant by
   (i) base year,
   (ii) weights.

(b) Calculate the missing value x, the weighting for housing, and y, the weighted arithmetic mean, the index for all items in the table below.

Index of Retail Prices for 1962 = 100

Group	Weights (1972)	Index (Sept. 1972)
Food	251	172
Alcoholic drink and tobacco	119	153
Housing	x	192
Fuel and light	60	173
Durable household goods	58	141
Clothing and footwear	89	144
Transport and vehicles	139	159
Other	163	177
All items	1000	y

Source: Monthly Digest of Statistics.

O.N.C.

5.11 (a) What is meant by the term 'index number'?

(b) *Index Numbers of Retail Prices in the U.K.*

Group	Index	Weight
Food	104	319
Housing	110	104
Durable household goods	100	64
Miscellaneous goods	108	63

(i) Using a weighted arithmetic mean calculate an index of retail prices for the group combining all four of these items.

(ii) If the index of retail prices for all household items (total weight = 1000) was 104, calculate the index for all household

O.N.C.

5.12 Two industries, A, labour-intensive and B, capital-intensive, find that the costs of their inputs had increased over the period 1970–4 as shown in the table, which also shows the distribution of their costs in 1970.

Input	Cost Distribution in 1970 (percentages)		% Increase in Costs over 1970
	Industry A	Industry B	
Labour	70	10	50
Raw materials	20	20	80
Capital	10	70	120
Totals	100	100	

(a) Calculate an index of total costs for each industry in 1974 based on 1970 = 100.
(b) Why do the two results in (a) differ?
(c) Why do you think your results may not accurately reflect the changes which have taken place from 1970 to 1974?
(d) What additional information would you require to give you
O.N.C.

5.13 The following information has been extracted from a company's payroll records:

	Unskilled Workers		Semi-skilled Workers		Skilled Workers	
	Average Weekly Wages (£)	Average Number Employed	Average Weekly Wages (£)	Average Number Employed	Average Weekly Wages (£)	Average Number Employed
1970	29.30	156	32.50	112	36.20	84
1973	38.60	207	39.50	125	42.20	78

(a) Calculate an index number of all average weekly wages for 1973 using 1970 as a base year and average numbers employed in 1970 as the basis for relative weights.
(b) Calculate an index number of all average weekly wages for 1970 using 1973 as a base year and average numbers employed in 1973 as the basis for relative weights.
(c) Discuss the relative advantages and disadvantages of using base year and current year weights. Are there any alternatives to these two methods?
O.N.C.

5.14

Commodity Prices

Commodity	Relative Quantities	Prices	
		June 1974	June 1975
A	3	27p	29p
B	8	16p	16p
C	14	48p	53p
D	9	47p	42p
E	7	87p	84p

(a) Calculate an all-items price index number for June 1975 based on June 1974 using the data of commodity prices given above.
(b) Convert the answer you have given to (a) to a base of June 1973 when the index stood at 94 (based on June 1974).
(c) Explain the relative advantages of base and current weighted index numbers.

(d) Explain the difference between an index number and a price relative.

5.15 From the following information calculate a weighted aggregate price index for three meat products for 1972, using
(a) Base year quantities as weights (1969 = 100), and
(b) 1972 quantities as weights.

Meat Product	Weights		Prices	
	1969 (q_0)	1972 (q_n)	1969 (p_0) (pence)	1972 (p_n) (pence)
A	1.0	0.1	50	65
B	0.5	0.5	60	70
C	0.1	1.0	70	125

(c) Explain clearly what your answers to (a) and (b) indicate about the movement of the prices of the three meat products between 1969 and 1972. A.C.A.

5.16 (a) Explain the function of index numbers and state why they are useful.
(b) From the following data calculate both the Laspeyre price index and Paasche price index:

Commodity	Unit of Purchase	Price per Unit		
		Base Period	Period 1	Period 2
		£	£	£
A	2 gallon drum	36	40	42
B	1 ton	80	90	100
C	10 pounds	45	41	41
D	1 kilogramme	15	16	18
E	100 yards	5	6	6
F	1 cwt	150	150	180

	Quantity in Units		
	Base Period	Period 1	Period 2
A	100	95	90
B	12	10	10
C	16	18	20
D	115	120	120
E	1100	1200	1400
F	70	60	60

I.C.M.A.

5.17   A company employs three grades of male direct operators, M1, M2 and M3, and three grades of female direct operators, F1, F2 and F3. The following represents numbers of operators employed and rates paid over three years:

Labour Grade	1971		1972		1973	
	Rate per hour	No. of Ops.	Rate per hour	No. of Ops.	Rate per hour	No. of Ops.
	£		£		£	
M1	0.66	32	0.73	33	0.80	35
M2	0.62	14	0.68	12	0.74	10
M3	0.56	16	0.60	14	0.66	12
F1	0.44	40	0.52	42	0.64	45
F2	0.41	18	0.47	18	0.58	16
F3	0.36	25	0.42	26	0.52	30

(a) Adopting 1971 as base calculate an index number for the average wage for 1972 and for 1973, using:

   (i) base weighting formula; and
   (ii) current weighting formula.

(b) State, with reasons, which method you would employ in a business situation.   I.C.M.A.

5.18   (a) Discuss the usefulness and shortcomings of price indices in general and of Laspeyre's and Paasche indices in particular.

(b) A tenants' association requires information about the relative increase in the weekly average rents paid to a certain borough council between 1945 and 1960. The data given below was collected from tenants.

1945		1950		1960	
Rents	No. of Tenants	Rents	No. of Tenants	Rents	No. of Tenants
£		£		£	
0.50	1280	0.70	1280	1.20	1280
0.75	760	1.00	750	1.65	750
1.00	410	1.25	580	2.00	590
1.50	86	1.85	400	2.50	700
2.00	70	2.45	250	3.25	950
4.00	10	4.60	190	5.00	1000

Calculate aggregate Laspeyre's and Paasche indices for 1950 and 1960 with 1945 = 100. Account for the differences in the answer obtained from the two indices.   C.I.P.F.A.

5.19 The prices and sales by value of four commodities are shown below for 1968 and 1972. Calculate the Laspeyre's and Paasche index numbers for 1972 taking 1968 = 100. Would you expect the two answers to have the same value?

Commodity	Price, £	1968 Sales by Value £m	Price, £	1972 Sales by Value £m
A	£2.00	8.0	£3.00	12.0
B	£1.00	6.5	£1.50	9.0
C	£4.50	9.0	£5.50	11.0
D	£7.00	14.0	£8.50	17.0

I.C.S.A.

5.20 (a) Why, in constructing a price index, are prices usually weighted by quantities?

(b) Under what circumstances is it preferable to weight prices by current quantities rather than by base year quantities?

(c) Carry out appropriate calculations to determine the overall percentage increase in price from 1970 to 1975 of the products listed below. Give your reasons for the choice of weighting selected.

Product	1970 Number Sold (millions)	1970 Price (£ per 1000)	1975 Number Sold (millions)	1975 Price (£ per 1000)
Buckles	1.6	6	2.4	10
Clips	3.4	9	3.0	12
Toggles	2.7	8	2.8	10

A.C.A.

5.21 A steel stockist notices that prices and values of sales for the main units of steel supply were (years 1969 and 1974 included):

Type of Steel Items	1969 Price per tonne £	1969 Sales £m	1974 Price per tonne £	1974 Sales £m
Ingots	162	324	200	600
Steel bars	188	564	190	760
Steel strip	220	880	275	1100

Calculate a Paasche index number for 1974 prices, taking 1969 = 100. I.C.S.A.

5.22 (a) From the information stated below construct a quantity index for the products made by Multiproducts Ltd. for the period 1966–9, weighted as to 1966 prices, and

(b) explain the purpose of preparing a quantity index, state what the indices calculated in (a) above indicate about the production of Multiproducts Ltd. for the years 1966–9, and discuss the influence of individual products on the index.

Multiproducts Ltd.

Product	1966 Average Price £	1966 Production (000's)	1967 Production (000's)	1968 Production (000's)	1969 Production (000's)
Pliers	2.00	62	65	66	90
Wrenches	3.00	138	120	110	80
Bolts	0.50	500	540	580	800
Drills	4.50	10	10	10	10

A.C.A.

5.23 Given the following data, calculate a measure of the increase in physical output in the U.K. of motor vehicles (passenger and commercial vehicles, taken together) in 1960 compared with 1958. For what reason may your measure be a poor guide to the actual change in the output level?

U.K. Motor Industry – Production and Deliveries

	Monthly Averages		Value of Deliveries	
	No. of Passenger Cars Produced '000s	No. of Commercial Vehicles Produced '000s	Cars £m	Commercial Vehicles £m
1958	87.6	26.1	34.4	16.3
1959	99.2	30.9	40.7	20.1
1960	112.7	38.2	44.3	23.7

Source: Monthly Digest of Statistics.

C.I.P.F.A.

5.24   *Index of Industrial Production (Average 1963 = 100)*

	Weight	Index 1969
Mining and quarrying	56	80.2
Total manufacturing	749	125.6
Construction	127	118.9
Gas, electricity, water	68	136.2
Total	1000	

Source: Annual Abstract of Statistics.

(a) Explain the purpose of weights.
(b) Calculate the index of industrial production for 1969.
(c) If the index for construction rises to 140 and the other data remains the same, find the change in the index of industrial production.
(d) Calculate to the nearest integer an index for 1963 taking the value from (b) as base.   O.N.C.

5.25   *The A.B. Co. Ltd. Indices of Production (1960 = 100)*

Dept.	Weights	Indices 1962	1964
A	15	108	116
B	26	122	112
C	4	92	106
D	35	134	130

(a) Calculate for each of the two years 1962 and 1964 an index number of production for the whole firm.
(b) Calculate index numbers for each department and for the whole firm for 1964 taking 1962 as the base year.

                                                                O.N.C.

5.26 (a) Define an Index Number.

(b)   *Exports of Selected Commodities*

	Quantities (tons) 1955	1960	Value (£) 1955
Tiles	104,150	139,350	476,200
Sanitary ware	212,350	120,200	1,286,800
China	13,210	13,820	848,800
Electrical ware	23,740	17,720	302,400
Other earthenware	250,450	213,520	3,886,450

Calculate, for this group of exports, an index number of volume for 1960 (1955 = 100).   O.N.C.

5.27 (a) What are the main problems to be faced in the construction of an index number?

(b) Compute a price and a quantity index number for 1974 from the following figures (1970 = 100).

Item	Quantity ('00s tons) 1970	1974	Cost (£'000s) 1970	1974
A	172	197	154	185
B	34	47	128	151
C	49	42	277	248
D	64	66	219	206

                                                                O.N.C.

5.28   New York Times *Weekly Index of Business Activity.*
        'Steel' Industrial Production Index (1946 = 100)

	1964	1965	1966	Weight
(i) Electricity output	123	135	160	32
(ii) Steel	131	142	153	35
(iii) Auto and truck production	112	124	133	11
(iv) Freight car loading weight	98	96	101	22

(a) Obtain the general index of industrial production for each of
    the three years (1946 = 100).
(b) Calculate the index numbers for 1965 and 1966 on 1964 as base
    using the same weights.
(c) Comment on the procedure you have adopted and indicate
    a possible alternative.   O.N.C.

5.29   (a) Explain the difference between a price relative and a price
index.

(b) The following data shows the price index numbers of three
groups of commodities from 1967 to 1971. Groups 1 and 2 have been
prepared on the fixed-base principle, but Group 3 numbers are chain
based and unlinked.

	1967	1968	1969	1970	1971
Group 1	100	106	113	122	128
Group 2	84	94	100	108	114
Group 3	100	102	104	101	103

(i) Recalculate the Group 2 index numbers to make them more
    easily comparable with the Group 1 numbers.
(ii) Convert the Group 3 numbers into a series linked to the index
    number of 100 for 1967.
(iii) Tabulate the figures for Group 1 and the revised figures for
    Groups 2 and 3 and briefly comment on the situation revealed.
                                                               O.N.C.

Chapter Six

The Analysis of the Time Series

The statistical analysis we have undertaken so far has been concerned with frequency distributions. We have calculated various measures of central tendency and index numbers – all giving us a picture of the variable at a given point in time. But suppose we wanted to know, for example, the Retail Price Index in 1960, and were interested in the way it had behaved since that date. We would have to construct a time series of the Retail Price Index showing its value each year from 1960 to the present day. Some of the data we are interested in will, of course, give us more interesting information if we can build a time series showing the value of the variable at time periods shorter than a year, say monthly, or more usually, quarterly. The Central Electricity Generating Board, for example, finds it very important to know how electrical power consumption varies as we move from summer to autumn and from autumn to winter. Other data, such as egg prices, may best be examined in a series giving the highest price each month. It is not beyond the bounds of possibility for a financial analyst to want a series showing the movement of the *Financial Times* Share Index daily over, say, the last three months.

You might well wonder why we should spend so much effort constructing series showing what has happened in the past. This is history, and should we not rather be looking to the future? As you know, the twentieth century is the age of planning. Governments plan the economy for many years ahead; public corporations plan output and investment; most states plan to keep the rate of inflation down to an acceptable level. No-one, surely, imagines that those who plan the future of the economy, or that those who make decisions affecting the livelihood of millions, sit in isolation and pluck their target figures out of thin air. No: good planning is based on information, and this is where the time series comes into its own. It provides information about the way in which economic and social variables have been behaving in the recent past, and provides an analysis of that behaviour that planners cannot ignore. Naturally, if we are looking into the future, there are certain assumptions we have to make, the most important of which is that the behavioural pattern that we have found in the past will continue into the future. We do not expect to find high prosperity one month and deep depression the next. If the economy has been expanding it will continue to do so. Gradually the rate of expansion may slow down; there may be fluctuations month by month, but the general trend of what is happening does not change overnight. At a much more modest level, if a fish and chip shop finds that over a period of a year its takings have been higher on Friday than on any other day of the week, we would expect this to continue – and would be truly amazed if it did not. Thus, in looking to the future, there are certain patterns that we assume will continue, and it is to help in the determination of these patterns that we undertake the analysis of the time series. To illustrate the type of pattern in which we are interested let us look at a time series showing the volume of imports of certain raw materials into the United Kingdom a few years ago.

Imports of Raw Materials into the United Kingdom
(1968 = 100)

Quarter / Year	1972	1973	1974	1975
1	114	116	128	137
2	142	150	158	180
3	155	153	169	
4	136	140	159	

If we graph these figures we get an immediate picture of the way in which imports were behaving (see diagram 6.1).

Two things are immediately apparent. There is a general upward trend of the figures as a whole. It is not an exceptional rise of course, but it is quite marked. With the solitary exception of the third quarter of 1973, the figures in any quarter are higher than those in the same quarter of the previous year. We will have more to say about this exception in a minute.

Secondly, although the figures fluctuate up and down, there is a pattern. The figures in the third quarter of any year are always the highest figures for that year; those in the first quarter are always the lowest of the year. There is, that is, a very marked seasonal fluctuation in the figures.

Finally, we would not expect import figures to be unaffected by day-to-day happenings, such as disputes in the docks or exchange rate fluctuations. Something like this must have happened in 1973 to reduce the figures for the third quarter below those of the previous year. Such variations as this which affect our figures are known as

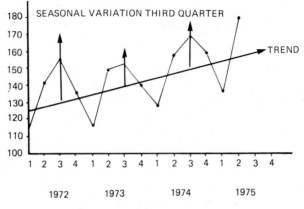

Imports of raw materials into the U.K. 1968 = 100

Diagram 6.1

residual or *random* variations. They cannot be foreseen nor pinpointed without a great deal of outside knowledge – but they can be important.

Thus, figures such as these, which fluctuate quite markedly, are responding to three sets of forces.

a. THE TREND. Or the general way in which the figures are moving. Some economists equate the trend with a general expansion or con-

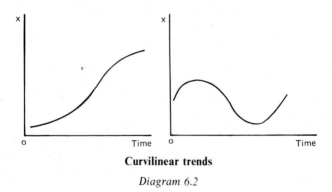

Curvilinear trends

Diagram 6.2

traction of the economy, or with such things as a changing pattern of consumer tastes. One would imagine, for example, that there has been a general upward trend in the sales of colour television sets, and a downward trend in the sales of black and white sets. The trend, of course, will not normally be a straight line as we have illustrated it. We would expect most trends to curve upwards or downwards, and, if our time period is long enough, perhaps to show a wave-like motion.

b. SEASONAL VARIATION. It is common knowledge that the value of many variables depends in part on the time of year we are considering. Every housewife knows that the price of flowers rises as we approach Mother's Day; or that the price of tomatoes is higher in winter than it is in summer. The consumption of electricity is higher in the December quarter than in the June quarter; sales of ice cream higher in June than in December. You can multiply these examples almost indefinitely, and anyone concerned with planning must take account of them.

c. RESIDUALS. These are random external events which affect our variables. Sometimes the effect is negligible; at other times it is great; some occurrences will increase our figures; others will reduce them. We cannot foresee what is going to happen in the future and so we cannot forecast such events. It is, however, reasonable to assume that in the long run they will tend to cancel each other out, and that in our analysis we may initially ignore their impact.

Now, it is one thing to isolate the factors which affect the fluctuations in our figures; it is quite another matter to disentangle one from the others and to measure its influence. Let us first try to measure the trend.

The Calculation of Trend

It is easy to see from the graph of any time series whether the trend is rising or falling. It is even easier to grab a pencil and sketch a line through the middle of the graph saying that the trend 'is something like this', or 'somewhere around here'. In fact, with a great deal of practice it is possible to sketch in quite an accurate trend in this way. For serious statistical work, however, it is no use proceeding by guesswork. A statistic is a piece of data we can rely on and use, and if we want to use the trend we must calculate it, not guess it. There are several methods of calculating the trend, depending on whether we believe it to be linear or non-linear, but the method you will almost certainly be called upon to use at this stage is a general all-purpose method – the method of *moving averages*. We will illustrate this method by calculating the trend of unemployment in the United Kingdom during a fifteen-year period from 1954 to 1969.

Unemployment in the United Kingdom

Year	% Unemployed	5-Year Total	5-Year Moving Average = Trend
1954	1.3		
1955	1.1		
1956	1.2	7.1	1.42
1957	1.4	8.0	1.60
1958	2.1	8.5	1.70
1959	2.2	8.8	1.76
1960	1.6	9.4	1.88
1961	1.5	9.8	1.96
1962	2.0	9.2	1.84
1963	2.5	9.0	1.80
1964	1.6	9.0	1.80
1965	1.4	9.4	1.88
1966	1.5	9.3	1.86
1967	2.4	10.1	2.02
1968	2.4		
1969	2.4		

Source: *Employment and Productivity Gazette.*

A moving average is a simple arithmetic mean. We select a group of figures at the start of the series, e.g. five or seven or nine, and average them to obtain our first trend figure. Then we drop the first figure and include the next item in the series to obtain a new group. The average of this group gives us our second trend figure. We continue to do this until all our figures are exhausted. Thus, in the table above, we selected firstly the first five years, 1954 to 1958. The total of this group was $1.3 + 1.1 + 1.2 + 1.4 + 2.1 = 7.1$, and the average was $\frac{7.1}{5} = 1.42$. Because we are concerned with averages, we place this trend figure opposite the centre of the group to which it refers, that is, 1956. This need to place the trend against the mid-point of a group of figures is one advantage of using an odd number of years in the first place. We now drop the first figure, i.e. 1.3, and include the next figure in our series to give us a new five-year total of $1.1 + 1.2 + 1.4 + 2.1 + 2.2 = 8.0$ and a second trend figure of $\frac{8.0}{5} = 1.60$. Next we drop the 1955 figure and take the group 1956 to 1960, giving us a third trend figure of 1.70. Now calculate the rest of the figures for yourself, and check your results with the table above.

In Fig. 6.3 we have drawn the graph of the original figures and superimposed the trend.

There is no doubt that the trend eliminates the large-scale fluctuations found in the original figures, but it is not, perhaps, as smooth as you expected. In fact, from 1962 to 1966 it does not seem able to make up its mind which way to turn. This was probably a result of variations in government policy as the United Kingdom struggled to counter inflation, prevent large-scale unemployment, and maintain expansion.

The rationale of the method of moving averages is easy to see. Some figures will be above the average, others below it, so by using the average figure we are offsetting one against the other – cancelling out, as it were, the fluctuations in our series. You are probably wondering why we chose to use a five-year moving average rather

Unemployed in the U.K. 1954–1969

Diagram 6.3

than, say, a seven-year or a nine-year. There is no infallible guide here. The best moving average is the one that gives the smoothest trend. But a good working rule is to look at the data and assess the number of years between successive peaks or successive troughs. In other words, assess the period of the cycle. In the unemployment data, the lowest levels of unemployment occurred in 1955, 1961 and 1965; the peak levels of unemployment were in 1959, 1963 and 1967–9. It looks very much as if unemployment in this period was subject to a five-year cycle, and in fact, economists confirm that this was so. Hence we chose a five-year moving average. It would be both interesting and useful if you now calculated the trend based on a seven-year moving average and compared it with the trend we have drawn.

You will readily appreciate that we cannot, from a series such as this, pursue the second of our investigations – that of analysing seasonal variation. How could we when the figures are given only annually? What we might discover is a *cyclical* pattern extending over a period of years, and while this might be useful in long-range forecasting, it does not really help us plan for the immediate future.

The Calculation of Seasonal Variation

We have already seen that seasonal variation in a series is a relatively short-term phenomenon, consisting of upswings and downswings at particular periods of time. When we come to measure these rises and falls, however, we are faced with a problem – we need a point of reference before we can assess the magnitude of the change. If, for example, sales of umbrellas rose to 187,000 in November, it makes a great deal of difference to what we think is happening if this rise was from 185,000 in October, or was from 95,000 in October.

We hope you will agree that it is reasonable to assess the size of the rise or fall season by season with reference to an average figure, and for this purpose the obvious point of reference is the trend. Armed with this knowledge, we can now formally define seasonal variation as a regular periodic deviation from trend. The first step in our calculation then is to calculate the trend; and for this purpose we will go back to the series we introduced at the beginning of the chapter.

Imports of Raw Material into the U.K. (1968 = 100)

Year	Quarter	Imports	Sum in 4's	Sum of two 4's	Trend	Deviation
1972	1	114				
	2	142				
	3	155	547	1096	137.0	+ 18.0
	4	136	549	1106	138.25	− 2.25
1973	1	116	557	1112	139.0	− 23.0
	2	150	555	1114	139.25	+ 10.75
	3	153	559	1130	141.25	+ 11.75
	4	140	571	1150	143.75	− 3.75
1974	1	128	579	1174	146.75	− 18.75
	2	158	595	1209	151.12	+ 6.88
	3	169	614	1237	154.62	+ 14.38
	4	159	623	1268	158.50	+ 0.50
1975	1	137	645			
	2	180				

The first thing you will notice is that although we gave the figures originally in the form of a simple table, we have had to rewrite them in columnar form for ease of calculation. Since almost every examination question you meet on this topic will involve this, let us warn you now that you must be very careful in extracting the figures. We know from experience that it is very easy, under the stress of examination conditions, to extract figures for the first quarter of every year, then the second quarter of every year and so on. Oh, we know very well that *you* will never do that – but every year someone does.

Secondly you will see that we have based the trend on a four-quarterly moving average. This becomes almost a rule for calculating the trend of figures given quarterly. The reason is that if the data exhibits seasonal characteristics, the period between successive peaks or troughs will usually be four quarters. In the same way, if the data is given monthly you will use a twelve-monthly moving average. This, of course, creates a problem. Our trend, or average, must be placed opposite to the centre of the group to which it relates, and the centre of a group of four is midway between the second and third item. This in itself is not bad, but we want to compare imports in, for example, the third quarter of 1973 with the trend in that quarter, and we cannot do this at the moment. To overcome this we use a technique known as *centreing* the figures. We take successive pairs of four quarterly totals, add them, and divide the total by eight to obtain the trend. We are, in effect, averaging the trend figures we would have had had we divided by four. Thus, we take the sum of the first two quarterly totals, $547 + 549$, and divide by eight to give us a trend of 137.0, which we can now place opposite 1972, quarter 3. Then we take the sum of the second and third quarterly totals, $549 + 557$. (Note: *not* the third and fourth four-quarterly totals.) This gives us a trend figure of 138.25 placed opposite 1972, quarter 4. Continue like this to the end of the series. The trend we have established gives us, for each quarter from the third quarter of 1972 to the fourth quarter of 1974, a reference figure, with which we can compare the data to establish the extent of the quarterly fluctuation in our figures. Thus, we can say that in the third quarter of 1972, seasonal fluctuations caused imports to rise by 18.0 points above trend ($155 - 137$), but in the fourth quarter imports were reduced to a level 2.25 points below trend.

Now these deviations are not, of course, pure seasonal variations. They are also influenced by what we have called residual events. If we take our deviations for the third quarter of each year, $+18.0$, $+11.75$ and $+14.38$, the differences between the deviations indicate that outside influences have been at work. It may well be that in 1972 these residuals reinforced the seasonal swing, but that in 1973 other residuals were operative which reduced the seasonal swing to

11.75. It is not easy to dispose of the effect of residual events, especially since we have no means of knowing just what those events were. Let us suppose, however, that we are right in our argument that these events sometimes reinforce, and sometimes oppose, the seasonal swing. Once again, by taking an average of the deviations in each individual quarter over a number of years, we can offset one residual event against another, and obtain something like the truth. So let us now tabulate the deviations from trend so as to bring together all those occurring in the first quarter, all those occurring in the second quarter and so on.

Year / Quarter	1	2	3	4
1972			+ 18.0	− 2.25
1973	− 23.0	+ 10.75	+ 11.75	− 3.75
1974	− 18.75	+ 6.88	+ 14.38	+ 0.50
Totals	− 41.75	+ 17.63	+ 44.13	− 5.50
Average	− 20.87	+ 8.81	+ 14.71	− 1.83
Adjustment	− .205	− .205	− .205	− .205
	− 21.075	+ 8.605	+ 14.505	− 2.035
Seasonal variation	− 21	+ 8.5	+ 14.5	− 2

You will see that when we took the average of the variations for each quarter, in two quarters we had to divide our totals by two, and in two quarters by three. Do be careful of this; it is easy to forget and make a mistake. Sometimes you will divide every total by the same figure; at other times the divisor will vary, depending on how many deviations you have for each quarter.

You will notice too that we have made a slight adjustment to our figures of −0.205 points each quarter. The reason for this is that if we had entirely eliminated the 'unexplained' deviations, the sum of our quarterly averages would be zero. (If you cannot see why this should be so, think back to what we said about arithmetic means in chapter four.) In fact our averages add up to +0.82 and we have to dispose of this somehow. We do not know where this difference arises, so we allocate the adjustment equally between each quarter. Thus, $\frac{0.82}{4} = 0.205$, and since we have to dispose of an excess positive figure, we knock this amount off each quarterly average. Admittedly, in this example the adjustment is trifling and makes almost no difference, but in some series you work with, you may have to add, or subtract, as much as eight or ten points from your quarterly average. The result is our estimate of seasonal variation for each quarter.

We have made a number of assumptions in this analysis, and however good the grounds for these assumptions, it would be unwise for us to say that we can rely on our estimate of seasonal variation being accurate to three decimal places. Instead of saying that seasonal variation is -21.075, $+8.605$, $+14.505$ and -2.035, we feel that it is far safer to say that it is -21, $+8\frac{1}{2}$, $+14\frac{1}{2}$ and -2, and accept that these are the most reliable estimates we can get from the figures available.

The importance of Residuals

We began this chapter by saying that the figures in our original series were a result of three sets of forces:

TREND + SEASONAL VARIATIONS + RESIDUALS = ORIGINAL FIGURES

We have now calculated a figure for trend and seasonal variation, and it is a simple matter of arithmetic to calculate the value of the residual. The residual for 1972, quarter 3, for example, is

$$155 - (137.0 + 14.5) = +3.5$$

		Original Series	= Trend	+ Seasonal Variation	+ Residual
1972	1	114			
	2	142			
	3	155	137.0	$+14.5$	$+3.5$
	4	136	138.25	-2.0	-0.25
1973	1	116	139.0	-21.0	-2.0
	2	150	139.25	$+8.5$	$+2.25$
	3	153	141.25	$+14.5$	-2.75
	4	140	143.75	-2.0	-1.75
1974	1	128	146.75	-21.0	$+2.25$
	2	158	151.12	$+8.5$	-1.62
	3	169	154.62	$+14.5$	-0.12
	4	159	158.5	-2.0	$+2.5$
1975	1	137			
	2	180			

We must agree that there is little one can say about the value of the residual, and that its calculation is not particularly useful. It does, however, give us an indication of the extent to which our figures are affected by unforeseen external factors. If we are using our calculations as a basis for forecasting this knowledge can be useful. In the example we have calculated, the value of the residual is relatively small, and, knowing this, we could argue that any forecast we made was likely to be fairly accurate, and unlikely to be seriously upset by external events to any great extent. If, however, the value of the

residual was large, we could place much less reliance on any forecast
we made.

Series with Seasonal Variation Eliminated

We often look at the time series in an effort to assess whether conditions are improving or getting worse. The Managing Director wishes
to know whether sales are rising; the Department of Health and
Social Security tries to determine whether deaths from lung cancer
or influenza are really falling; the police authorities try to assess
whether particular crimes are on the increase or decrease.

Sometimes, of course, the figures speak for themselves, but more
often than not constant wide fluctuations hide the general picture.
Statisticians often eliminate the effect of seasonal fluctuations from
a series in order to bring out clearly the underlying pattern. Naturally
you will say that they could equally well calculate the trend, and
once we have eliminated seasonal variation we will get a pattern very
close to trend. Against this is the fact that the calculation of trend
is often, in practice, a far more complex affair than the mere calculation of moving averages, and it is far easier to raise or lower figures
as they become available by an amount which has already been
established as a result of earlier work. Then, too, in eliminating
seasonal factors, we are leaving in the series not only the trend, but
also the residual factors. A comparison of trend figures with the new
figure with seasonal factors eliminated gives a very clear picture of
the strength of the residual factors in a particular quarter or month.

The general rule is that we subtract the seasonal variation we have
calculated from the figures in the original series, remembering that
if seasonal variation is negative, minus a minus quantity is a plus.
Eliminating the seasonal variation from the series we have worked
on, we get:

		Imports −	Seasonal Variation =	Series with S.V. eliminated
1972	1	114	− 21.0	135.0
	2	142	+ 8.5	133.5
	3	155	+ 14.5	140.5
	4	136	− 2.0	138.0
1973	1	116	− 21.0	137.0
	2	150	+ 8.5	141.5
	3	153	+ 14.5	138.5
	4	140	− 2.0	142.0
1974	1	128	− 21.0	149.0
	2	158	+ 8.5	149.5
	3	169	+ 14.5	154.5
	4	159	− 2.0	161.0
1975	1	137	− 21.0	158.0
	2	180	+ 8.5	171.5

The importance of this series can be seen if we interpret the figures we have calculated. Firstly, the figures of imports show a steady and sustained growth over the period when we eliminate the effects of seasonal variation. Since this growth is almost continuous it is unlikely to be seriously influenced by residual items. Thus we can say that over this period imports were certainly rising. Secondly, if we

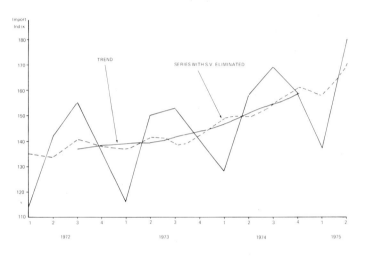

Imports of raw materials into the U.K. 1968 = 100

Diagram 6.4

look at the first two quarters of 1972 we find that although imports rose in the second quarter, when we eliminate the effects of seasonal variation the series shows a fall in the second quarter. Our analysis tells us that the low level of imports in the first quarter was not a result of a lack of demand for imports so much as a result of seasonal factors. It does not tell us, of course, what these factors were, but we could surmise that the winter weather may have affected shipping, or that importers who had built up stocks for, perhaps, the Christmas period were now allowing them to run down to a more normal level. Such factors as these would be present in the first quarter of every year and when we allow for them we find that if they were not present imports would have been much higher.

We conclude this section by summarising what we have done in a graph, diagram 6.4, which shows the original figures, the trend and the series with seasonal variation eliminated on the same diagram.

The Time Series and Forecasting

Whatever anyone may tell you, there is no way of predicting the future with certainty; but experience tells us that once we have calculated a trend line, that trend is going to continue virtually unchanged for some little time ahead. This is almost certainly true of the next two or three quarterly trend figures, and we make this a basic assumption in forecasting techniques. It is possible, then, for us to project the trend some way into the future with reasonable confidence, and to use this trend as the basis of forecasting.

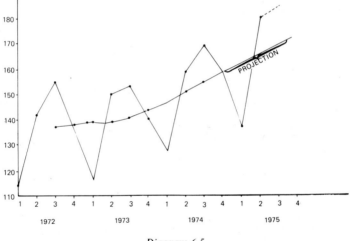

Diagram 6.5

In diagram 6.5 we have redrawn the trend of the series we have been examining and projected it two or three quarters forward. Obviously, there is a great deal of room for error here, and our results will be no better than the projection we make. Equally, you will appreciate that the further ahead we look, the greater the possibility of error. But bearing all this in mind let us see what we have got.

Our projection shows that we estimate the trend figure for the third quarter of 1975 to be 170.0. The seasonal variation for the third quarter is +14.5, so, subject to the influence of residuals, we could forecast the volume index for imports in the third quarter of 1975 as 184.5. As you can see from the graph, this follows closely the pattern of the previous years when figures in the third quarter rose above those in the second quarter. Our result is at least logical.

Now, you may object that projecting the trend forward for three quarters is asking too much. Let us check our forecast by estimating the figure in a different way. We will project the trend forward one quarter only, to the first quarter of 1975. Our projected trend gives us a value of 163.0 for the trend at this date. You will remember that this figure is obtained by totalling (the last two quarters of 1974 and the first two quarters of 1975) plus (the last quarter of 1974 and the first three quarters of 1975) and dividing the total by eight. Since we know every figure but that for the third quarter of 1975 it is a matter of simple arithmetic to calculate the estimated figure for that quarter:

$$(169 + 159 + 137 + 180 + 159 + 137 + 180 + x) = 163 \times 8 = 1304$$

from which it follows that x, the figure for the third quarter of 1975, is 183, pretty much the same as our previous forecast.

If you look at the trend line in this example you will see that it is almost linear, or a straight line, so let us conclude this chapter by an example of how to 'fit' a straight line trend to this series.

Fitting a Linear Trend

The algebraic formulae for fitting a straight line trend are many, and some of them are extremely complex. In a later chapter dealing with correlation and regression analysis we explain one of the simpler of the algebraic methods of fitting a straight line to a series of figures. What we are concerned with here is a very simple arithmetic method, which is commonly asked for in examinations – the method of semi-averages.

Nothing could be simpler than this method. All we have to do is to divide the series into two equal parts, and find the average of the figures for each part. As usual, this average is placed against the centre of the group to which it refers, and this gives us two points through which the linear trend will pass. Naturally we need only two points to draw a straight line.

Let us illustrate from the series you now know so well. We have fourteen figures so we will initially divide them into two groups of seven.

			Total	Average				Total	Average
1972	1	114			1973	4	140		
	2	142			1974	1	128		
	3	155				2	158		
	4	136	966	138		3	169	1071	153
1973	1	116				4	159		
	2	150			1975	1	137		
	3	153				2	180		

We now place a point at 138 opposite the fourth quarter of 1972, another at 153 opposite the third quarter of 1974, and join these two by a straight line to give us our trend. Purists may dislike this method, but it is quick and easy, and provided the trend fits the series reasonably well, there is nothing to stop you from calculating seasonal variation from the trend you have inserted.

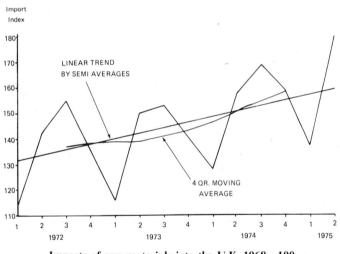

Imports of raw materials into the U.K. 1968 = 100

Diagram 6.6

In diagram 6.6 we have drawn the original trend and the linear trend calculated above on the same graph. As you can see the linear trend fits the original data fairly well and is a good approximation to the four-quarterly moving average trend.

EXERCISES TO CHAPTER SIX

6.1   Describe the components into which statistical data relating to business and economic events may be analysed by the use of time series analysis.   A.C.A.

6.2   Specify and describe the various movements which may be identified when analysing economic and business statistics over a long time span.   A.C.A.

6.3   Required: In the analysis of time series
  (1) explain what is meant by a trend line and describe very briefly two principal methods of calculating it;
  (2) explain what is meant by residual variations and why they are important;
  (3) give two situations where it is important to adjust the data prior to analysis, with reasons;
  (4) sketch a graph of a time series which shows a trend and also cyclical and seasonal movements.   A.C.A.

6.4   The table below shows the number of components produced by a factory during the morning, afternoon and evening shifts last week.

Day	Shift	No. of Components Produced
Monday	morning	127
	afternoon	114
	evening	134
Tuesday	morning	130
	afternoon	115
	evening	138
Wednesday	morning	128
	afternoon	117
	evening	142
Thursday	morning	131
	afternoon	116
	evening	141
Friday	morning	132
	afternoon	120
	evening	144

Plot these values on a graph. On the same graph plot a moving average with the period chosen to remove variation between shifts. Calculate an estimate of the shift variation.   O.N.C.

6.5   The table shows the number of passengers ('000s) flying from
U.K. airports to destinations on the continent of Europe and to the
Mediterranean Sea area:

Number of Passengers Flown ('000s)

Year	Quarters			
	1	2	3	4
1967				800
1968	690	1580	2250	940
1969	830	1900	2670	1130
1970	1040	2160	3070	1360
1971	1190	2580		

Source: Monthly Digest of Statistics.

Plot the data and obtain the moving average trend. Plot the trend
line on the same graph. What conclusions may be deduced from your
graph?   O.N.C.

6.6   (a) State four components of a time series.
      (b) What is meant by seasonally adjusted?
      (c) The following table shows the quarterly sales of a company
          in thousands of tons for a period of four years:

Sales	Quarter			
	1	2	3	4
Year 1	70	41	52	83
2	78	44	48	85
3	83	54	51	96
4	85	49	54	89

You are required using the information given above to:

  (i) plot on a graph the quarterly sales;
  (ii) derive and plot the appropriate moving average.

                                                          I.C.M.A.

6.7   A traffic census taken at the same time each day during July
on a busy road approaching a coastal holiday resort revealed that
the number of vehicles passing per hour was as follows (to nearest
10):

	Week 1	Week 2	Week 3	Week 4	Week 5
Monday		840	840	830	820
Tuesday		860	860	830	
Wednesday		1190	1200	1220	
Thursday		840	830	840	
Friday		970	1020	1080	
Saturday	1800	1860	1950	2100	
Sunday	1460	1480	1520	1550	

(a) Plot the data on a graph.
(b) Calculate a suitable moving average and plot the trend line. Explain your choice of time period.
(c) If the survey had been carried out in say November, what do you think the figures would have looked like then? (You may illustrate by a rough sketch or by providing possible figures for one or two weeks.) O.N.C.

6.8   *Annual Production of Paper Sacks*

Year	Production ('000s)
1963	50.0
1964	36.5
1965	43.0
1966	44.5
1967	38.9
1968	38.1
1969	32.6
1970	38.7
1971	41.7
1972	41.1
1973	33.8

(a) Construct a five-year moving average, graphing the trend line against the original data. Comment on your results. If the interval for the moving average had not been suggested, how would you have determined it? What is the purpose of a moving average?

(b) With which characteristic movement of a time series would you mainly associate each of the following?

(i) a minor fire delaying production for three weeks;
(ii) an increase in unemployment during the winter months;
(iii) the increasing demand for small cars since 1971;
(iv) a recession. O.N.C.

6.9   *Unemployment Expressed as a Percentage of Total Employees*

	March	June	September	December
1970	2.3	2.4	2.6	2.6
1971	2.9	3.2	3.6	3.7
1972	3.9	3.5	3.6	3.2
1973	2.8	2.6	2.4	2.1
1974	2.4	2.5		

(a) Smooth this time series by means of a centred four-quarterly moving average.
(b) Plot the original and the moving average figures on the same graph.
(c) Discuss whether this moving average has any value for forecasting future percentage unemployment. O.N.C.

6.10   The number of prescriptions dispensed by chemists under the National Health Service in England and Wales from 1969 to 1973 is shown in the table below.

N.H.S. prescriptions ('000,000s)

Year	Quarter			
	1	2	3	4
1969			60	71
1970	69	67	62	69
1971	73	66	62	68
1972	72	66	65	67
1973	75			

Source: Monthly Digest of Statistics.

(a) Plot the data on a graph.
(b) Calculate and plot a suitable moving average on the same graph.
(c) Explain what additional calculations would be necessary to obtain the average seasonal variation.
  (Do *not* make these calculations.)   O.N.C.

6.11   *Percentage Turnover of Labour Force*

	1st Quarter	2nd Quarter	3rd Quarter	4th Quarter
1970	11	23	16	8
1971	14	29	16	9
1972	18	34	17	9
1973	19	42	23	12

(a) Smooth this time series by means of a centred four-quarterly moving average.
(b) Calculate the average seasonal variations.
(c) Explain how your calculations could be used as a basis for forecasting percentage turnover figures for the four quarters of 1974.   O.N.C.

6.12   Explain what is meant by the terms trend and seasonal variation. The table below shows the quarterly sales of a certain product during 1969, 1970 and 1971.

Quarterly Sales (thousands)

	1st Quarter	2nd Quarter	3rd Quarter	4th Quarter
1969	19	30	63	8
1970	20	32	67	16
1971	23	35	74	14

Calculate the average seasonal variation for each quarter of the year and, using the second quarter as an example, state what is meant by your calculated figure.   O.N.C.

6.13   *No. of Houses Completed in*
England and Wales

Year	Quarter	Completions
1969	1st	32,458
	2nd	32,881
	3rd	35,049
	4th	39,462
1970	1st	33,310
	2nd	31,953
	3rd	33,628
	4th	35,983
1971	1st	30,808
	2nd	27,935
	3rd	27,526
	4th	30,946
1972	1st	28,674

Source: Department of the Environment.

(a) Rewrite the number of houses completed to the nearest hundred.

(b) Using the rounded data:

    (i) calculate, by means of four-quarterly moving averages, the trend of the series;

    (ii) calculate the seasonal variations.

(c) State the main factors affecting a time series.   O.N.C.

6.14   The following data give the index numbers for Industrial Production for the years 1970–3. By calculating an appropriate moving average obtain the trend and hence the seasonal factors for each quarter. Explain how to obtain a forecast of the index for the fourth quarter of 1973.

Year	\multicolumn{4}{c}{Quarters}

Year	1	2	3	4
1970				103.5
1971	102.2	101.2	95.1	103.5
1972	99.1	103.8	96.8	109.0
1973	112.1	110.5	105.2	

Source: Monthly Digest.   O.N.C.

6.15   The following table shows the quarterly sales figures in £'000's.

Quarterly Sales

Years	I	II	III	IV
1970	81	46	42	76
1971	79	40	31	70
1972	64	31	34	66
1973	71	30	32	—

You are required to:

(a) use moving averages to calculate the trend;
(b) calculate the average seasonal variation;
(c) explain how this information could be used in forecasting.

I.C.M.A.

6.16 *Supplies and Deliveries of Crude Steel. Weekly Averages – Thousand Tons*

Year	Quarters			
	1	2	3	4
1968	480	520	466	526
1969	541	541	440	510
1970	538	544	493	531

Source: Department of Trade and Industry.

(a) Calculate the average seasonal variation for this data.
(b) Deseasonalise the series.
(c) Briefly comment on your findings.

O.N.C.

6.17 The following data give the index numbers for the total value of sales in catering in Great Britain for the years 1970–3. By calculating an appropriate moving average obtain the trend and hence the seasonal factors for each quarter.

Deseasonalise the quarters of 1972.

Year	Quarters			
	1	2	3	4
1970		110	120	140
1971	110	124	130	154
1972	123	134	143	176
1973	139			

Source: Department of Trade and Industry.

O.N.C.

6.18 *Average Weekly Earnings of Agricultural Workers in Great Britain*

Half-yearly Periods Commencing		Men £	Women £
1959	April	10.20	6.45
	October	9.75	6.36
1960	April	10.58	6.63
	October	10.35	6.72
1961	April	11.20	7.34
	October	10.75	6.83
1962	April	11.58	7.16
	October	11.41	7.13
1963	April	12.40	7.37
	October	12.13	7.39

Half-yearly Periods Commencing		Men £	Women £
1964	April	13.08	7.93
	October	12.50	8.14
1965	April	13.98	9.19
	October	13.63	8.33
1966	April	12.99	9.10
	October	14.31	9.54

(a) Explain the purpose of moving averages.

(b) Calculate the trend of earnings (i) for men and (ii) for women using a two-point centred moving average.

(c) What conclusions can be drawn? O.N.C.

6.19 What is meant by seasonal variation? Using a three-term moving average, find the trend and hence calculate the average 'seasonal' variation for each of the three 'seasons' in the data below and hence obtain de-seasonalised sales figures for 1971 and 1972. Using a forecasting method of your choice, estimate the sales in the three seasons of 1973.

Sales (£000s)

	1969	1970	1971	1972
Jan.–Apr.	425	431	434	428
May–Aug.	312	300	291	300
Sept.–Dec.	445	451	454	451

O.N.C.

6.20

Rainfall in Millimetres

Year	1st Quarter	2nd Quarter	3rd Quarter	4th Quarter
1964	152	204	134	213
1965	187	198	311	299
1966	210	257	231	323
1967	201	225	236	318
1968	180			

Source: Annual Abstract of Statistics 1968.

From the data given in the table calculate the average seasonal variation in rainfall in the years 1964 to 1967 inclusive. Hence predict the rainfall for the first quarter of 1968. For what reasons might your prediction differ from the actual rainfall? C.I.P.F.A.

6.21

	Quarters			
	1	2	3	4
1972	58	85	97	73
1973	64	96	107	89
1974	76	102	115	94

The above table shows the number of visitors (in hundreds) to an hotel over a period of three years. By using the method of moving averages rewrite the series without seasonal variations. Estimate as accurately as you can the quarterly figures for 1975 and say how reliable you think your estimates are.   O.N.C.

6.22   The following table gives the sales in hundreds of components manufactured by Company A.

Quarterly Sales in Hundreds

Quarters

	1	2	3	4
1972				13
1973	14	16	9	14
1974	16	17	12	17
1975	18	20	13	

Calculate the seasonal fluctuations and rewrite the series with the seasonal variations removed. Draw a graph of the trend values and project it into 1976. Hence, or otherwise, calculate the expected sales for the next four quarters.   O.N.C.

6.23   *Manufacturers' Sales of Floorcoverings – Carpets and Rugs*

| Year | Millions of Square Metres | | | |

Quarter

Year	1st	2nd	3rd	4th
1970	24.7	28.7	27.8	33.6
1971	27.2	31.4	32.1	39.3
1972	33.5	37.0	36.9	44.2

Source: Department of Trade and Industry (adapted).

(a) Calculate the average seasonal variation for the data given above relating to Manufacturers' Sales of Floorcoverings.
(b) De-seasonalise the data for 1972.
(c) Suppose the trend value for the third quarter of 1975 is estimated to be 46.0 million square metres. Using the answer you have given to (a) estimate the sales for the third quarter of 1975. What criticism can you make of this means of estimating a figure for 1975?   O.N.C.

6.24   *Educational Building in Great Britain*

Projects Approved – Primary and Secondary

		£ thousands
1968	third quarter	18,787
	fourth quarter	15,562
1969	first quarter	33,771
	second quarter	28,711

Projects Approved – Primary and Secondary

£ thousands

	third quarter	21,235
	fourth quarter	19,669
1970	first quarter	69,584
	second quarter	27,115
	third quarter	28,376
	fourth quarter	26,900
1971	first quarter	90,384

Source: Department of Education and Science.

(a) Round off the above data to the nearest £100,000. Using a four-quarterly basis, calculate the moving average of the rounded-off figures.

(b) Graph the rounded-off series and the moving average values.

(c) From your graph, estimate the trend value of projects in the first quarter of 1972. Would this estimate be satisfactory as an estimate of the actual value of the projects in the first quarter of 1972? If not, state why not. O.N.C.

6.25   *United Kingdom Outward Passenger Movement by Sea*

Year	Quarter	Total Passengers (thousands)
1970	1st	2133
	2nd	4334
	3rd	7484
	4th	2655
1971	1st	2228
	2nd	5018
	3rd	7859
	4th	3206
1972	1st	2912
	2nd	5167
	3rd	8202
	4th	3786
1973	1st	3210
	2nd	5817

Source: Department of Trade and Industry.

(a) From the above data:
   (i) calculate, by means of four quarterly moving averages, the trend of the series;
   (ii) calculate the average seasonal variations.

(b) Explain how the figures you have calculated could be used to estimate the quarterly figures for the next four quarters.

O.N.C.

6.26   *Sea Departures from the United Kingdom for the Irish*
                          Republic 1966–70

		(thousands)
1966	1st quarter	65
	2nd quarter	103
	3rd quarter	432
	4th quarter	91
1967	1st quarter	69
	2nd quarter	157
	3rd quarter	478
	4th quarter	57
1968	1st quarter	54
	2nd quarter	191
	3rd quarter	530
	4th quarter	96
1969	1st quarter	58
	2nd quarter	195
	3rd quarter	573
	4th quarter	102

Source: Board of Trade.

By applying a moving average technique calculate the centred trend
and seasonal component in the data given above. Hence obtain an
estimate of departures for the first quarter of 1970. For what reasons
may the actual figure, which was 81,000, differ from your estimate?

C.I.P.F.A.

6.27   The following data have been artificially constructed to contain an exact n-year cycle with constant fluctuations around a constantly increasing trend. Find n and hence fit the appropriate moving
average trend line to the data. Find the magnitude of the fluctuations
around the trend. Assuming the pattern to continue into the future,
forecast the values of the variable for years 15 and 16. Do you think
that any real-world variables would exhibit such a pattern?

Year	Value of Variable
1	100
2	105
3	95
4	115
5	120
6	110
7	130
8	135
9	125
10	145
11	150
12	140
13	160
14	165

C.I.P.F.A.

6.28 Quarterly production for a paper-making plant was reported as follows:

Years	Quarterly Production ('00 tonnes)			
	I	II	III	IV
1972	38.8	41.3	39.0	45.6
1973	44.7	45.2	42.0	49.9
1974	46.7	48.2	44.5	51.3
1975	50.1	54.6	—	—

Using the method of moving averages, find the average seasonal deviations, and thus estimate the production figures for the last two quarters of 1975. I.C.S.A.

Chapter Seven

Dispersion

If you have carefully read the last three chapters, then you cannot fail to be impressed with the power and importance of averages in statistics. We started with the simple goal of obtaining a figure that was representative of a distribution, and expanded this to cover methods of measuring economic change, and methods of analysing data over time – all based on the simple concept of an average. However, we have now reached the end of the road, and any further advance that we can make is dependent on our being able to measure *dispersion* or *spread* within a series or distribution. Let us first examine why we need a measure of dispersion.

Do you remember Fred, the candidate for a job as a salesman? The average income earned by the sales force was £8000 per year, and Fred felt cheated when he learned that the sales force consisted of four salesmen earning £2500 a year and the sales director earning £30,000 a year. We suggested that the median income of £2500 would be more representative, giving Fred a clearer picture of his prospects as a salesman. However, we also suggested that the median has serious drawbacks and wherever possible the arithmetic mean should be used in preference. One way out is to quote a measure of the spread of incomes – here the spread is quite large and Fred would have been warned to examine the implications of the arithmetic mean carefully.

A second problem with quoting a measure of central tendency only is that it often masks information that is vitally important. To take an example, suppose a brewer sells lager in bottles marked 'contents not less than $9\frac{1}{2}$ fluid ounces', and he would be in trouble under the Trade Descriptions Act if he violated this claim. Now if he checks the contents by finding the average contents of samples of (say) twenty bottles, then the mean contents may well be in excess of $9\frac{1}{2}$ fluid ounces, but this by no means guarantees that all bottles have contents above the specified minimum. As we shall see later, a measure of spread is extremely useful in such cases. It can be used not merely to check that the claim is not violated, but to positively ensure that it isn't.

Thirdly, we should note that in statistical investigations spread may be just as important as an average, and reveal information that is vital to the problem in hand. Economists are often more interested in examining changes in income distribution than in examining changes in average income. It is usually held that a more equal distribution of income increases economic welfare. Suppose, then, that we examine income at two time periods and we find that there has been no change in average income. We might be tempted to conclude that economic welfare has not changed. However, although average incomes may not have changed, it is quite possible that welfare did increase through a more equal distribution of income. We have already seen how we can examine this using a Lorenz curve, but a quantitative measure of the extent to which the distribution has altered can be obtained through a measure of dispersion.

Finally, we will find that a measure of spread is absolutely essential when dealing with sampling. Later, we will be examining how to discover certain characteristics about populations by drawing samples from that population. We will be particularly interested in estimating population means from sample evidence (for example average age, or average weekly consumption of beer). Now if the spread of items within the population is quite narrow, then we can estimate the population mean from a fairly small sample, but if the population has a fairly wide spread, then small samples could give us estimates very wide of the mark. If, then, we have some idea of the spread of the population, we can calculate the sample size necessary to obtain an efficient estimator.

So you can see that there is a strong case for quoting a measure of dispersion. As with measures of central tendency, a number of different measures are available. However, we can conveniently put these measures into two groups – measures of range and measures of average deviation. Just as with measures of central tendency, we will be equally concerned with their uses and limitations as well as their calculation.

Measures of the Range

To measure dispersion, we could simply take the difference between the greatest and the least value in a series or distribution. We call this measure the *range*. Earlier, we considered the price per fine ounce of gold on the London Bullion Market, and the details were as follows:

End of –	$ per fine ounce
Aug. 1975	155
Sept.	143
Oct.	144
Nov.	139
Dec.	140
Jan. 1976	141

So the highest price during the period was $155, and the lowest price was $139, giving a range of $16. Nothing, then, could be more simple both in concept and calculation. However, the range does have two great faults. Firstly, it ignores the bulk of data available to us, being concerned only with the extreme values. In this sense then, it suffers from the same defects as the median and the mode. The second disadvantage is that, being concerned with the extreme values only, the range may be quite unrepresentative of the spread of items, especially as the extreme values are probably quite untypical of the distribution. Suppose, for example, the salaries of the salesmen in Fred's firm had been

£2000   £2000   £2500   £2500   £3000   £3000   £30,000

Now the salary range is £30,000 – £2000 = £28,000, but the bulk of salaries are within £500 of £2500! Despite these criticisms, the range is used considerably – especially in statistical quality control. The reason is that in this field a measure of dispersion is often required quite quickly, and the range is eminently suited to this condition. However, it should be pointed out that, in these circumstances, the range will be found repeatedly from a number of samples, and this does minimise the chances of obtaining untypical values at the extremes.

Because the range can be so misleading, statisticians have turned to alternative measures of dispersion. The one we shall now examine finds the range containing the central 50% of a distribution. In chapter four we examined the distribution of weekly incomes of adult male workers – let us examine it again. We want to find the range of incomes earned by the central 50% of workers. We can do this by finding the income of the $\frac{1}{4} \times 11 = 2.75$th million worker and the income of the $\frac{3}{4} \times 11 = 8.25$th million worker. First let us find the income of the 2.75th million worker. Consulting the cumulative frequency distribution, we see that his weekly income is between £22 and £24. Using arguments similar to those for calculating the median, we estimate his income to be

Weekly Income	Cumulative Frequency (millions)
Under £16	0.2
„ £18	0.6
„ £20	1.2
„ £22	1.9
„ £24	2.8
„ £26	3.8
„ £28	4.7
„ £30	5.6
„ £35	7.5
„ £40	8.9
„ £45	9.7
„ £50	10.2
„ £60	10.6
„ £70	10.9
„ £100	11.0

$$22 + 2 \times \frac{(2.75 - 1.9)}{0.9}$$

$$= £23.89 \text{ per week}$$

The income of the 8.25th million worker is in the group £35–£40 and we estimate his income to be

$$35 + 5 \times \frac{(8.25 - 7.5)}{1.4}$$

$$= £37.68 \text{ per week}$$

So the range of incomes earned by the central 50% of workers is £13.79. We call this range the *interquartile range* or *quartile deviation* (it is the range of incomes earned by the central two quarters of the distribution). We call the lower end of this range (£23.89) the *lower quartile* (Q_1), and 25% of workers earn a wage less than this figure. Likewise, the upper end of the range is called the *upper quartile* (Q_3) and 25% of workers earn wages above this figure.

Fig. 7.1 shows this information on an enlarged cumulative diagram. Notice that calling the lower quartile Q_1 and the upper quartile Q_3 would naturally lead us to call the median Q_2. Notice also that although the median *worker* lies midway between the upper quartile worker and the lower quartile worker, the median *income* is not at the centre of the quartile deviation. Beware of this – many students fall into this trap.

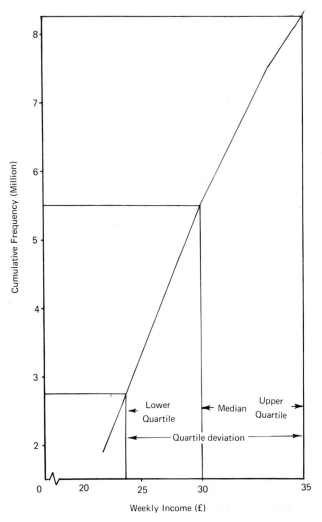

Cumulative frequency distribution of weekly income – median and quartiles

Figure 7.1

Sometimes you will come across the *semi-quartile range* – this is merely half the quartile deviation, i.e.

$$\frac{Q_3 - Q_1}{2}$$

so the semi-quartile range of incomes is £6.89.

Notice that we could not calculate the range of incomes, as we have no way of knowing what the lowest income is. Just as with the mean, then, the range cannot be used for open-ended distributions. This disadvantage will probably not apply to the quartile deviation as it is unlikely that the central 50% of frequencies will penetrate the open-ended classes. However, the quartile deviation does have the same disadvantage as the range – it uses only two values and ignores the rest. What we shall now examine is measures of dispersion that use all of the data available to us.

Measures of Average Deviation

So far, we have examined two predetermined points in a series or distribution and calculated the difference between them. We have fixed the points either at the ends of the distribution (the range) or about the central 50% (the quartile deviation). We could, of course, have fixed these two points anywhere we wished; for example, covering the central 40% or 60% of the items. But let us now consider dispersion in an entirely different way: we could choose some central value and calculate the deviation of the items from this value. What central value should we choose? Well, the arithmetic mean is one choice that automatically springs to mind. However, there is a snag with choosing the arithmetic mean – can you see what it is? Clearly, we are not going to be interested in the individual deviations themselves – we would still have a series of numbers rather than a single measure of dispersion. Surely, it would be more sensible to consider the average deviation from the mean. Now here's where the snag comes in. If you remember the ground covered in chapter four, then you will appreciate that the sum of the deviations from the mean is zero. Hence the average deviation from the mean must always be zero! Clearly, this will not do – we cannot use the average deviation from the mean as a measure of dispersion, because irrespective of the distribution under consideration our measure of dispersion will always be zero.

One way out of this problem is to find the *absolute* deviations from the mean, irrespective of whether they are positive or negative. Let us do this for the price of gold quoted on the London Bullion Market, August 1975 to January 1976. The average price was

$$\frac{155 + 143 + 144 + 139 + 140 + 141}{6} = \frac{862}{6}$$

$= \$143\frac{2}{3}$ per fine ounce

and the deviations from this price are

Price (x)	Deviation $x-\bar{x}$	Absolute Deviation
155	$11\frac{1}{3}$	$11\frac{1}{3}$
143	$-\frac{2}{3}$	$\frac{2}{3}$
144	$\frac{1}{3}$	$\frac{1}{3}$
139	$-4\frac{2}{3}$	$4\frac{2}{3}$
140	$-3\frac{2}{3}$	$3\frac{2}{3}$
141	$-2\frac{2}{3}$	$2\frac{2}{3}$
	0	$23\frac{1}{3}$

So the average absolute deviation from the mean is

$$\frac{23\frac{1}{3}}{6} = 3.89$$

The measure of dispersion we have just calculated is called the *mean absolute deviation*, and using the Σ notation we calculate it like this:

$$\text{Mean absolute deviation} = \frac{\Sigma |x-\bar{x}|}{n}$$

The vertical lines enclosing $x-\bar{x}$ simply means take the absolute deviations, whereas brackets would imply that we must take account of signs. Only a minor adjustment is needed to this formula if we are confronted with a frequency distribution.

$$\text{Mean absolute deviation} = \frac{\Sigma f|x-\bar{x}|}{\Sigma f}$$

where f represents the frequencies and x represents the centre point of the various classes.

The mean absolute deviation has a number of disadvantages. Because we have taken absolute deviations and ignored the signs, it is not capable of being manipulated mathematically in the ways that the statistician requires. A second disadvantage is that it will be quite complicated to calculate when the mean is not a whole number. Thirdly, we cannot combine a number of mean absolute deviations to obtain an overall measure of dispersion. Suppose, for example, a number of samples will be made available to us over a period of time, and we intend to use the samples to estimate dispersion in the population. We cannot calculate the mean deviation of each sample, and pool them, adjusting our estimate as more samples become available. We would have to pool all the samples, making one single sample. We do not wish, however, to leave you with the impression that the mean absolute deviation is of little use – far from it. One thing it cannot be criticised for is its ability to be representative of dispersion. Probably no other measure of dispersion does this quite so well. The advantage of the mean absolute deviation is that conceptually it is so easy to understand. So what advice can we give you about when to use it? If you are interested merely in representing dispersion, then you can do no better than to use the mean absolute deviation, but if further statistical analysis is required we must look to other measures.

The main problems surrounding the mean absolute deviation arise because we took all the deviations as being positive in order to prevent the sum of the deviations being zero. Is there any other course of action open to us? Well, we could square all the deviations – the square of a negative number is a positive number, so the pluses and minuses will no longer cancel each other out. If we find the average of the square of the deviations, then we have a measure called the *variance*,

$$\text{Variance} = \frac{\Sigma (x - \bar{x})^2}{n}$$

So we could calculate the variance of gold prices as follows:

Price (x)	$(x - \bar{x})$	$(x - \bar{x})^2$
155	11.33	128.44
143	−0.67	0.44
144	0.33	0.11
139	−4.67	21.78
140	−3.67	13.44
141	−2.67	7.11
		171.32

$$\text{Variance} = \frac{171.32}{6} = \$28.55$$

The trouble with the variance is that (in this example) it is measured in units of the square of the price deviations. It would seem more sensible, then, to take the square root of the variance. We give the name *standard deviation* (σ) to this measure of dispersion, and of all the measures this is the one that is most commonly used.

$$\sigma = \sqrt{\frac{\Sigma (x - \bar{x})^2}{n}}$$

So the standard deviation of the price of gold is $\sqrt{28.55} = \$5.34$.

It is quite easy to show that an alternative form of the standard deviation is

$$\sqrt{\frac{\Sigma x^2}{n} - \left(\frac{\Sigma x}{n}\right)^2}$$

Notice that this expression does not ask us to calculate the deviations from the arithmetic mean – and this will be very useful when the mean is an awkward number. We do not intend to prove that the two expressions are the same (you can do this for yourself) but we shall demonstrate that both expressions give the same result by calculating the standard deviation of the price of gold bullion, this time using the second expression.

x	x^2
155	24,025
143	20,449
144	20,736
139	19,321
140	19,600
141	19,881
862	124,012

$$\sigma = \sqrt{\frac{124012}{6} - \left(\frac{862}{6}\right)^2} = \$5.34$$

If we wish to find the standard deviation of a frequency distribution, we simply replace x with fx and n with f.

$$\sigma = \sqrt{\frac{\Sigma fx^2}{\Sigma f} - \left(\frac{\Sigma fx}{\Sigma f}\right)^2}$$

where x is the centre point of the class and f is the frequency. In chapter four we calculated the arithmetic mean of the age of adult workers – let us now calculate the standard deviation. The distribution was

Age	No. in Employment (millions)
15, but under 20	1.1
20–	1.7
25–	1.5
30–	1.3
35–	1.3
40–	1.4

Age	No. in Employment (millions)
45–	1.5
50–	1.3
55–	1.4
60	1.1
65, but under 70	0.4

So we need to find the centre point of each class

Centre Point (X)	f	fx	$fx^2 = fx \times x$
17.5	1.1	19.25	336.875
22.5	1.7	38.25	860.625
27.5	1.5	41.25	1,134.375
32.5	1.3	42.25	1,373.125
37.5	1.3	48.75	1,828.125
42.5	1.4	59.50	2,528.750
47.5	1.5	71.25	3,384.375
52.5	1.3	68.25	3,583.125
57.5	1.4	80.50	4,628.750
62.5	1.1	68.75	4,296.875
67.5	0.4	27.00	1,822.500
	14.0	565.00	25,777.500

$$\sigma = \sqrt{\frac{25777.5}{14} - \left(\frac{565}{14}\right)^2}$$

$$= \sqrt{1841.25 - 1628.6989}$$

$$= 14.58 \text{ years}$$

Notice that in constructing the table for calculating the standard deviation, we have also obtained all the information we need to calculate the arithmetic mean. It would make sense, then, to calculate the mean as well as the standard deviation

$$\bar{x} = \frac{\Sigma fx}{\Sigma f} = \frac{565}{14} = 40.36 \text{ years}$$

Unless you have a calculator at your disposal, it can be very tedious to calculate the standard deviation using this method. Fortunately, we can simplify the calculations as we did with the arithmetic mean. We can multiply all the frequencies by 10, and calculate the deviations from the assumed mean (we again take 42.5 as our assumed mean). Notice that all the deviations are divisible by 5 – we have done this in the column headed d.

x	$x-42.5$	d	f	fd	fd^2
17.5	-25	-5	11	-55	275
22.5	-20	-4	17	-68	272
27.5	-15	-3	15	-45	135
32.5	-10	-2	13	-26	52
37.5	-5	-1	13	-13	13
42.5	0	0	14	0	0
47.5	5	1	15	15	15
52.5	10	2	13	26	52
57.5	15	3	14	42	126
62.5	20	4	11	44	176
67.5	25	5	4	20	100
			140	-60	1216

Calculating the standard deviation as before we have

$$\sigma = \sqrt{\frac{1216}{140} - \left(\frac{-60}{140}\right)^2}$$
$$= \sqrt{8.686 - 0.184}$$
$$= 2.916$$

However, we divided all the deviations by 5, so we must now multiply our standard deviation by 5

$$\sigma = 2.916 \times 5 = 14.58 \text{ years}$$

which agrees exactly with our previous result. Let us see if we can write a formula which describes the above calculation. If d is the deviation from an assumed mean, and if d is divided by a constant c, then

$$\sigma = c \times \sqrt{\frac{\Sigma fd^2}{\Sigma f} - \left(\frac{\Sigma fd}{\Sigma f}\right)^2}$$

Whether you use this formula for calculating the standard deviation, or the previous formula, is a matter of personal preference. If you have a calculating machine, then the first formula is probably preferable – it is certainly less messy! Although the second formula simplifies the multiplications, finding the deviations can often be so awkward that this outweighs its advantages. However, if we could offer some advice, it would be this: if the class width is constant, and if no calculating machine is available, then you will certainly find the second formula easier to use.

Again, the table gives us all the information we require to calculate the arithmetic mean. We have taken an assumed mean of 42.5, so

$$\bar{x} = 42.5 + \frac{5 \times -60}{140}$$

$$= 40.36 \text{ years}$$

Relative Dispersion

So far, we have been trying to measure dispersion *within* a series or distribution. We shall now attempt to measure dispersion *between* distributions, and we shall find that the standard deviation cannot do this. Consider the two series below:

A = 8, 9, 10, 11, 12, 13, 14   Mean = 11
B = 1008, 1009, 1010, 1011, 1012, 1013, 1014   Mean = 1011

Both A and B have the same standard deviation – can you see why? The deviations from the mean are identical in both series $(-3, -2, -1$ etc.) and both series have the same number of observations, so $\Sigma(x - \bar{x})^2$, and n would be the same whichever series we examined. You should verify that the standard deviation is, in fact, 2 for both series. Now does this mean that both series show the same degree of spread? Surely not! An increase from the smallest to the largest value in A is an increase of

$$\frac{14-8}{8} \times 100 = 75\%$$

but the same increase for series B is only

$$\frac{1014-1008}{1008} \times 100 = 0.595\%!$$

Clearly, A has a much greater percentage spread than B, and if we are going to compare dispersion between series we must take into account not only dispersion within each series (i.e. the standard deviation) but also the mean of the series. We can do this by calculating the *coefficient of variation*

$$V = \frac{100 \times \sigma}{\bar{x}}\%$$

For the series above, the coefficients of variation are

$$\frac{100 \times 2}{11} = 18.18\% \text{ (for A)}$$

and

$$\frac{100 \times 2}{1011} = 0.198\% \text{ (for B)}$$

confirming our suspicion that A has a greater relative spread than B. Notice that the coefficient of variation is a percentage, and not a particular measurement (centimetre, dollar, kilogram, etc.), and so it can be used for comparing distributions which have different units.

Now we would like to issue a word of warning. If you attempt to quantify the differences in dispersion using the coefficient of variation, ask yourself whether the result you have obtained 'feels right'. Compare your result with a 'gut feeling' you have obtained by visually examining the histogram of each distribution. If your results do not feel right, then you would be well advised to compare the distributions using the quartiles. Earlier, we defined the semi-interquartile range as $\frac{1}{2}(Q_3 - Q_1)$, and we could take the median Q_2 as a measure of central tendency, so an alternative measure of relative dispersion is

$$\frac{100 \times \frac{1}{2}(Q_3 - Q_1)}{Q_2}\% = \frac{50(Q_3 - Q_1)}{Q_2}\%$$

and we shall call this measure the *quartile coefficient of variation*. We shall say no more about it now, but in the exercises at the end of this chapter you will find an example where its use is obviously required.

Standard Scores

Suppose at a particular examination a candidate scored 65 marks, and at a later examination he scored 55 marks. Now his lower performance could be due to a genuine worsening in his performance, but it could also be due to the fact that the second examination was more difficult than the first. Suppose the average mark at the first examination was 50, and at the second examination was 45; this would indeed indicate that the second examination was more difficult than the first. But how can we compare his performance in the two examinations? Suppose that in the first examination the standard deviation was 10 marks, then his score of 65 marks is $\left(\frac{65-50}{10}\right)=$ one and a half standard deviations above the mean. If the standard deviation for the second examination was 5 marks, then his score of 55 marks is $\left(\frac{55-45}{5}\right)=$ two standard deviations above the mean. So we can see that in the second examination his relative performance (i.e. his performance with respect to other candidates) was better than in the first examination: he was nearer to the top of the group. Marks calculated in this way – in terms of standard deviations measured from the mean – are called *standard scores* or Z scores, and for any quantity x we can calculate the Z score like this –

$$Z = \frac{x - \bar{x}}{\sigma}$$

Notice that the Z score is in relative, not absolute units; so they can be used to compare values in distributions that do not use the same unit of measurement. These Z scores are often used by educationalists to standardise examination marks.

Now Z scores are very important to statisticians: under certain conditions Z scores can be used to predict the proportion of a distribution less than a certain measurement. Let us first examine the conditions necessary for us to be able to do this. The distribution must be continuous, it must be symmetrical (we will tell you later how to test for this) and it must be bell-shaped. In other words, the distribution must be shaped like the one in Fig. 7.2. We call such a distribution a *normal distribution*, and call its shape *mesokurtic*. Now you may (with some justification) think that these conditions are very

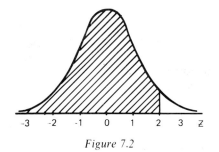

Figure 7.2

stringent and will not often be met in practice. We will have more to say about this later and for the moment we will concentrate on learning how to make predictions based on the normal distribution.

If you consult the tables at the end of this book you will find a table headed the Normal Distribution Function. In the column headed x are the various Z scores and in the column next to this (headed $\Phi(x)$) is the proportion of the distribution with a Z score less than x. Suppose we wished to find the proportion in a normal distribution with a Z score less than 2 (i.e. a value of two standard deviations greater than the mean). The shaded area in Fig. 7.2 represents the proportion diagrammatically. Consulting the table for $x = 2$, we read that $\Phi(x) = 0.9772$ (or 97.72%), so 97.72% of any normal distribution has a Z score less than 2. This being so, it must follow that $100 - 97.72 = 2.28\%$ of a normal distribution has a Z score greater than 2 (we imply here that a negligible proportion will have Z scores *exactly* equal to 2).

How can we apply this knowledge? Suppose we know that electric-light bulbs have an average life of 2000 hours and a standard deviation of 60 hours. Furthermore, we know that the lives of bulbs are normally distributed (this would be a reasonable assumption) and we wish to know the proportion of bulbs failing before 2120 hours. We could represent the problem diagrammatically like this:

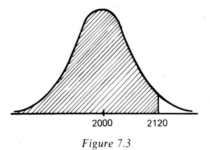

Figure 7.3

Notice that as the distribution is symmetrical, the mean bisects the distribution, and the mean and mode coincide. The shaded area will, of course, represent the proportion of bulbs failing before 2120 hours, and by far the majority of them will do so. The first thing we do is calculate the Z score

$$Z = \frac{2120 - 2000}{60} = 2 \text{ standard deviations}$$

Now we already know that 97.72% of items in a normal distribution have a Z score of less than 2, and in this particular normal distribution any bulb with a life below 2120 hours has a Z score less than 2. So it must follow that 97.72% of bulbs must fail before 2120 hours.

So far, we have considered cases where the Z score is positive, but it is perfectly possible for a Z score to be negative. This will occur when an item under consideration has a value less than the arithmetic mean. Suppose, for example, we wished to find the proportion of bulbs with lives less than 1850 hours. This involves finding the proportion of items with Z scores less than

$$\frac{1850 - 2000}{60} = -2.5$$

If we consult the table, we notice that only positive Z scores are given – but the table can also be used for negative Z scores. A glance at Fig. 7.4a and 7.4b will confirm that as the distribution is symmetrical, the proportion of items with Z scores less than −2.5 is the same as the proportion with Z scores greater than 2.5. Reading from the table, we see that 99.379% of items have Z scores less than 2.5, so 0.621% have Z scores greater than 2.5, and equally 0.621% must have

Z scores less than -2.5. So we can see that only 0.621% of bulbs can be expected to fail before 1850 hours.

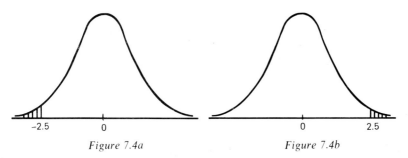

Figure 7.4a	*Figure 7.4b*

Now you may find this all a bit confusing – sometimes the Z score is positive, and sometimes it is negative; sometimes we read the percentage directly from the table, and sometimes we subtract it from 100. Can we at this point offer some advice? When considering problems involving the normal distribution, *always* draw a sketch of the problem and shade the area under consideration. You can then see at a glance whether the area required is greater or less than 50%. If the area is greater than 50%, then the proportion in the table is the one required. If the area required is less than 50%, subtract from 100 the percentage obtained from the table.

Suppose we know that the weights of bags of flour are normally distributed with a standard deviation of 0.01 kilograms. The bags are marked 'weight not less than 1 kilogram', and the machine is set to fill bags to an average weight of 1.015 kilograms. We require to know the proportion of bags that are underweight. Firstly, let us draw a sketch of the problem (see Fig. 7.5).

The Z score is

$$\frac{1-1.015}{0.01} = -1.5$$

and looking up 1.5 in the table we see that $\Phi(x) = 93.32\%$. Now the diagram tells us immediately that this cannot be the percentage we require – it obviously should be less than 50%. So the proportion of underweight bags is $100 - 93.32 = 6.68\%$.

Sometimes it is necessary to use the normal distribution tables in reverse, i.e. given a Z score, we must find a value in the distribution which it corresponds to. Suppose that in the last example, legislation states that only 5% of bags may be underweight. Clearly, the firm does not comply with the requirements, and in order to do so the

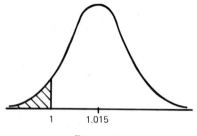

Figure 7.5

average weight of bags must be increased (by resetting the machine filling the bags). We wish to find the machine setting that will meet the legal requirements. Fig. 7.6 illustrates the situation, and $\bar{x}$ is the machine setting required. We cannot look up 5% in the table (50%

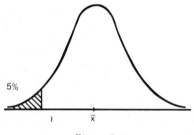

Figure 7.6

is the lowest proportion), but as the distribution is symmetrical, 5% has the same Z score as 95%. We notice that in the $\Phi(x)$ column that 94.95% of items have a Z score of less than 1.64, and 95.05% have a Z score less than 1.65, so it would seem reasonable to assume that 95% have a Z score less than 1.645. Now notice that the weight we are considering (1 kilogram) is *less than* the mean, so its Z score must be negative. In other words,

$$\frac{1 - \bar{x}}{0.01} = -1.645$$

so $\bar{x} = 1.01645$ kilograms.

We shall now examine a case which shows how the normal distribution can help in the decision-taking process.

In order to satisfy legal requirements, a pork pie manufacturer may only produce 0.2% of pies below a weight of 75 grams. The pie-producing machine operates with a standard deviation of 0.5 grams. If

weights are normally distributed, to what weight should the machine
be set? A new pie-producing machine is available; operating with
a standard deviation of 0.2 grams, but costs an additional £225 per
week to operate. The pie manufacturer's weekly output is 200,000
pies. Pies with weights in excess of 77 grams require additional packaging at a cost of 0.5p per pie. The pie contents cost 5p per 100 grams.
Would you recommend that the pie manufacturer purchases the new
machine?

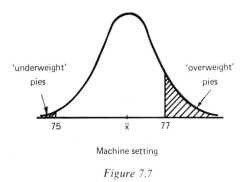

Machine setting

Figure 7.7

Firstly, we calculate the setting for each machine. If only 0.2% of
pies may be underweight then $\Phi(x) = 99.8\%$, and $Z = -2.88$. The Z
score for the old machine is $\frac{(75-\bar{x})}{0.5}$, and for the new machine is $\frac{(75-\bar{x})}{0.2}$.
To calculate the machine setting for the old machine, we have

$$\frac{75-\bar{x}}{0.5} = -2.88$$

so the machine setting is 76.44 grams. For the new machine we have

$$\frac{75-\bar{x}}{0.2} = -2.88$$

so the setting for the new machine is 75.576 grams.
Now let us calculate the proportion of pies that need extra packaging. Using the old machine we have

$$Z = \frac{77 - 76.44}{0.5} = 1.12, \quad \text{so} \quad \Phi(x) = 86.86\%$$

So 13.14% of pies will need extra packaging. Using the new machine

$$Z = \frac{77 - 75.576}{0.2} = 7.12$$

Now the Z values in the normal distribution only go up to 4, so for $Z = 4$, $\Phi(x) = 100\%$, so with the new machine we will not expect any of the pies to need extra packaging. We can now calculate the weekly cost using the two machines. Using the old machine,

Weekly pie content requirement is $200{,}000 \times 76.44 =$ 15,288,000 gm
Weekly cost of contents is $15{,}288{,}000 \times 0.05\text{p} = £7644$
Each week 13.14% of $200{,}000 = 26{,}280$ pies need extra packing
Weekly cost of extra packing is $26{,}280 \times 0.5\text{p} = £131.40$

So weekly cost using old machine is $£7644 + £131.40 = £7775.40$. Using the new machine

Weekly pie content requirement is $200{,}000 \times 75.576 =$ 15,115,200 gm
Weekly cost of contents is $15{,}115{,}200 \times 0.05\text{p} = £7557.60$

As no pies will need extra packing with this machine, £7557.60 is the weekly cost of the new machine. So the new machine involves a saving of £217.80, and as it costs an extra £225 to operate, the manufacturer would be well advised to retain the use of the old machine.

The normal distribution is of paramount importance to statistics, and you would be well advised to master it before moving on to the following chapters. Before we finish this chapter, we must return to a point made earlier; that the conditions attached to using the normal distribution are so stringent that they will seldom be satisfied in practice. Now while it is probably true that the conditions will seldom be met in populations, we will find later that the conditions *will* be expected to be met when considering certain aspects of *sampling*. This is a fact that we will examine in some detail in later chapters. Finally, we promised earlier to tell you how to test a distribution for symmetry. We can test for symmetry by calculating the coefficient of skewness,

$$\frac{3\,(\text{mean} - \text{median})}{\text{standard deviation}}$$

If the distribution is symmetrical, then the mean and median are the same, so the coefficient of skewness is zero. With negative skewness, the median exceeds the mean, and the coefficient is negative. With positive skewness, the mean exceeds the median and the coefficient is positive. The nearer the coefficient is to zero, the more symmetrical is the distribution.

Although perfect symmetry is seldom achieved, many cases occur in which there is a very good approximation, and in all the questions involving the use of this method we assume that the skewness is insufficient to make any material difference to our results.

EXERCISES TO CHAPTER SEVEN

7.1 The monthly production in 2 factories in thousands of units is as follows:

A: 23, 30, 28, 31, 29, 26, 34, 36, 28, 32, 25, 26
B: 53, 65, 70, 50, 62, 58, 52, 63, 69, 72, 64, 54

(a) Compare the variability of production in the 2 factories by calculating the standard deviation in each case.
(b) Calculate the coefficient of variation in each case.   O.N.C.

7.2 From the figures given below state what is:

(a) the range;
(b) the arithmetic mean;
(c) the median;
(d) the lower quartile;
(e) the upper quartile;
(f) the quartile deviation;
(g) the mean deviation.

Explain what is meant by the mean deviation and the quartile deviation.

8	35	45	50	60	68
13	37	46	52	61	70
26	40	47	55	65	71
29	41	48	58	67	75
33					

I.C.M.A.

7.3 The table shows the age distribution of the estimated U.K. population at 30th June 1972.

Age in Years	Total U.K. Population (millions)
0 and under 5	4.4
5 and under 10	4.7
10 and under 15	4.3
15 and under 20	3.9
20 and under 25	4.1
25 and under 30	4.0
30 and under 35	3.3
35 and under 40	3.2
40 and under 45	3.3
45 and under 50	3.4

Age in Years	Total U.K. Population (millions)
50 and under 55	3.4
55 and under 60	3.3
60 and under 65	3.2
65 and over	7.5

Source: Monthly Digest.

(a) Draw an appropriate graph and from it estimate the median and the upper and lower quartiles. Hence obtain the semi-interquartile range.

(b) Detail how the quartiles could be obtained other than by using the graph. O.N.C.

7.4   Details of the annual bonuses paid to sales staff employed by a large wallpaper manufacturer have recently been made available (1974):

Annual Bonus (£)	Number of Bonuses
Under 60	8
60 and under 70	10
70 and under 80	16
80 and under 90	14
90 and under 100	10
100 and under 110	5
110 and over	2

Source: Company Records.

(a) Using graphical methods, estimate the median bonus paid and comment on the suitability of the median in interpreting this type of data. How many sales staff receive an annual bonus of

 (i) Less than £88?

 (ii) At least £63 but less than £75?

 (iii) £96 or more?

(b) From the graph, estimate a measure of dispersion, using the quartiles. What is meant by *dispersion*? O.N.C.

7.5   *Estimated Wealth of Individuals in Gt. Britain in 1968*

Ranges of Net Wealth (£)	No. of Cases (thousands)
Under 1,000	5,190
1,000–under 3,000	5,415
3,000–under 5,000	2,918
5,000–under 10,000	2,191
10,000–under 15,000	598
15,000–under 20,000	288
20,000–under 25,000	148
25,000–under 50,000	326
50,000–under 100,000	121
100,000–under 200,000	40
200,000 and over	20
Total	17,255

Source: Board of Inland Revenue.

(a) Calculate (i) the median net wealth,
           (ii) the quartile deviation.

(b) How appropriate are these measures to this distribution?

(c) State briefly the advantages and disadvantages of using quartile deviation and standard deviation as measures of dispersion.   O.N.C.

7.6   Profits made by a sample of firms in a certain industry in a given year are as follows:

Profits (£)	% of Firms
Up to 2,000	6.8
2,001–	11.4
4,001–	14.1
6,001–	13.5
8,001–	11.5
10,001–	24.1
12,001–	6.4
13,001 or more	5.8
Showing a loss	6.4
All firms	100%
Number of firms	5231

Calculate the median and quartile deviation of the profits made by the 5231 firms included in the sample. Construct a block diagram to represent the distribution and discuss whether the mean is likely to be higher or lower than the median.   C.I.P.F.A.

7.7   The following data gives the monthly expenditure on advertising in 1969 of the branches of Cosmetics Ltd.:

Cosmetics Ltd. Monthly Advertising Expenditure in 1969

£	Number of Branches
800 and less than 1000	50
1000 and less than 1200	200
1200 and less than 1400	350
1400 and less than 1600	150
1600 and less than 1800	100
1800 and less than 2000	75
2000 and less than 2200	50
2200 and less than 2400	25

(a) From the above data calculate the median monthly expenditure, and explain what it indicates about the branches' advertising expenditure in 1969.
(b) Calculate the semi-interquartile range from the data and explain the purpose of this calculation.   A.C.A.

7.8   *Deliveries of Gravel from a Quarry*

Weight of Load	No. of Loads	
(cwt)	Week 1	Week 2
5 and under 10	84	45
10 and under 20	86	63
20 and under 30	122	140
30 and under 40	86	77
40 and under 60	16	21
60 and under 80	6	4
	400	350

(a) Express the frequencies as percentages of their respective totals and use these figures to draw, on the one graph, cumulative frequency curves for the loads of gravel delivered in Week 1 and Week 2.
(b) Use your graph to find the median weight and the semi-interquartile range for the two weeks.
(c) Comment briefly on your results.   O.N.C.

7.9   *Local Authorities with Central Purchasing Organisations*

Average % Discount Obtained	Number of Authorities
8 and under 12	0
12 and under 16	0
16 and under 20	2
20 and under 24	0
24 and under 28	3
28 and under 32	0

Average % Discount Obtained	Number of Authorities
32 and under 36	6
36 and under 40	7
40 and under 44	2
44 and under 48	3

Local Authorities without Central Purchasing Organisations

Average % Discount Obtained	Number of Authorities
8 and under 12	5
12 and under 16	16
16 and under 20	12
20 and under 24	8
24 and under 28	13
28 and under 32	1
32 and under 36	0
36 and under 40	1
40 and under 44	1
44 and under 48	0

Source: L.G.O.R.U.

For each of these distributions calculate

(a) the arithmetic mean of the average % discount obtained;
(b) the standard deviation of the average % discount obtained.

Compare the arithmetic means and suggest what conclusions might be drawn from these statistics. O.N.C.

7.10 The table below gives an analysis of the debtors' balances of Fuel Suppliers Ltd. at 30th November 1974.

Fuel Suppliers Ltd. Debtors' Balances at 30th November 1974

Balance Outstanding (£)	Number of Accounts
20– 39.9	1
40– 59.9	3
60– 79.9	6
80– 99.9	10
100–119.9	5
120–139.9	3
140–159.9	2

You are required to:

(a) calculate the mean balance and the standard deviation, and
(b) explain the value of knowing the standard deviation in respect of the outstanding balances due to Fuel Suppliers Ltd.

A.C.A.

7.11   The distribution shown below is the output of the factories of Quality Clothing Ltd., for the month of May 1972. You are required to:

(a) calculate the standard deviation from these figures, and
(b) contrast the mean deviation and the standard deviation as measures of dispersion and indicate briefly what the standard deviation calculated in (a) means for the monthly output of Quality Clothing Ltd.

Quality Clothing Ltd.

Monthly Output Men's Suits (000's)	Number of Factories
23 and under 28	10
28 and under 33	20
33 and under 38	20
38 and under 43	24
43 and under 48	20
48 and under 53	16
53 and under 58	8
58 and under 63	2

A.C.A.

7.12   From the following frequency distribution of the weekly overtime earnings of the staff of Catering Ltd., you are required to:

(a) calculate (i) the mean and (ii) the standard deviation, and
(b) indicate what the value of the standard deviation tells you about the weekly overtime earnings of the staff of Catering Ltd.

Catering Ltd.

Weekly Overtime Earnings (pence)	Number of Staff
50– 74.9	2
75– 99.9	5
100–124.9	10
125–149.9	17
150–174.9	10
175–199.9	4
200–224.9	2

A.C.A.

7.13   A furnace whose size is nominally 200 tons is used to cast steel ingots of 10 tons weight. The amount of steel in the furnace cannot be controlled accurately, so that an incomplete ingot is normally produced when ingots are cast. For example, a furnace load of 198 tons will produce 19 full ingots and one 8-ton ingot. The following data show the weight of 100 furnace loads of steel.

Weight of Furnace Load (tons)	Frequency
190.0 and under 192.5	1
192.5 and under 195.0	4
195.0 and under 197.5	8
197.5 and under 200.0	19
200.0 and under 202.5	36
202.5 and under 205.0	20
205.0 and under 207.5	8
207.5 and under 210.0	4

Required: Compile a frequency distribution of the weight of incomplete ingots, and calculate its mean and standard deviation.

A.C.A.

7.14   *Distribution of Personal Incomes before Tax*
(1970–1 Annual Survey)

Lower Limit of Range of Income (£)	Number of Incomes (thousands)
400	883
500	1,161
600	1,270
700	1,212
800	2,322
1,000	5,720
1,500	4,296
2,000	3,341
3,000	836
5,000	328
Total	21,369

Source: Board of Inland Revenue.

(a) Rewrite the numbers of incomes to the nearest hundred thousand.
(b) Using the rounded data calculate the standard deviation.
(c) Explain the importance of this measure of dispersion.
(d) The source gives the number of all incomes as 21,368 (thousands). Why is this number different from the total in the above table?   O.N.C.

7.15 A survey of house prices in a local newspaper yielded the following information:

Price of House (£'000s)	Number of Houses for Sale
below 10	16
10 and under 12	41
12 and under 14	39
14 and under 16	22
16 and under 18	10
18 and under 20	11
20 and under 22	4
22 and under 24	5
24 and under 26	1
26 and under 28	5
28 and under 30	4
30 and over	2
	160

(a) Calculate the mean price of houses in the area and the standard deviation, stating clearly any assumptions you may make.

(b) For what reason may the mean and standard deviation be inappropriate for such a distribution? Suggest better alternatives.

O.N.C.

7.16 At the General Election in February 1974, the sizes of constituencies were distributed as shown in the table below:

Number of Voters ('000s)	Number of Constituencies
20 and under 30	7
30 and under 40	17
40 and under 50	74
50 and under 60	176
60 and under 70	183
70 and under 80	115
80 and under 90	48
90 and under 100	13
100 and over	2
Total	635

(a) Calculate the average number of voters per constituency and also the standard deviation.

(b) In order that constituencies may be kept to a roughly similar size, constituency boundaries are from time to time revised. From your results in (a) suggest a range of sizes outside which changes might be made, and give reasons for your suggestions.

O.N.C.

7.17   *Electric Lamps*

Hours of Life (hundreds)	Number of Lamps
0–5	5
5–10	10
10–20	38
20–40	36
40 and over	15

(a) Calculate the mean and standard deviation of the life of the whole batch of lamps whose pattern of duration is given in the table above.

(b) Compare and contrast the standard deviation and the quartile deviation as measures of dispersion.   C.I.P.F.A.

7.18   (a) Explain the meaning of absolute and relative measures of dispersion and compare their use.

(b) In Department A of a firm the average weekly earnings are 366 sh. with a standard deviation of 28.2 sh. Calculate the relative dispersion.

(c) In Department B the earnings in shillings in a certain week of the 10 members are as follows:

237   245   283   296   253   249   236   254   305   242

Calculate the mean and the standard deviation of this department. Compare this result with Department A and comment.

O.N.C.

7.19   Explain the use of the coefficient of variation.

A company has two factories A and B, situated in different parts of England. Labour turnover in factory B is much higher than in factory A. The consultant engaged by the firm to investigate the causes of labour turnover suggests that a possible cause of the higher turnover in factory B is a wider variation in the annual wages of workers in factory B than in factory A: he found that the standard deviation of wages of workers in factory B was £600 compared with a standard deviation of £500 for factory A. Given the information that the mean annual wage of workers in factory B is £2000 and in factory A £1500. Show how the consultant's suggestion may be tested by use of the coefficient of variation, and say whether he is right.

A.C.A.

7.20   *Projected Population in Scotland in 1972*
(*tens of thousands*)

Age Group	Males	Females
0–14	75	72
15–29	59	58
30–44	46	47
45–59	43	48
60–74	31	41
75 and over	6	14
All ages	260	280

(a) Calculate the standard deviation for each distribution.
(b) Calculate the arithmetic mean of the male distribution and hence obtain a relative measure of dispersion.   O.N.C.

7.21

Monthly Salary £	Number of Trainee Draughtsmen
under 72	4
72 and under 76	9
76 and under 80	16
80 and under 84	28
84 and under 88	45
88 and under 92	66
92 and under 96	85
96 and under 100	72
100 and under 104	54
104 and under 108	38
108 and under 112	27
112 and under 116	18
116 and under 120	11
120 and under 124	5
124 and over	2

(a) The above figures relate to the monthly salaries of the trainee draughtsmen of a local company. Calculate the arithmetic mean and the standard deviation.
(b) Information relating to the trainees employed by a rival firm gives a coefficient of variation of 18%. Are they, or the local company's trainees, more variable with respect to salaries?
    O.N.C.

7.22　A company selling a consumer product directly to retail outlets has collected the following information:

Average Number of Orders Taken per Month by Individual Salesmen	Number of Salesmen
20 and under	3
21–30	7
31–40	16
41–50	22
51–60	19
61–70	8
71 and over	2

Calculate　(a) the approximate range;
　　　　　　(b) the standard deviation;
　　　　　　(c) the coefficient of variation.

All of these are measures of dispersion. Describe, with additional examples, when the use of each would be appropriate.　　O.N.C.

7.23　The following table shows the distribution of weekly incomes for two towns:

Weekly Income	Town A		Town B	
	No.	Income (£)	No.	Income (£)
£0 and under £10	0	0	1	5
£10 and under £20	4	60	5	75
£20 and under £30	9	225	9	225
£30 and under £40	17	595	13	455
£40 and under £50	23	1035	19	855
£50 and under £60	19	1045	23	1265
£60 and under £70	13	845	17	1105
£70 and under £80	9	675	9	675
£80 and under £90	5	425	4	340
£90 and under £100	1	95	0	0
Totals	100	5000	100	5000

(i) Show that the arithmetic mean income is the same in both towns. In the light of this result do you feel that the arithmetic mean is a useful measure to use for comparison of the two towns' 'average' income? If not, derive an alternative measure that you consider better, giving reasons for your choice.

(ii) Show that the standard deviation of incomes is the same in both towns. In the light of this result do you feel that the standard deviation is a useful measure to use for comparison of the two towns' dispersion of income? If not, derive an alternative measure that you consider better, giving reasons for your choice.

(iii) Given your discussion of (i) and (ii) above, what do you consider to be the essential differences between the two towns' distributions of income? How *might* you express this by a statistical measure?

(iv) Construct a visual presentation of the data in the table that highlights the differences as discussed by you in (iii) above.

C.I.P.F.A.

7.24 The table below shows the salaries of the 600 manual employees of a certain company.

No. of Employees	Range of Salary
0	Under £600
80	£600 but under £800
170	£800 but under £1000
90	£1000 but under £1200
80	£1200 but under £1400
70	£1400 but under £1600
50	£1600 but under £1800
40	£1800 but under £2000
20	£2000 but under £2200
0	£2200 and over

(a) Calculate the mean and standard deviation salary of the employees.

(b) Obtain and comment on an arithmetical measure of the skewness of the salary distribution.

(c) State the main reason for normally using the median salary as a measure of position rather than the arithmetic mean or average; illustrate your answer with reference to the above data.

O.N.C.

7.25 The table shows the age distribution of those males receiving retirement pensions at 31st December 1972. Calculate the arithmetic mean and standard deviation for this distribution. If the median is 71.8 years, obtain a measure of skewness and comment on what this tells you about the shape of the frequency curve of the distribution.

Retirement Pensions (Male) at 31st December 1972

Age (years)	Number Receiving Pensions (thousands)
65–69	1030
70–74	820
75–79	460
80–84	240
85–89	80
90 and over	20

Source: Dept. of Health and Social Security.   O.N.C.

7.26 (a) What are the more important characteristics of the normal distribution?

(b) Discuss the importance of the mean and standard deviation in the use of the normal distribution. I.C.S.A.

7.27 The length of rods in a large batch is normally distributed with mean 120 mm and standard deviation 1.5 mm. What percentage of the rods would you expect to measure

(i) over 122.5 mm;
(ii) between 116 mm and 124 mm? O.N.C.

7.28 A random sample was taken of 200 candidates who had submitted scripts in a certain question paper at a public examination. The results obtained by the 200 candidates in the examination were as follows:

Marks Obtained out of a Possible 100	Number of Candidates
Under 20	0
20–29	6
30–39	18
40–49	41
50–59	68
60–69	49
70–79	14
80–89	4
90 and over	0
Total	200

(a) Calculate:

(i) the mean;
(ii) the standard deviation.

(b) (i) What does the standard deviation measure?
(ii) How does the standard deviation you have calculated differ from what might be expected if results were normally distributed? I.C.M.A.

7.29 (a) What are the principal features of the normal distribution?

(b) Suppose that the distribution of women by size of feet is normal, with an arithmetic mean length of 8 in. and a standard deviation of 1 in. A manufacturer of women's shoes has an output of 10,000 pairs per week and he wants to know how many pairs of shoes of each length to produce. How could a table of the area under a normal curve help him to plan his output? How many pairs per week should be (a) above $8\frac{1}{2}$ in.; (b) below $6\frac{1}{2}$ in.; (c) above $7\frac{1}{2}$ in.; (d) below 9 in.? C.I.P.F.A.

7.30   (a) Sketch a normal distribution curve. On this sketch indicate the approximate proportions of the area under the curve which are contained within the following limits:

arithmetic mean ± 1 standard deviation,
arithmetic mean ± 2 standard deviations, and
arithmetic mean ± 3 standard deviations.

(b) Explain why this distribution and the proportions of the total area you have indicated are so important to the process of statistical inference based on sampling.

(c) A company packing biscuits knows that the weights of 500 packets form a normal distribution with a mean weight of 16 ounces and a standard deviation of 0.2 ounces. How many of these 500 packets can be expected to weigh:

(i) less than 15.6 ounces;
(ii) between 15.8 and 16.4 ounces;
(iii) at least 16.2 ounces?   O.N.C.

7.31   Describe a normal distribution, paying particular attention to precise definitions of its most important properties. Give examples of statistical data which might be expected to conform closely to a normal distribution.

An automatic machine produces packages whose weights are normally distributed with a standard deviation of 0.07 ounces. To what weight should the machine be set so that at least $97\frac{1}{2}\%$ of the packages are over 1 lb in weight?   O.N.C.

7.32   (a) Illustrate graphically the relationship between the standard deviation and areas under the normal curve of distribution.

(b) Assuming that the hub thickness of a certain type of gear is normally distributed around a mean thickness of 2.00 inches, with a standard deviation of 0.04 inches, say:

(i) approximately how many gears will have a thickness between 1.96 and 2.04 inches in a production run of 5000 gears;
(ii) in a random selection of one gear from this production run of 5000, with what degree of confidence could it be predicted that its thickness would be between 1.92 and 2.08 inches?
                                  A.C.A.

N.B. The tables given with these two questions are different to the table at the end of the book.

7.33   A manufacturer makes chocolate bars with a mean weight of 110 grams and a standard deviation of 2 grams. The weights are normally distributed. What proportion of the bars are likely to be less in weight than 106 grams? The manufacturer decides to make 'bigger' bars with a mean weight of 115 grams, with the same standard deviation as before. What proportion of the new bars is likely to be less in weight than the old ones? (The weights of the 'bigger' bars are also normally distributed.)

It is decided that the covers of these 'bigger' bars will be marked 'Minimum weight 115 grams'. What mean weight will have to be aimed at if no more than 1 bar in 100 is to be less than 115 grams in weight?

Table of Normal Probability
(T is the standardised normal variate)

T	Area to the right of T	T	Area to the right of T
0.0	0.500	2.5	0.994
0.5	0.691	3.0	0.999
1.0	0.841		
1.5	0.933		
2.0	0.977		

I.C.S.A.

7.34 (a) In quality control it is the practice to take at intervals a sample of items, around 4 or 5 in number, and to note the mean and the range of the items. Explain why it would be inadequate to take a single item, rather than 4 or 5.

(b) Components made by a certain process have a thickness which is normally distributed about a mean of 3.00 cm and a standard deviation of 0.03cm. A component is classified as defective if its thickness lies outside the range 2.95 cm to 3.05 cm.

Required:
(1) What is the proportion of defective components?
(2) Find the change in the proportion of defective components if the mean thickness is increased to 3.01 cm, the variability remaining the same.

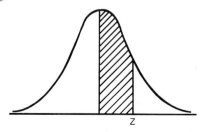

Proportion Lying in Shaded Area of Standard Normal Distribution

Z	0.0	0.1	0.2	0.3	0.4	0.5	0.6	0.7	0.8	0.9
proportion	0.000	0.040	0.079	0.118	0.155	0.192	0.226	0.258	0.288	0.316
Z	1.0	1.1	1.2	1.3	1.4	1.5	1.6	1.7	1.8	1.9
proportion	0.341	0.364	0.385	0.403	0.419	0.433	0.445	0.455	0.464	0.471
Z	2.0	2.1	2.2	2.3	2.4	2.5	2.6	2.7	2.8	2.9
proportion	0.477	0.482	0.486	0.489	0.492	0.494	0.495	0.496	0.497	0.498

A.C.A.

More exercises can be found on the normal distribution at the end of chapter nine.

Chapter Eight

Probability

If you have read the previous chapters carefully, you will have realised by now that much of a statistician's time is spent measuring
data and drawing conclusions based on his measurements. Sometimes, all the data is available to the statistician, and the measurements are bound to be accurate. In such circumstances, we can say
that he has perfect knowledge of the population he is investigating.
Unfortunately, this will not be the usual situation. In most cases,
the statistician will not have the details he wants about the entire
population, and will be unable to collect all the information he wants
because of the cost and labour involved. To take an example; suppose it is required to find the average height of adult males in a particular country; it would not be possible to measure the height of
every male. Instead, the statistician would have to make do with the
average height of a sample. Now if he is careful about how his sample
is drawn, and if the sample is not too small, then the sample average
will give a good approximation to the population average. However,
because the entire population has not been examined, the statistician
can never be completely sure of his results, so when quoting conclusions based on sample evidence it is usual to state just how confident we are of our results. So you will often see estimates quoted
'with 95% confidence', i.e. the probability that the estimate is right
is 95%. In order to understand the principles of sampling, then, we
must first understand the meaning and theory of probability.
Furthermore, the emphasis of this book will now undergo a change.
Previously, we have been concerned with statistical measurement
and representation, but from now on we will concentrate on *statistical analysis*. The basis for all statistical analysis is the theory of probability – something that must be mastered if we are to appreciate fully
the work of the statistician.

Some Definitions

Let us suppose that we toss a coin. This experiment can have two outcomes: the coin can land with either heads showing or tails showing.

The result of such an experiment is called an *event*. Notice that in this case the events are *mutually exclusive*, that is, if a head occurs, then a tail cannot occur at the same time. Now not all events are mutually exclusive, and we must be careful to recognise when events are mutually exclusive and when they are not. Suppose, for example, we are selecting a card from a pack; and the first event is that the card is red and the second event is that the card is an ace. If we draw the ace of hearts or the ace of diamonds, then both events have occurred simultaneously. Clearly, the events are *not* mutually exclusive. Usually, we use a capital E with a suitable subscript to identify the events in an experiment. We could write the events in the coin-spinning experiment like this:

$$E_1 = \text{the coin shows a head}$$
$$E_2 = \text{the coin shows a tail}$$

Notice too that E_1 and E_2 are *collectively exhaustive*: that is, they account for all the logical possibilities (we treat with contempt the suggestion that the coin lands on its edge!).

Sometimes we will find it convenient to consider the situations when the event would not occur, and we can do this by placing a dash after the symbol for the event. So we could write

$$E_1' = \text{the coin does not show a head}$$

Can you see that in this case E_1' and E_2 are equivalent events? If the coin does not show a head then it must show a tail. We can conclude that if $E_1' = E_2$, then E_1 and E_2 must be both mutually exclusive and collectively exhaustive.

How we Measure Probability

Let us consider a certain experiment, and list all the possible events; that is, we will ensure that the events are collectively exhaustive. Events that are equally likely will be assigned the same 'weighting'. Suppose, for example, we again consider tossing a coin. We have

$$E_1 = \text{the coin shows a head}$$
$$E_2 = \text{the coin shows a tail}$$

If we make the assumption that the coin is unbiassed, then E_1 and E_2 must be equally likely. What we will now do is to assign 'weights' to the events in proportion to the likelihood that they will occur. So we have

	Weight
E_1	1
E_2	1

Now the probability that the event E occurs is

$$P(E) = \frac{\text{Weighting for event } E}{\text{Sum of the weights}}$$

So $\qquad P(E_1) = \frac{1}{2} \text{ (or } 0.5)$

and $\qquad P(E_2) = \frac{1}{2}$

So we can see that the probability of obtaining a head with a single throw of a coin is one half. Just what do we mean by this? Well, it is obvious that we cannot demonstrate probability with a single toss of a coin. In fact, the outcome of a single toss depends on the force we exert together with the way the coin was originally facing. It has nothing to do with probability! When we state that the probability of a head is a half, we are surely making some prediction as to the proportion of heads occurring if we repeat this experiment many times. The outcome of each *individual* toss is determined by the forces mentioned earlier, but the outcome of many tosses obeys a law of 'mass behaviour', and it is this 'mass behaviour' that our probability measure is trying to predict. So when we state that the probability of a head is a half, we mean that if the coin is tossed a large number of times, then we would expect heads to occur on 50% of occasions.

Let us now see if we can restate our measure of probability. If an experiment has N *equally likely* outcomes, n of which constitute event E, then we can state that

$$P(E) = \frac{n}{N}$$

Suppose, then, we wished to find the probability of drawing an ace from a well-shuffled pack of cards. Here we have $N = 52$ (there are 52 cards in a pack, all of them having an equal chance of being drawn) and $n = 4$, so

$$P(\text{ace}) = \frac{4}{52} = \frac{1}{13}$$

Easy, isn't it?

Now suppose that $n = N$. This implies that each and every outcome must constitute event E. In other words, if we perform the experiment we are absolutely certain that event E will occur. Moreover, if $n = N$, then $P(E) = 1$, so we assign a probability measure of 1 to events that are absolutely certain to occur. If the event E cannot possibly occur, then $n = 0$ and $P(E) = 0$, so we assign a zero probability measure to events that are absolutely impossible. As absolute certainty and absolute impossibility are at opposite ends of the spectrum, we have now obtained limits to our measure of probability –

$P(E)$ must lie between zero and one. We can write this statement mathematically like this:

$$0 \leqslant P(E) \leqslant 1$$

So let this be a warning to you – if you are calculating the probability of an event, and your result is either negative, or greater than one, then you have made a mistake somewhere. We, as examiners, have frequently met solutions to probability problems in the form of (say) $P(E) = 1.5$. Now not only has the candidate obviously performed the calculations incorrectly, but also he has demonstrated that he does not know that $P(E)$ cannot exceed one – you cannot be more certain than absolute certainty! So if you obtain an answer like this in an examination, and you cannot discover where you have gone wrong, please do state that your answer *is* wrong, and state *why* it is wrong!

Earlier, we stated that an experiment has N equally likely outcomes, n of which constitute event E. Hence, it must follow that $N - n$ of the outcomes would *not* constitute event E. We can now formulate that

$$P(E') = \frac{N-n}{N}$$

$$= 1 - \frac{n}{N}$$

So $P(E') = 1 - P(E)$

We have already discovered that the probability of drawing an ace from a pack of cards is $\frac{1}{13}$, so it must follow that the probability of not drawing an ace is $1 - \frac{1}{13} = \frac{12}{13}$. Later, we will find this formula extremely useful.

The Three Approaches to Probability

Well, we have now seen how to measure probability. However, we have so far been making an assumption without actually spelling it out. We have assumed that we not only know all the possible outcomes of an experiment, but also that we can weight the probability of each outcome in proportion to its likelihood. More importantly, we have assumed we can do both of these things *before the experiment is performed*. In other words, we assume a prior knowledge of the outcomes – we have been using the so-called *a priori* approach to probability. Now although it is true that in many cases we will have the necessary information to use an a priori approach (it is true, for example, when considering games of chance), there are many cases in which an a priori approach cannot be used.

Suppose we have a large case of wood screws, and we wish to find the probability that one screw chosen at random is defective. Clearly, it is possible here to define all the events (the screw is either defective or it isn't) but it is not possible to weight the events in proportion to their likelihood. The only way we can determine probability in this case is to draw a sample of N screws, and count the number of defectives (call this n). We can then *estimate* the probability that a randomly chosen screw is defective is $\frac{n}{N}$. This is the so-called *empirical approach* – there is just no way of estimating the probability without drawing that sample!

An appreciation of these two approaches to probability helps to explain a problem that confuses so many students. The problem runs something like this – if I spin a penny 100 times, and on 99 occasions the coin shows heads, what is the probability that it will show heads on the next spin? Some people would argue that the outcome can be either a head or a tail, and the coin has no memory of the 100 previous tosses. So the probability that the coin will show heads on the next spin must be $\frac{1}{2}$. Others would argue that the coin is more likely to show heads than tails, and would estimate the probability of obtaining a head on the next spin to be $\frac{99}{100}$. Well, which approach is the correct one? Surprisingly, the answer is both! In the first case, we are using an a priori approach, reasoning that the experiment has produced a fluke result which does not detract from the fact that the coin is unbiassed. In the second case, we are using an empirical approach, stating that the experimental evidence indicates that the coin is biassed in favour of heads. Now ask yourself this – if you were a gambler, which approach would you prefer to use?

There is a third approach to probability that we must now examine. Suppose we wished to find the probability that a particular horse wins the Derby – clearly we cannot use an a priori approach. Nor can we use an empirical approach, as this would demand that the same race be repeated many times under identical conditions! The only way we can obtain this probability is to give a personal, 'gut feeling' of the horse's chances. This is the so-called *subjective* approach to probability, and it is the method used by bookmakers when fixing odds for a particular horse to win a race. Initially, the odds will be determined by the personal view of the bookmaker, and will be modified as the race approaches according to the collective, subjective views of the punters.

These three distinct approaches to probability raise an interesting philosophical problem. We know that $P(E)$ can never exceed one, but does $P(E) = 1$ imply absolute certainty? It all depends on the approach used. If we use an a priori approach then $P(E) = 1$ means that E *must always* occur. However, using an empirical approach

$P(E) = 1$ means that *E has always* occurred – which does not imply that it *must* occur in the future. Likewise, using a subjective approach $P(E) = 1$ means that *we think that E will occur* – which again does not imply that it must occur.

Without doubt, the empirical and subjective approaches are more interesting and more useful than the a priori approach. However, in an introductory book such as this, it is preferable to concentrate our attention on a priori probability, and, unless we state to the contrary, you should assume that an a priori approach is being used.

The Laws of Probability

Let us suppose that we cast two dice, and add the scores of the dice. We could represent all the outcomes in a table like this:

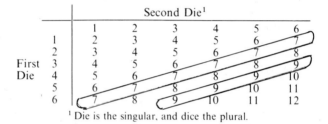

¹ Die is the singular, and dice the plural.

The number in front of each row represents the possible scores of the first die, and the number at the head of each column represents the possible scores of the second die. The numbers in the main body of the table represent the sums of the two possible scores. So we see that if we score a total of 11, we must have thrown either a six with the first die and a five with the second, or a five with the first die and a six with the second. We see, then, that there are 36 equally likely total scores ($N = 36$). Let us now define two events

$$E_1 = \text{the sum of the scores is 7}$$
$$E_2 = \text{the sum of the scores is 9}$$

Now there are 6 ways of scoring a total of 7, so $P(E_1) = \frac{6}{36} = \frac{1}{6}$. Again, there are 4 ways of scoring a total of 9, so $P(E_2) = \frac{4}{36} = \frac{1}{9}$. Now suppose we wished to find the probability that the sum of the scores is *either* 7 *or* 9. We can write the probability symbolically like this:

$$P(E_1 \cup E_2)$$

where $\cup$ is a shorthand way of writing 'either – or'. Consulting the table, we see that there are 10 ways of obtaining a total score of either 7 or 9, so $P(E_1 \cup E_2) = \frac{10}{36} = \frac{5}{18}$. Notice that the 10 ways are obtained by adding the number of ways for E_1 and E_2. This gives us our first law of probability: the so-called addition law.

$$P(E_1 \cup E_2) = P(E_1) + P(E_2)$$

a law which is true only if E_1 and E_2 are mutually exclusive. If the events are not mutually exclusive, then using this law will not yield the correct probability. Suppose we draw a card from a pack, and E_1 is that the card is an ace. So $P(E_1) = \frac{4}{52}$. If E_2 is that the card is a heart, then $P(E_2)$ is $\frac{13}{52}$. If we want to find the probability that the card is either a heart or an ace, we notice that there are 52 equally likely outcomes, 16 of which would be either a heart or an ace (i.e. 13 hearts plus the three other aces). So the probability that the card is either a heart or an ace is $\frac{16}{52}$. Notice that if we had applied the law, we would have obtained $\frac{13}{52} + \frac{4}{52} = \frac{17}{52}$ – the wrong probability! So beware – before using this law make absolutely sure that the events are mutually exclusive!

Look again at the table we obtained earlier which refers to the sum of the possible scores from casting two dice. Notice that there are 36 equally likely total scores. We could deduce this as follows: there are six ways the first die can fall, each of which can combine with any one of the six ways that the second die can fall. So there are $6 \times 6 = 36$ ways that both dice can fall. Now suppose we have two piles of cards. The first pile contains the two red aces and the four kings, and the second pile contains the two red aces and the ace of spades and the four kings. Suppose we draw a card from each pile – as there are six cards in the first pile and seven cards in the second, there will be $6 \times 7 = 42$ ways of drawing a pair of cards, one from each pile. We could represent the situation in a table like this:

		Second Card						
		A♡	A♢	A♠	K♡	K♢	K♠	K♣
	A♡	1	2	3	4	5	6	7
	A♢	8	9	10	11	12	13	14
First	K♡	15	16	17	18	19	20	21
Card	K♢	22	23	24	25	26	27	28
	K♠	29	30	31	32	33	34	35
	K♣	36	37	38	39	40	41	42

In this table we have numbered all the possible 42 combinations of events with 1, 2, 3, ... etc., so combination 25, for example, means drawing the king of diamonds with the first card and the king of hearts with the second. Let us now define two events.

$E_1 = $ the first card is an ace, so $P(E_1) = \frac{2}{6}$
$E_2 = $ the second card is an ace, so $P(E_2) = \frac{3}{7}$

Suppose we wanted to find the probability that both cards were aces:
We could write it symbolically like this

$$P(E_1 \cap E_2)$$

where the symbol $\cap$ is a shorthand form for 'both ... and'. Notice
that there are six ways of obtaining two aces, so $P(E_1 \cap E_2) = \frac{6}{42}$.
Now we could have obtained this result by multiplying $P(E_1)$ and
$P(E_2)$ together $(\frac{2}{6} \times \frac{3}{7} = \frac{6}{42})$. This gives us the second law of probability:
the so-called multiplication law.

$$P(E_1 \cap E_2) = P(E_1) \cdot P(E_2)$$

a law which applies only if E_1 and E_2 are *independent* (i.e. as long
as the outcomes in no way affect each other). We will discuss this
point more fully later, but it is worth noting now that independent
events cannot be mutually exclusive, and mutually exclusive events
cannot be independent.

The second law of probability enables us to modify the first law
to take account of events that are not mutually exclusive. A little
earlier, we considered the case of drawing a card from a pack, calling
E_1 that the event was an ace (so $P(E_1) = \frac{4}{52}$), and calling E_2 that the
card is a heart (so $P(E_2) = \frac{13}{52}$). We stated that the probability that the
card is either a heart or an ace $P(E_1 \cup E_2)$ is *not* $\frac{4}{52} + \frac{13}{52} = \frac{17}{52}$. Now
why doesn't the addition law work? Surely the fault here is that the
card we draw could be the ace of hearts *and we have counted this
card twice* – once as a heart and once as an ace. So the probability
that the card is either an ace or a heart is $\frac{17}{52}$ minus the probability
that the card is the ace of hearts. Using the second law, the prob-
ability that the card is the ace of hearts is $P(E_1 \cap E_2) = \frac{4}{52} \times \frac{13}{52} = \frac{1}{52}$,
so the probability that the card is either an ace or a heart is $\frac{17}{52} -
\frac{1}{52} = \frac{16}{52}$ – which agrees precisely with the result we obtained from first
principles. We can now restate the addition law to take account of
situations when the events are not mutually exclusive:

$$P(E_1 \cup E_2) = P(E_1) + P(E_2) - P(E_1 \cap E_2)$$

This is the so-called *general law of addition*, and it works whether
the events are mutually exclusive or not (if the events are mutually
exclusive, then they cannot both occur, so $P(E_1 \cap E_2)$ will be zero).

Conditional Probability

In the last section, we stated that events cannot be both mutually
exclusive and independent. This should not be taken to mean that
if events are not mutually exclusive then they must be independent:
there is a third category that we must now examine. When we state

that events are independent, we mean that the outcome of one event in no way affects the outcome of the other. Now there are many cases where this is not true: the outcome of the second event is *conditional* on the outcome of the first event. Two examples may clarify this point.

Suppose we draw a card from a well-shuffled pack, and this card happens to be an ace. We now draw a second card – what is the probability that this card is also an ace? Well, having removed one card already, there must be 51 equally likely outcomes left, three of which would yield an ace. So the probability of an ace with the second card is $\frac{3}{51}$. Suppose the first card was not an ace: there would be 51 equally likely outcomes of which four would yield an ace. In this case, the probability of an ace with the second card would be $\frac{4}{51}$. In the first case, we are drawing from a pack with a lower proportion of aces than originally, and in the second case the pack has a higher proportion. Whichever way you consider this problem, the outcome of the first trial affects the outcome of the second. Now this raises an interesting philosophical problem: we cannot predict the outcome of the second event until we know the outcome of the first. If I deal a card to you, and you do not reveal it to me, the probability that I deal myself an ace must be $\frac{4}{52}$. Why is this so when a card has been removed from the pack? It is the *information* from the first card that is important, not the fact that it has been dealt. In this case, as you do not reveal the card it has a zero information value to me: from the information viewpoint, it is irrelevant to me whether the card is in your hand or in the pack. However, if your card is revealed to me, then I can use this information to calculate the probability that I deal myself an ace – the probability will be $\frac{4}{51}$ or $\frac{3}{51}$, depending on whether you have an ace or not. We need a new notation to take into account the fact that events can be conditional upon each other. If we have two events E_1 and E_2 then $P(E_2 | E_1)$ is the probability that E_2 occurs given that E_1 has occurred. So we can now modify our multiplication law to take account of conditional probability

$$P(E_1 \cap E_2) = P(E_1) . P(E_2 | E_1)$$

If E_1 is draw an ace with the first card, then $P(E_1) = \frac{1}{13}$. If E_2 is draw an ace with the second card, then $P(E_2 | E_1) = \frac{3}{51}$. The probability of drawing an ace with both cards is $P(E_1 \cap E_2) = \frac{1}{13} \times \frac{3}{51} = \frac{1}{221}$.

Now let us consider a second example. Suppose we have a box of ten machine parts, three of which are defective. From this we draw a sample of two parts – what is the probability they are both defective? If E_1 is that the first part is defective, and E_2 is that the second part is defective, then the events are conditional. $P(E_1) = \frac{3}{10}$, $P(E_2 | E_1) = \frac{2}{9}$ and $P(E_1 \cap E_2) = \frac{3}{10} \times \frac{2}{9} = \frac{1}{15}$. Can you see that if we had replaced the first part before drawing the second then E_2 would not be conditional on E_1, and $P(E_2)$ would also be $\frac{3}{10}$? Using the statisticians' jargon, we would say that *sampling without replacement makes the events conditional.* Is this always true? We might have drawn two parts from a very large consignment indeed, and it would seem rather pedantic to state that the consignment is poorer in defectives if the first item drawn is defective. Moreover, the proportion of defectives in a very large consignment can only be an estimate. When sampling from a large population, then E_1 and E_2 can for all intents and purposes be considered independent.

Applications of the Laws of Probability

To conclude this chapter, let us examine some examples of how the laws of probability can be applied.

EXAMPLE 1
(i) Define mutually exclusive events.

(ii) Firm A is one of many firms competing for a government contract to build a bridge. The probability that firm A will obtain the contract is $\frac{1}{9}$, and the probability that firm A is the second choice is $\frac{1}{3}$, and the probability that firm A is the government's third choice for building the bridge is $\frac{1}{2}$. What is the probability that firm A will not be the government's first, second or third choice of firm to build the bridge?

(Part question, Scottish National Cert. in
Business Studies)

Well, we have already defined mutually exclusive events, so we will move directly to the second part of the question. The probability that firm A is the first choice is $\frac{1}{9}$, so the probability that firm A is not the first choice is $\frac{8}{9}$. Likewise, the probability that the firm is not the second choice is $\frac{2}{3}$, and the probability that the firm is not the third choice is $\frac{1}{2}$. If, then, we wish to calculate the probability that the firm is neither the first nor the second nor the third choice, we must multiply these probabilities together:

$$\tfrac{8}{9} \times \tfrac{2}{3} \times \tfrac{1}{2} = \tfrac{8}{27}$$

The rest of the question is as follows. Two types of metal A and B, which have been treated with a special coating of paint, have probabilities of $\frac{1}{4}$ and $\frac{1}{3}$ respectively of lasting four years without rusting.

If both types of metal are given the special coating on the same day, what is the probability that

(i) both last 4 years without rusting
(ii) at least one of them lasts 4 years without rusting

For part (i), we can again use the multiplication law to obtain a probability of $\frac{1}{4} \times \frac{1}{3} = \frac{1}{12}$ that both last for four years. Turning to the second part, we should first notice that four distinct outcomes are possible

(a) both last 4 years   (probability is $\frac{1}{4} \times \frac{1}{3} = \frac{1}{12}$)
(b) A lasts, B doesn't   (probability is $\frac{1}{4} \times \frac{2}{3} = \frac{2}{12}$)
(c) B lasts, A doesn't   (probability is $\frac{3}{4} \times \frac{1}{3} = \frac{3}{12}$)
(d) neither lasts   (probability is $\frac{3}{4} \times \frac{2}{3} = \frac{6}{12}$)

Now any of the outcomes (a), (b) or (c) satisfies the condition that at least one lasts four years, so the probability we require is $\frac{1}{12} + \frac{2}{12} + \frac{3}{12} = \frac{6}{12} = \frac{1}{2}$. Notice that we could have calculated the probability more directly by using the fact that

$$P \text{ (at least one lasts)} = 1 - P \text{ (neither lasts)}$$

This second method can save quite a lot of time, and you should always use it in preference to writing out all the possible outcomes.

EXAMPLE 2
An item is made in three stages. At the first stage, it is formed on one of four machines, A, B, C or D, with equal probability. At the second stage it is trimmed on one of three machines, E, F or G, with equal probability. Finally, it is polished on one of two polishers, H and I, and is twice as likely to be polished on the former as this machine works twice as quickly as the other. Required:

(1) what is the probability that an item is:
 (i) polished on H?
 (ii) trimmed on either F or G?
 (iii) formed on either A or B, trimmed on F and polished on H?
 (iv) either formed on A and polished on I, or formed on B and polished on H?
 (v) either formed on A or trimmed on F.

(2) Suppose that items trimmed on E or F are susceptible to a particular defect. The defect rates on these machines are 10% and 20% respectively. What is the probability that an item found to have this defect was trimmed on F? (A.C.A.)

First, we shall determine the probabilities for each machine. As the formation stage is equally likely to occur on any one of the four machines, we have

$$P(A) = P(B) = P(C) = P(D) = \tfrac{1}{4}$$

Again, trimming is equally likely to occur on any one of the three machines, so

$$P(E) = P(F) = P(G) = \tfrac{1}{3}$$

Polishing is twice as likely to occur on machine H as machine I, so

$$P(H) = \tfrac{2}{3}, \quad P(I) = \tfrac{1}{3}$$

(i) The probability that an item is polished on $H = P(H) = \tfrac{2}{3}$.

(ii) The probability that an item is trimmed on either F or $G =$
$P(F \cup G) = P(F) + P(G) = \tfrac{2}{3}$.

(iii) Formed on either A or B, trimmed on F and polished on H

$$\begin{aligned}
&= P(A \cup B) \cap F \cap H \\
&= [P(A) + P(B)] \cdot P(F) \cdot P(H) \\
&= (\tfrac{1}{4} + \tfrac{1}{4}) \times \tfrac{1}{3} \times \tfrac{2}{3} = \tfrac{1}{9}
\end{aligned}$$

(iv) Either formed on A and polished on I or formed on B and polished on H

$$\begin{aligned}
&= P[(A \cap I) \cup (B \cap H)] \\
&= [P(A) \cdot P(I)] + [P(B) \cdot P(H)] \\
&= (\tfrac{1}{4} \times \tfrac{1}{3}) + (\tfrac{1}{4} \times \tfrac{2}{3}) \\
&= \tfrac{1}{4}
\end{aligned}$$

(v) Either formed on A or trimmed on F. These events are *not* mutually exclusive as it is possible to form on A *and* trim on F, so we need the general rule of addition, i.e.

$$\begin{aligned}
P(A \cup F) &= P(A) + P(F) - P(A \cap F) \\
&= \tfrac{1}{4} + \tfrac{1}{3} - (\tfrac{1}{4} \times \tfrac{1}{3}) \\
&= \tfrac{1}{2}
\end{aligned}$$

Dealing with the second part of this question, we notice that F is twice as likely to produce a defective item as is machine E. So, given that the item is defective, the probability that it was trimmed on F must be $\tfrac{2}{3}$.

EXAMPLE 3

In the past, two building contractors, A and B, have competed for twenty building contracts of which ten were awarded to A and six were awarded to B. The remaining four contracts were not awarded to either

A or *B*. Three contracts for buildings of the kind in which they both specialise have been offered for tender.

Assuming that the market has not changed, find the probability that

(a) *A* will obtain all three contracts;
(b) *B* will obtain at least one contract;
(c) Two contracts will not be awarded to either *A* or *B*;
(d) *A* will be awarded the first contract, *B* the second, and *A* will be awarded the third contract.

(C.M.A.)

The probability that *A* gets the contract $P(A) = \frac{10}{20} = \frac{1}{2}$, the probability that *B* gets the contract is $P(B) = \frac{6}{20} = \frac{3}{10}$, and the probability that neither *A* nor *B* gets the contract is $P(A \cup B)' = \frac{4}{20} = \frac{1}{5}$.

(a) The probability that *A* will obtain all three contracts is $\frac{1}{2} \times \frac{1}{2} \times \frac{1}{2} = \frac{1}{8}$

(b) The probability that *B* will obtain at least one contract

$$= 1 - P(B \text{ obtains no contracts})$$
$$= 1 - (\tfrac{7}{10} \times \tfrac{7}{10} \times \tfrac{7}{10}) = \tfrac{657}{1000}$$

(c) The probability that a contract is awarded to *A* or *B* = $P(A \cup B) = \frac{4}{5}$. We require to know the probability that two contracts will not be awarded to either *A* or *B*: this is equivalent to finding the probability that one of the contracts is awarded to either *A* or *B*. But the contract awarded to either *A* or *B* could be either the first, second or third contract. So the probability we require is

$\frac{4}{5} \times \frac{1}{5} \times \frac{1}{5}$ (*A* or *B* wins the first contract)
plus $\frac{1}{5} \times \frac{4}{5} \times \frac{1}{5}$ (*A* or *B* wins the second contract)
plus $\frac{1}{5} \times \frac{1}{5} \times \frac{4}{5}$ (*A* or *B* wins the third contract)
$$= 3 \times \tfrac{4}{5} \times \tfrac{1}{5} \times \tfrac{1}{5} = \tfrac{12}{125}$$

(d) The probability that *A* is awarded the first contract, *B* the second and *A* the third is $\frac{1}{2} \times \frac{3}{10} \times \frac{1}{2} = \frac{3}{40}$

Now a few words to conclude this chapter. The concepts underlying probability are extremely easy to understand, and there are very few rules that must be learnt. However, putting these rules (or combinations of these rules) into practice can be very tricky indeed. You would be well advised to re-read the section on the laws of probability to make absolutely sure that you understand them. Also, make certain that you understand the logic employed in the previous examples before you attempt the following exercises. Before you attempt any calculations on the exercises, you should be certain you know the way or ways the desired event can occur (for example, 'at

least one' means one or more). Also, you should decide on the relationship between the events – whether they are mutually exclusive,
independent, or conditional. Suppose that, after all this, you still cannot cope with probability – what then? Well, at least you can console
yourself with the knowledge that although some students find probability a highly stimulating intellectual exercise, by far the bulk of
students find probability problems the nearest thing to purgatory!
Frequently you will find that although you can see that your answer
is wrong, it is extremely difficult to see just where you have gone
wrong! Fortunately, a lack of capability at solving probability problems need not hold you up in a statistics course, as a knowledge of
what probability means and how it is measured are the important
things.

EXERCISES TO CHAPTER 8

8.1   Explain carefully what is meant by 'the probability of an event'.
Outline the main differences in philosophy of the Classical as
opposed to the Beyesian School.   I.C.A.

8.2   A bag contains nineteen balls, each of which is painted in two
colours. Four are red and white, seven are white and black, and eight
are black and red. A ball is chosen at random and seen to be partly
white. What is the probability that its other colour is red?

O.N.C.

8.3   (a) Explain what is meant by the terms

(i) mutually exclusive
(ii) independent

(b) A manufacturer purchases two machines A and B. The probability that A will last 5 years is $\frac{4}{5}$ and the probability that B will
last 5 years is $\frac{3}{4}$. Find the probability that

(i) both machines will last 5 years
(ii) only machine A will last 5 years
(iii) at least one machine will last 5 years   O.N.C.

8.4   (a) Explain what you understand by

(i) independent events
(ii) conditional probability

(b) 8% of the items produced in a manufacturing process are
known to be faulty. A sample of 5 items is drawn at random. Calculate the probability that the sample

(i) does not contain any faulty items

(ii) only contains one faulty item

(c) Two independent events A and B are such that $P(A) = 0.2$ and $P(B) = 0.4$. Find the values of (i) $P(AB)$, (ii) $P(A + B)$ and (iii) the probability of A occurring given that B has already occurred.   O.N.C.

8.5 (a) State the theorems of addition and multiplication of probabilities.

(b) An analysis of the national origins of the employees of a manufacturing company produced the following result:

English	488
Scots	230
Irish	112
Welsh	108
American	30
Other European	16

If two employees of this company are chosen at random, state the probability that

(i) both will be other European

(ii) both will be English

(iii) both will be either Irish or Welsh

(iv) at least one of the two will be a Scot.   O.N.C.

8.6 (a) Explain what is meant by (i) mutually exclusive events and (ii) independent events.

(b) (i) What is the chance of throwing a number greater than four with an ordinary die?

(ii) If the probability of throwing a seven with a pair of dice is $\frac{1}{6}$, what is the probability of rolling two sevens in a row?

(iii) If three dice are thrown together, what is the probability of obtaining at least one five?

(iv) Out of 10 steel valve springs 3 are defective. Two springs are chosen at random for testing. What is the probability that both test specimens are:

(a) not defective;

(b) defective?   O.N.C.

8.7 The following results were obtained from interviews with 500 people who changed their cars recently, cars being classified as large, medium or small in size, depending on their length.

Previous Car Size	Present Car Size			Total
	Large $(>15')$	Medium $(13'-15')$	Small $(<13')$	
Large	75	47	22	144
Medium	36	75	69	180
Small	11	63	102	176
Total	122	185	193	500

Required:

(1) What proportion of people in the survey changed to:

   (i) a smaller car?

   (ii) a larger car?

(2) What effect would such car-changing habits have generally on the size of car owned in the future?

(3) What is the probability that a person from the survey selected at random who bought a large car, previously had a small or medium car?

(4) Estimate the average length of car owned at present by the 500 people surveyed, if no owner has a car less than 9 feet or greater than 19 feet. A.C.A.

8.8   The probability that machine A will be performing a useful function in five years' time is $\frac{1}{4}$ while the probability that machine B will still be operating usefully at the end of the same period is $\frac{1}{3}$.

Find the probability that in five years' time:

   (a) both machines will be performing a useful function;

   (b) neither will be operating;

   (c) only machine B will be operating;

   (d) at least one of the machines will be operating.   I.C.M.A.

8.9   The probability that a man now aged 55 years will be alive in 1993 is $\frac{5}{8}$ while the probability that his wife now aged 53 years will be alive in 1993 is $\frac{5}{6}$.

Determine the probability that in 1993:

   (a) both will be alive;

   (b) at least one of them will be alive;

   (c) only the wife will be alive.   I.C.M.A.

8.10   A sub-assembly consists of three components A, B and C. Tests have shown that failures of the sub-assembly were caused by faults in one, two and sometimes all three components. Analysis of 100 sub-assembly failures showed that there were 70 faulty components A, 50 faulty components B, and 30 faulty components C. Of the failures 44 were caused by faults in two components only (i.e. *A* and *B*, or *A* and *C*, or *B* and *C*) and 10 of the 44 faults were faults in *B* and *C*.

If a faulty component is randomly selected, find the probability that it has faults in:

    (a) all three components;
    (b) component *A* on its own.   I.C.M.A.

8.11   (a) One bag contains 4 white balls and 2 black balls; another contains 3 white balls and 5 black balls. If one ball is drawn from each bag, find the probability that (i) both are white, (ii) both are black, (iii) one is white and one is black.

(b) A purse contains 2 silver coins and 4 copper coins, and a second purse contains 4 silver coins and 3 copper coins. A coin is selected at random from one of the two purses. What is the probability that it is a silver coin?

(c) A box contains *M* components of which *N* are defective. Selection occurs without replacement. Find the probability that:

   (i) the first selection is defective;
  (ii) the first two selections consist of one defective and one non-defective;
 (iii) the second selection is defective.   I.C.A.

8.12   An amplifier circuit is made up of three valves. The probabilities that the three valves are defective are $\frac{1}{20}$, $\frac{1}{25}$ and $\frac{1}{50}$ respectively. Calculate the probability that (a) the amplifier workers, (b) that the amplifier has one defective valve.

A bag contains *r* red balls and *w* white balls, $r > w$. If they are drawn one by one, show that the chance of drawing first a red, then a white and so on alternately until only red balls are left is

$$\frac{r!\,w!}{(r+w)!}$$ I.C.A.

N.B. Do not attempt the second part of this question until you have read the next chapter.

8.13
Weekly Wages (shillings)	*f*
200 and under 210	4
210 and under 220	54
220 and under 230	244
230 and under 240	115
240 and under 250	56
250 and under 260	15
260 and under 270	8
270 and under 280	4
	500

An individual is taken at random from this group. State the probability that:

- (a) (i) his wage is 250/- or over;
    - (ii) his wage is either between 220/- and 230/- or between 210/- and 220/-;
    - (iii) his wage is under 230/-.

- (b) Two individuals are taken at random from the wage group. State the probability that:

    - (i) both their wages are 250/- or over;
    - (ii) both are either in 220/- to 230/- class or in the 210/- to 220/- class;
    - (iii) both wages are under 230/-;
    - (iv) at least one of them is in receipt of 240/- or over.

O.N.C.

8.14 In a particular factory, an automatic process identifies defective items produced. Defectives can be classified as lacking strength, incorrect weight or incorrect diameter. A random sample of 1000 items were checked and the following results recorded:

120 have a strength defect;
 80 have a weight defect;
 60 have a diameter defect;
 22 have strength and weight defects;
 16 have strength and diameter defects;
 20 have weight and diameter defects;
  8 have all three defects.

Find the probability that a randomly chosen item

- (i) is not defective;
- (ii) has exactly two defects.   I.C.A.

8.15 A manufacturer supplies transistors in boxes of 100. A buyer takes a random sample of 5 transistors and if one of them is faulty he rejects the box; otherwise he accepts the box.

- (i) If there are 10 faulty transistors in the box what is the probability that the buyer will accept it?
- (ii) What is the probability that he will reject a box which in fact only contains one faulty transistor?   O.N.C.

8.16   The table given below shows a frequency distribution of the lifetimes of 500 light bulbs made and tested by ABC Limited:

Lifetime (hours)	Number of light bulbs
400 and less than 500	10
500 and less than 600	16
600 and less than 700	38
700 and less than 800	56
800 and less than 900	63
900 and less than 1000	67
1000 and less than 1100	92
1100 and less than 1200	68
1200 and less than 1300	57
1300 and less than 1400	33
	500

(a) Using the information in this table construct an ogive.
(b) Determine the percentage of light bulbs whose lifetimes are at least 700 hours but less than 1200 hours.
(c) What risk is ABC Limited taking if it guarantees to replace any light bulb which lasts less than 1000 hours?
(d) Instead of guaranteeing the life of the light bulb for 1000 hours, ABC Limited suggests introducing a 100-day money-back guarantee. What is the probability that refunds will be made, assuming the light bulb is in use:

  (i) 7 hours per day;
  (ii) 11 hours per day?   A.C.A.

8.17   A businessman estimates that the probability of gaining an important contract to build a factory is 0.65. If this contract is obtained he will certainly have a probability of gaining a further contract of building an associated computer block – he estimates that this probability is 0.8. If he fails to obtain the contract to build the factory, he will not be asked to deal with the computer block construction. As an alternative to the factory/block contract, there is a probability of 0.35 that the businessman could obtain the contract to build an office block – he could only deal with this if the first set of contracts was not obtained. What is the probability that both factory and computer block contracts will be gained? Also, what is the probability that the businessman will obtain either the computer block contract or the office block contract?   I.C.S.A.

8.18   A company in which the training period for apprentices is five years is considering its intake for the coming year. Information concerning apprentices recruited in previous years is given overleaf:

Year of intake	1963	1964	1965	1966
Number of apprentices recruited	700	500	150	250
Number of apprentices leaving in				
First year	28	18	8	14
Second year	29	18	6	10
Third year	17	8	2	1
Fourth year	13	8	1	2
Fifth year	2	2	1	1

(a) What is the probability that an apprentice will qualify?

(b) What is the probability that an apprentice will stay for longer than two years?

(c) How many apprentices should be recruited in 1971 to provide the company with 300 qualified men in 1976?   I.C.M.A.

8.19   (a) Explain briefly the value of conditional probability calculations to the businessman.

(b)   *Table: Number of Boxes*

Firm	Defective Electron Tubes per box of 100 units			
	0	1	2	3 or more
Supplier *A*	500	200	200	100
Supplier *B*	320	160	80	40
Supplier *C*	600	100	50	50

From the data given in the above table, calculate the conditional probabilities for the following questions:

(i) If one box had been selected at random from this universe what are the probabilities that the box would have come from Supplier *A*; from Supplier *B*; from Supplier *C*?

(ii) If a box had been selected at random, what is the probability that it would contain two defective tubes?

(iii) If a box had been selected at random, what is the probability that it would have no defectives and would have come from Supplier *A*?

(iv) Given that a box selected at random came from Supplier *B*, what is the probability that it contained one or two defective tubes?

(v) If a box came from Supplier *A*, what is the probability that the box would have two or less defectives?

(vi) It is known that a box selected at random has two defective tubes. What is the probability that it came from Supplier *A*; from Supplier *B*; from Supplier *C*?   A.C.C.A.

8.20   Two companies *A* and *B* regularly bid against each other for building contracts. *A* has a probability of $\frac{2}{3}$ of winning any given contract while *B* has a probability of $\frac{1}{3}$. Assuming independence, calculate the probabilities that, of the next two contracts, (i) *A* wins both (ii) *B* wins both, (iii) each company wins one. O.N.C.

8.21 (a) If an 'event' is defined as an outcome of an experiment, explain what is meant by

  (i) mutually exclusive events,

 (ii) independent events, and

(iii) conditional events.

Give examples of events that would fall into each category.

  (b) To control the quality of output, a sample of ten items is examined each hour and if no defective items are found the process continues, otherwise the process is stopped and adjustments are made. What is the probability that the process will be stopped after a sample is drawn if 10% of the items produced by this process is defective? How large a sample should be drawn to ensure that if 10% of items is defective, then the probability that the process is stopped is at least 99%? I.C.A.

8.22 A circuit is protected by two fuses, *F* and *G*, so arranged that the correct operation of either of them is sufficient to stop the circuit being damaged. The reliability (i.e. the probability that the device operates successfully when required) of the fuses, *F* and *G*, is 0.95 and 0.90 respectively. What is the probability that on a given occasion the circuit will not be protected? O.N.C.

8.23 In an experiment the probability of success is $\frac{1}{3}$. If it is performed 6 times, what is the probability of occurrence of (i) 5 successes, (ii) more than 4 successes? O.N.C.

8.24 (a) Explain what are meant by mutually exclusive events, independent events and dependent events.

  (b) A public company holds two accounts: an account *A* with a government department and an account *B* with a merchant bank. It has been established that on any given day there is a finite and distinct probability that each account will exceed its overdraft facilities. It may be assumed that the probability that either or both accounts exceed their overdraft facilities is 0.55 whilst the probability that account B exceeds its overdraft facility is 0.25.

  (i) If the fluctuations of the accounts are independent what is the probability that account *A* exceeds its overdraft facilities on any given day?

(ii) Had the fluctuations of the accounts been dependent what would have been the probability that account A exceeded its overdraft facilities on any day in which account B also exceeded its overdraft facilities if the probability that both accounts exceeded their overdraft facilities had been 0.12?

I.C.A.

Chapter Nine

Probability Distributions

In the last chapter, we examined the basic concepts of probability. We can now use our knowledge to examine aspects of probability under certain rigidly defined conditions. The main difficulty that you have probably experienced so far in dealing with probability problems is that there is no one, assured method of dealing with them. However, when the conditions underlying a problem match the conditions we shall examine in this chapter, there will be a well-defined route to the solution. So although the concepts explained here are probably more involved than in the last chapter, you can rest assured that the applications of these concepts will be much simpler. Our first task will be to examine what is meant by a probability distribution.

What is a Probability Distribution?

Suppose in an experiment we define all the outcomes, and choose one of the outcomes as an attribute. We could then form a frequency distribution by finding the probability that the attribute does not occur, occurs once, occurs twice – and so on. The distribution we have formed is called a *probability distribution*. An example will clarify what we mean by this. Suppose we spin a coin, and choose as our attribute the number of heads occurring. The probability distribution would look like this:

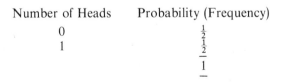

Number of Heads	Probability (Frequency)
0	$\frac{1}{2}$
1	$\frac{1}{2}$
	$\overline{1}$

Notice that the sum of the frequencies is one – a feature of all probability distributions. This is because the number of times the attribute can occur (in this case zero or one), form mutually exclusive, collectively exhaustive events.

In forming the above probability distribution, we have been using *a priori* concepts: we calculated the probabilities *before* the experiment was performed. However, it is certainly possible to form a probability distribution using empirical evidence, i.e. after the experiment is performed. Suppose, for example, we know that in a large batch of components some of them will be defective. We decide to draw a sample of six items, so the sample could be free from defectives, or contain 1, 2, 3, 4, 5 or 6 defectives. We wish to find the probability of each outcome. Well, we could draw, say, 100 samples and count the number of defectives in each. Our result may look like this:

Number of defectives	0	1	2	3	4	5	6
Frequency	75	15	7	2	1	0	0

To form the probability distribution we divide each of the frequencies by 100 (the total frequency). So we have:

Number of defectives	0	1	2	3	4
Probability	0.75	0.15	0.07	0.02	0.01

In this chapter we will examine certain standard types of probability distributions and use them as a basis for calculating a priori probabilities. You may feel that we are devoting too much time to a priori probability and ignoring the other forms. However, if we *suspect* that the outcome of an experiment would conform to one of the standard types of probability distributions then we can make some very useful predictions. We can always check our assumptions by obtaining empirical probabilities and comparing them with a priori probabilities. Later, we will show you how to test how well an a priori distribution fits or corresponds to the empirical evidence.

The Binomial Distribution

The first probability distribution we will examine is the so-called Binomial distribution, and we shall examine how it arises by considering a very simple example. Let us suppose that three coins are tossed together and take as our attribute the number of heads occurring. Well, the probability that none of the coins is a head can be calculated very simply using the multiplication law,

$$P_{(0)} = \tfrac{1}{2} \times \tfrac{1}{2} \times \tfrac{1}{2} = \tfrac{1}{8}$$

Now let us calculate the probability that one of the coins shows a head. The problem here is that whereas there is only one event where no heads occur, there are a number of events where just one head occurs, namely HTT, THT, TTH (where H is a head occurring and T is a tail occurring). Fortunately, each of the events are equally likely $(\frac{1}{2} \times \frac{1}{2} \times \frac{1}{2})$, so

$$P_{(1)} = 3 \times \frac{1}{2} \times \frac{1}{2} \times \frac{1}{2} = \frac{3}{8}$$

Two heads can occur in three equally likely ways (HHT, HTH, THH) so

$$P_{(2)} = 3 \times \frac{1}{2} \times \frac{1}{2} \times \frac{1}{2} = \frac{3}{8}$$

but three heads can occur in one way only (HHH) so

$$P_{(3)} = \frac{1}{2} \times \frac{1}{2} \times \frac{1}{2} = \frac{1}{8}$$

We have now calculated the full probability distribution, and we could represent it like this

No. of Heads Occurring	Probability	or Probability
0	$\frac{1}{8}$	0.125
1	$\frac{3}{8}$	0.375
2	$\frac{3}{8}$	0.375
3	$\frac{1}{8}$	0.125
	1	1.000

A binomial distribution is concerned with two terms (hence its name) – the probability that the event we are considering occurs (we will call this p) and the probability that the event does not occur (we call this $1-p=q$). We have just considered an example where $p=q$ (the probability of obtaining a head is identical to the probability of obtaining a tail), but we can use a very similar analysis for cases where p and q are unequal *as long as the experiment is performed three times.* Suppose we have a very large consignment of components, and we know from past experience that 10% of components are defective. We randomly select three components from the consignment – what is the probability distribution of the number of defectives in the sample? We let p be the probability that an item in the sample is defective. Hence we have $q=0.9$, $p=0.1$.

$$P_{(0)} = q \times q \times q = q^3 = (0.9)^3 \qquad\qquad = 0.729$$
$$P_{(1)} = 3 \times q \times q \times p = 3q^2p = 3 \times 0.9^2 \times 0.1 = 0.243$$
$$P_{(2)} = 3 \times q \times p \times p = 3qp^2 = 3 \times 0.9 \times 0.1^2 = 0.027$$
$$P_{(3)} = p \times p \times p = p^3 = 0.1^3 \qquad\qquad = 0.001$$
$$\overline{\phantom{P_{(3)} = p \times p \times p = p^3 = 0.1^3 \qquad\qquad\quad} 1.000}$$

Notice that we are using the results of the previous example. There is only one way for the sample to contain no defectives, and only one way for it to contain three defectives. There are three equally likely ways that the sample can contain one defective, and three equally likely ways that the sample can contain two defectives.

Examining the above examples, we can see that to calculate the individual probabilities in a binomial distribution, we must find the number of equally likely events comprising the outcome we require, and multiply this by the probability of any one of the events. Suppose we increased the sample size in the question above to five items, and wished to find the probability that three of the items were defective. Now we know that this outcome can occur in a number of equally likely ways, and it is easy to calculate the probability of any one of these ways. For example

$$q \times q \times p \times p \times p = q^2 p^3 = (0.9)^2 (0.1)^3 = 0.00081$$

is the probability that the first two items are non-defective and the last three are defective. We now need to know the number of equally likely ways of obtaining this outcome. We could write out all the events (as we did previously) but this would be very tedious – there are 10 equally likely events in this case. Also, we could never be sure that we have included all of the outcomes! How do you think we could go on writing out all the outcomes of drawing, say, two defectives if the sample contained 100 items?

Pascal's Triangle

A very useful device for finding all the equally likely events in a binomial distribution is *Pascal's Triangle*, and an example of it is constructed below

1	1						n = no. of items in
1	2	1					2 the sample
1	3	3	1				3
1	4	6	4	1			4
1	5	10	10	5	1		5
1	6	15	20	15	6	1	6

Number of defectives 0   1   2   3   4   5   6

Reading off from the triangle, we see that if we draw a sample of 5 items ($n = 5$) there is one way that a sample can contain no defectives, there are 5 equally likely ways that the sample can have one defective, 10 ways for it to have two defectives – and so on. Using this information we can calculate the complete binomial distribution.

No. of Defectives	No. of Equally Likely Events	Probability of One of these Events	Required Probability
0	1	$(0.9)^5$	$(0.9)^5 = 0.59049$
1	5	$(0.9)^4(0.1)$	$5(0.9)^4(0.1) = 0.32805$
2	10	$(0.9)^3(0.1)^2$	$10(0.9)^3(0.1)^2 = 0.0729$
3	10	$(0.9)^2(0.1)^3$	$10(0.9)^2(0.1)^3 = 0.0081$
4	5	$(0.9)\ (0.1)^4$	$5(0.9)\ (0.1)^4 = 0.00045$
5	1	$(0.1)^5$	$(0.1)^5 = 0.00001$
			1.00000

So you can see that Pascal's Triangle is a useful way of finding the number of equally likely events. But if you are going to use Pascal's Triangle, it will be necessary for you to be able to construct it. The first thing you should notice is that the first and last number in any row is one. The rest of the numbers are obtained by adding the numbers in the previous row together in pairs. So the numbers for row six would be

$$\begin{array}{cccccccc}
1 & 1+5 & 5+10 & 10+10 & 10+5 & 5+1 & 1 \\
=1 & 6 & 15 & 20 & 15 & 6 & 1
\end{array}$$

and the numbers in row seven would be

$$\begin{array}{cccccccc}
1 & 1+6 & 6+15 & 15+20 & 20+15 & 15+6 & 6+1 & 1 \\
=1 & 7 & 21 & 35 & 35 & 21 & 7 & 1
\end{array}$$

The numbers that we are obtaining in the rows of Pascal's Triangle are called the *binomial coefficients*, and certainly it is easy to obtain them. But suppose we are drawing a sample of 20 items. If we don't have a copy of Pascal's Triangle available, it will be necessary to construct its first 20 rows, and this is going to be quite a task! It is possible, of course, but let us examine an alternative to Pascal's Triangle which we think that in the long run you will find easier.

Combinations

Most gamblers are aware that if you want the bookmaker to choose a stated number of results (say three) from a larger number of selections (say six) he will do so. In fact, this is one of the most popular forms of betting both on the football pools and on the racetrack. So popular is it that many bookmakers issue tables telling us how much it will cost to bet on any number of results chosen from a larger number. Such a table is a copy of Pascal's Triangle, but instead of reading off 'the number of defectives' we read off the 'number of correct results'. So gamblers can now look at the table and see that if they want to select six football teams and win the bet if any three of them draw, then we must make 20 bets. Bookmakers call these tables 'permutation tables', and instruct us to write our bets in the form 'Perm any 3 results from 6 selections $= 20$ bets'.

Now strictly, the bookmaker is wrong – when we are betting on three results from six we are dealing not with a permutation but with a combination, and we will now show you how to calculate how many combinations of 'r' results there are if you make 'n' selections. We can write this problem symbolically like this:

$$^nC_r$$

and to calculate the number of combinations we apply the formula

$$^nC_r = \frac{n(n-1)(n-2)\dots[(n-r)+1]}{r(r-1)(r-2)\dots \times 1}$$

This formula looks very fearsome, but in fact it is very easy to apply. If we examine Pascal's Triangle we see that if we select 7 football teams to win then there are 35 equally likely ways of just 3 of them winning. Now let us check this by using the formula for combinations. Here we have $n = 7$, $r = 3$, so $(n-r)+1 = (7-3)+1 = 5$, and

$$^7C_3 = \frac{7 \times 6 \times 5}{3 \times 2 \times 1} = 35$$

We are now in a position to derive a general expression for a binomial distribution. Suppose that within a population a proportion p has a certain attribute (call it 'defective') – it follows that $1 - p = q$ is the proportion of non-defectives. Now suppose we draw a sample of n items.

The probability that the sample is free from defective items $= P_{(0)} = q^n$.

The probability that the sample has one defective item is $P_{(1)} = {}^nC_1 q^{n-1} p$ (if one item is defective than $n - 1$ must be non-defective)

The probability that the sample has two defective items is $P_{(2)} = {}^nC_2 q^{n-2} p^2$

We could continue in this way until we reach the probability that all the items in the sample are defective, which must be $P_{(n)} = p^n$. Now we know that all the probabilities must sum one, so

$$q^n + {}^nC_1 q^{n-1} p + {}^nC_2 q^{n-2} p^2 + {}^nC_3 q^{n-3} p^3 + \dots + p^n = 1$$

We also know that $q + p = 1$, so $(q + p)^n$ must equal one. Now we can write

$$(q+p)^n = q^n + {}^nC_1 q^{n-1} p + {}^nC_2 q^{n-2} p^2 + {}^nC_3 q^{n-3} p^3 + \dots + p^n$$

and call the right-hand side of this expression the *expansion of the binomial* $(q+p)^n$. The individual terms of the right-hand side give the probabilities of 0, 1, 2 ... n defectives.

The great advantage of using the general expression for the binomial distribution is that we often do not wish to calculate the entire distribution, but just part of it. If we knew that a bag of seeds had a 95% germination rate, and we planted 10 of these seeds, we could quite easily calculate the probability that (say) 2 of the seeds fail to germinate. We have

$$q=0.95, \quad p=0.05, \quad n=10, \quad r=2, \quad (n-r)+1=9$$

$$P_{(2)} = \frac{10 \times 9}{1 \times 2}(0.95)^8(0.05)^2 = 0.0746$$

We would like to point out that when we state that it is quite easy to calculate probabilities using the general expression for the binomial distribution, we really mean that it is easy to decide *what* to do. We are only too willing to admit that the actual arithmetic operations are most tedious.

The Mean and Standard Deviation of a Binomial Distribution

Let us begin by calculating the probabilities of the binomial distribution $(\frac{3}{4}+\frac{1}{4})^5$ (for example, sampling in groups of 5 from a population with 25% defectives). We shall use the general expression rather than Pascal's Triangle.

$$(\tfrac{3}{4}+\tfrac{1}{4})^5 = (\tfrac{3}{4})^5 + {}^5C_1(\tfrac{3}{4})^4(\tfrac{1}{4}) + {}^5C_2(\tfrac{3}{4})^3(\tfrac{1}{4})^2 + {}^5C_3(\tfrac{3}{4})^2(\tfrac{1}{4})^3$$
$$+ {}^5C_4(\tfrac{3}{4})(\tfrac{1}{4})^4 + (\tfrac{1}{4})^5$$

$$= (\tfrac{3}{4})^5 + 5(\tfrac{3}{4})^4(\tfrac{1}{4}) + \frac{5.4}{2.1}(\tfrac{3}{4})^3(\tfrac{1}{4})^2 + \frac{5.4.3}{3.2.1}(\tfrac{3}{4})^2(\tfrac{1}{4})^3$$

$$+ \frac{5.4.3.2}{4.3.2.1}(\tfrac{3}{4})(\tfrac{1}{4})^4 + (\tfrac{1}{4})^5$$

$$= 0.2373 + 0.3955 + 0.2637 + 0.0879 + 0.0146 + 0.001$$

We can now calculate the mean and standard deviation of the number of defectives in samples of 5 items.

Number of Defectives (x)	Probability (f)	fx	fx^2
0	0.2373	0	0
1	0.3955	0.3955	0.3955
2	0.2637	0.5274	1.0548
3	0.0879	0.2637	0.7911
4	0.0146	0.0584	0.2336
5	0.0010	0.0050	0.0250
	1.0000	1.2500	2.5000

$$\bar{x}=\frac{\Sigma fx}{\Sigma f}=\frac{1.25}{1}=1.25 \text{ defectives per sample}$$

$$\sigma=\sqrt{\frac{\Sigma fx^2}{\Sigma f}-\left(\frac{\Sigma fx}{\Sigma f}\right)^2}=\sqrt{\frac{2.5}{1}-\left(\frac{1.25}{1}\right)^2}$$

$$=0.968 \text{ defectives per sample}$$

In fact, there is no need to go through this procedure to obtain the mean and standard deviation. For any binomial distribution w know that

$$\text{mean}=np$$
$$\text{standard deviation}=\sqrt{npq}$$

We have just been considering the distribution $(\frac{3}{4}+\frac{1}{4})^5$, in which $p=\frac{1}{4}$, $q=\frac{3}{4}$ and $n=5$. The mean is $np=5\times\frac{1}{4}=1.25$, and the standard deviation is $\sqrt{5\times\frac{1}{4}\times\frac{3}{4}}=0.968$.

The Normal Approximation to the Binomial Distribution

Earlier, we considered the normal distribution, and used it to find the proportion in a distribution that was greater than or less than a given value. Now in fact, the normal distribution is another type of probability distribution. Earlier, we asked what *proportion* of electric lamps failed before (say) 1000 hours – but in fact we were also finding the probability that a lamp failed before 1000 hours. Can you see why? Surely, the proportion of lamps failing before 1000 hours can be taken as a measure of the probability that a particular lamp fails before this period. So when we are considering a normal distribution, *we can consider the words proportion and probability to be interchangeable.* The binomial distribution and the normal distribution, then, are two types of probability distributions. However, there is a subtle difference between them – the normal distribution is continuous in so far as the measurements considered can have any value (they are a continuous variable). The binomial distribution is discrete (we are concerned with integers only).

The greatest problem in using the binomial distribution is that it involves awkward arithmetic. Now if the sample size is very large, we can use the normal distribution as an approximation to the binomial distribution, and this will save a considerable amount of arithmetic. Suppose we draw a sample of 1000 packets of soap powder from a batch in which 20% of items are underweight, and we require to know the probability of obtaining more than 220 underweight packets in our sample. The appropriate binomial distribution is $(0.8+0.2)^{1000}$, and the probability we require is $P_{(221)}+$

$P_{(222)} + P_{(223)} + \ldots + P_{(1000)}$. Obviously, this is going to be quite some task! Now the appropriate normal distribution to use is the one with the same mean and standard deviation as the binomial distribution. In this case, we have

$$\bar{x} = np = 1000 \times 0.2 = 200$$
$$\sigma = \sqrt{npq} = \sqrt{1000 \times 0.2 \times 0.8} = 12.65$$

In the diagram below we have drawn part of the histogram of the probability distribution $(0.8 + 0.2)^{1000}$ – it is *not* drawn to scale. If we want to find the probability of obtaining more than 220 packets, we must add the areas of the rectangles enclosing 221, 222, 223, ... 1000.

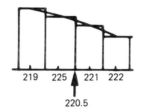

Diagram 9.1

The line joining the mid-points at the top of each rectangle represents the normal distribution that we are using as an approximation. If we wish to use this normal distribution as an approximation, then the diagram clearly shows that we require the proportion to the right of 220.5. This 0.5 adjustment is always used when we use the normal distribution as an approximation to a discrete distribution. So the situation looks like this:

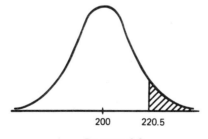

Diagram 9.2

The z score for 220.5 is

$$\frac{220.5 - 200}{12.65} = 1.62$$

and consulting the normal distribution tables we see that the probability we require is $100 - 94.74 = 5.26\%$.

Before we leave the binomial distribution, one very important point must be emphasised (though it is hoped that many of you will have realised it already). A binomial distribution assumes that the events are independent, that is, when we are drawing the sample the outcome of the first item drawn in no way affects the outcome of the second item drawn. This is only true if we are drawing from a large population.

The Poisson Distribution

Suppose we draw samples of two items from a population with 50% of items defective, and samples of 100 from a population with 1% of items defective. In both cases the mean is the same (one defective per sample) – but we could not expect to get the same probability distribution. In the first case, the number of defectives per sample can range between zero and two, but in the second case it can range between zero and 100. But if we draw large samples from a population containing a small proportion of defectives, then a very remarkable thing happens. The probability distributions for such samples tends to become the same *as long as the mean is constant*. To illustrate this feature we consider three cases: drawing samples of 100 from a population containing 1% defectives, samples of 1000 from a 0.1% defective population and samples of 10,000 from a 0.01% defective population. In each case then the mean is the same (one defective per sample).

$$(0.99 + 0.01)^{100} = 0.366 + 0.370 + 0.185 + 0.061 + 0.014$$
$$+ 0.003 + 0.001 + \ldots$$
$$(0.999 + 0.001)^{1000} = 0.368 + 0.368 + 0.184 + 0.061 + 0.015$$
$$+ 0.003 + 0.001 + \ldots$$
$$(0.9999 + 0.0001)^{10000} = 0.368 + 0.368 + 0.184 + 0.061 + 0.015$$
$$+ 0.003 + 0.001 + \ldots$$

It would seem reasonable to suppose that we could discover the probability distribution for such samples as long as we know the mean number of defectives per sample. A third probability distribution – the *Poisson distribution* will enable us to do this.

Before we examine the Poisson distribution and discover how it works, let us examine another condition which calls for its use. So far, we have been considering a sample of known and determinable size, and counting the number of times that an event occurred. We could also count the number of times the event did not occur. However, there are many cases where we cannot count the number of times the event did not occur. Suppose, for example, we wished to investigate the incidence of industrial accidents in a particular trade. We could count the number of accidents within (say) one year and use this as an estimate of the mean number of accidents. But we cannot count the number of times the accident did not occur! For problems such as this, we would have to use the Poisson distribution, as we have no way of evaluating p, q or n.

The Poisson distribution looks like this:

$$e^{-x}\left[1 + x + \frac{x^2}{2!} + \frac{x^3}{3!} + \frac{x^4}{4!} + \cdots\right]$$

Let us look at this distribution and examine certain features of it that you might not have met before. Firstly, notice the numbers 2!, 3!, 4! (pronounce them '2 factorial, 3 factorial', etc.). This is just a convenient way of writing 'multiply the number n by $(n-1)$, then by $(n-2)$ and so on until finally we multiply it by one'. So

$$2! = 2 \times 1$$
$$3! = 3 \times 2 \times 1$$
$$4! = 4 \times 3 \times 2 \times 1$$
$$5! = 5 \times 4 \times 3 \times 2 \times 1$$

and so on. Secondly, there is the number e. This is a well-known constant and has a value 2.7183 (to four decimal places). In fact, most books of mathematical tables will have a table giving values of e^{-x}. Thirdly, the expression contains x, which is the mean of the distribution. We obtain probabilities from the expression like this:

$$P_{(0)} = e^{-x} \times 1$$
$$P_{(1)} = e^{-x} \times x$$
$$P_{(2)} = e^{-x} \times \frac{x^2}{2!}$$
$$P_{(3)} = e^{-x} \times \frac{x^3}{3!}$$

and so on. Now as e is a constant, the only variable in the expression is the mean x. So provided we know the mean of a distribution we should be able to calculate the probabilities. Let's try it and see.

In a particular industry, there are on average two fatal accidents per year. We want to find the probability that (a) the industry is free from fatal accidents and (b) the industry has three fatal accidents in a year.

In this case, we have $x = 2$, and the appropriate Poisson distribution is

$$e^{-2}\left[1 + 2 + \frac{2^2}{2!} + \frac{2^3}{3!} + \dots\right]$$

$$P_{(0)} = e^{-2} \times 1$$

$$P_{(3)} = e^{-2} \times \frac{2^3}{3!}$$

Consulting a book of mathematical tables, we see that $e^{-2} = 0.1353$. However, in some examinations you are asked to calculate e^{-x} from first principles. To do this, we make use of the fact that

$$\log e^{-x} = \log 1 - x \log e$$

Using logarithm tables, $\log e = 0.4343$.

so
$$\log e^{-2} = 0 - (2 \times 0.4343)$$
$$= \bar{1}.1314$$
and
$$e^{-2} = 0.1353$$

Returning to our example,

$$P_{(0)} = 0.1353$$

so the probability that the industry is free from fatal accidents is 0.1353, or 13.53%

$$P_{(3)} = 0.1353 \times \frac{2^3}{3!}$$

$$= 0.1804$$

The probability that the industry has three fatal accidents in a year is 18.04%.

Conditions Necessary for using the Poisson Distribution

We can calculate probabilities using the Poisson distribution provided that we know the arithmetic mean of the distribution, and provided that p is small and n is large. A further condition is that the mean must remain constant. However, perhaps the most important condition is that the occurrence of the event must be purely at random. A good illustration of this is the flow of traffic along a highway. If we choose an isolated point on a highway and count the number of vehicles passing that point, then we would probably find a random flow of vehicles. However, if the point we choose is near a set of traffic lights, then we will not find a random flow – the flow will be 'bunched', i.e. the flow will be heavy when the lights show green. So we should be able to tell whether the occurrence of the event is random or not by using the Poisson distribution. In fact, this distribution was used for an important piece of statistical investigation during the Second World War. In 1944, London was subjected to bombardment by German V1 rockets (called doodlebugs). This was a pilotless vehicle packed with high explosive and equipped with sufficient fuel to carry it to London. When the fuel ran out, the vehicle would fall out of the sky and explode on impact. The problem was to decide whether the V1 rockets were guided to particular targets with a great degree of precision, or whether they fell on London at random. In other words, were the V1 rockets falling in clusters to a greater degree than could be ascribed to chance? R. D. Clark divided an area of 144 square kilometres into 576 equal squares, and counted the number of rockets falling in each square.

No. of bombs per square	0	1	2	3	4	5	Total
No. of squares	229	211	93	35	7	1	576

Now if we divide the frequencies by 576, then we can find the empirical probability distribution of the number of bombs per square

No. of bombs per square	0	1	2	3	4	5
Probability	0.3976	0.3663	0.1615	0.0608	0.0121	0.0017

If the bombs were falling at random, then we should be able to predict this probability distribution using the a priori Poisson distribution. To do this, we need to know the mean number of bombs per square.

x	f	fx	fx^2
0	0.3976	0.0000	0.0000
1	0.3663	0.3663	0.3663
2	0.1615	0.3230	0.6460
3	0.0608	0.1824	0.5472
4	0.0121	0.0484	0.1936
5	0.0017	0.0085	0.0425
	1.0000	0.9286	1.7956

For the moment, ignore the column headed fx^2. The mean is

$$\frac{\Sigma fx}{\Sigma f} = \frac{0.9286}{1} = 0.93 \text{ bombs per square}$$

and the Poisson distribution we require is

$$e^{-0.93}\left[1+0.93+\frac{(0.93)^2}{2!}+\frac{(0.93)^3}{3!}+\frac{(0.93)^4}{4!}+\frac{(0.93)^5}{5!}\right]$$

Using the tables at the end of this book we find that

$$e^{-0.93}=0.3946 \quad \text{so}$$

$$P_{(0)}=0.3946$$

$$P_{(1)}=0.3946\times0.93=0.3670$$

$$P_{(2)}=0.3946\times\frac{(0.93)^2}{2!} \quad \text{or using the previous term}$$

$$P_{(2)}=0.3670\times\frac{0.93}{2}=0.1706$$

$$P_{(3)}=0.3946\times\frac{(0.93)^3}{3!}$$

$$=0.1706\times\frac{0.93}{3}=0.0529$$

$$P_{(4)}=0.3946\times\frac{(0.93)^4}{4!}$$

$$=0.0529\times\frac{0.93}{4}=0.0123$$

$$P_{(5)}=0.3946\times\frac{(0.93)^5}{5!}$$

$$=0.0123\times\frac{0.93}{5}=0.0023$$

Let us now write the empirical and Poisson probabilities adjacent to each other so that we can compare them.

No. of bombs per square	0	1	2	3	4	5
Empirical probabilities	0.3967	0.3663	0.1615	0.0608	0.0121	0.0017
Poisson probabilities	0.3946	0.3670	0.1706	0.0529	0.0123	0.0023

We feel sure that you will agree that there is a fantastically good agreement between the empirical and Poisson probabilities, and we must conclude that the V1 rockets were falling at random over the area.

Before we leave the Poisson distribution, we should note that its mean equals its variance (do you remember that the variance is the square of the standard deviation?). Now as the empirical and Poisson probabilities show such close agreement, we would expect the mean of the empirical probabilities to be approximately equal to the variance. We have already obtained the mean – it is 0.9286. The variance is

$$\frac{\Sigma f x^2}{\Sigma f} - \left(\frac{\Sigma f x}{\Sigma f}\right)^2$$

$$= \frac{1.7956}{1} - \left(\frac{0.9286}{1}\right)^2$$

$$= 0.9333$$

Again, we find a very close agreement between the mean and variance.

Of the two discrete probability distributions we have examined in this chapter, the Poisson distribution is the most widely used. It has been found to describe 'accidents', traffic flows, and the arrivals into queueing situations, very well indeed. Without doubt, both distributions are very important. However, the probability distribution that is the most important in statistical analysis is the one we examined in an earlier chapter – the normal distribution. Because it is so important, we have included some more questions on the normal distribution in the exercises following this chapter.

EXERCISES TO CHAPTER NINE

9.1 (a) A large company's records show that they have an average of 6% of their employees off work on any one day. They employ 6 van drivers. You may assume that the probability of absence from work of a van driver on any one day is the same as that for any other employee.

(i) What is the probability that all their van drivers will be at work on a given day?
(ii) What is the probability that at least 5 of their van drivers will be at work on a given day? O.N.C. (part question)

9.2 The probability of a missile hitting a warship is $\frac{2}{5}$, and 3 hits are needed to put the warship out of action. If a salvo of six missiles are fired, show that the probability of putting the ship out of action is

$$\frac{19 \times 3^3}{5^4}$$

and evaluate to 4 decimal places.

Razor blades are sold in packets of five. The distribution below shows the number of faulty blades in 100 packets.

No. of faulty blades	0	1	2	3	4	5
No. of packets	84	10	3	2	1	0

Calculate the mean number of faulty blades per packet. Assuming the distribution is binominal, estimate the probability that a blade taken at random from a packet will be faulty. (Hint: mean $= np$.)

I.C.A.

9.3   It is expected that 10% of the production from a continuous process will be defective and scrapped. Determine the probability that in a sample of ten units chosen at random:
  (a) exactly two will be defective; and
  (b) at the most two will be defective; using in each case both:
      (i) the binomial distribution; and
      (ii) the Poisson approximation to the binomial distribution. (It is given that the value of $e = 2.718$.)   C.I.P.F.A.

9.4   A buying department is considering an acceptance sampling scheme for incoming lots of a manufactured item that can be classified as either good or defective. The plan calls for a random sample of 50 items from each lot. If there is one or less defectives in the sample the lot is accepted, otherwise it is rejected.

  (a) Find (i) from the binomial distribution, the probability of rejecting a lot that is 1% defective, and (ii) accepting a lot that is 10% defective.
  (b) Find, using the Poisson distribution, the Poisson approximations to the above probabilities.

Comment on your results.   I.C.A.

9.5   Ten per cent of males suffer from a certain disease. Use the normal approximation to the binomial distribution to find the probability that more than 60 men in a randomly selected group of 500 will suffer from the disease.   O.N.C.

9.6   (a) The mean inside diameter of a sample of 400 washers produced by a machine is 8.92 millimetres and the standard deviation is 0.12 millimetres. Washers with inside diameters within the range of 8.74 to 9.10 millimetres are acceptable. Calculate the percentage of defective washers produced by the machine, assuming the diameters are normally distributed.
  (b) Five per cent of the units produced in a manufacturing process

turn out to be defective. Find the probability that in a sample of ten units chosen at random exactly two will be defective using:

(i) the binomial distribution,
(ii) the Poisson approximation to the binomial distribution.

I.C.M.A.

9.7 An insurance salesman sells policies to 5 men, all of identical age and in good health. The probability that a man of this age will be alive in 30 years is $\frac{2}{3}$. Show that the probability of at least 3 men surviving the 30 years is:

$$\frac{2^3 \times 8}{3^4}$$

The probability that an individual suffers a bad reaction from an infection of a given serum is 0.001. Use the Poisson distribution to determine the probability that out of 2000 individuals, more than 2 will suffer a bad reaction.

I.C.A.

9.8 A manufacturer uses high-speed weighing and packing machines with an accuracy adequate to ensure that only one bag in twenty is likely to be underweight when the machines are set to weigh a given weight. A customer receives a consignment of 60 bags. What are the chances that four or more will be underweight? (It is given that $e = 2.718$.)

I.C.M.A.

9.9 At a certain time of day, the number of telephone calls coming in to a particular switchboard follows a Poisson distribution with a mean of 2 calls per minute. Calculate the probability of more than 4 calls in a minute.

O.N.C.

9.10 The number of failures per week, of a certain type of machine, has been found to follow a Poisson distribution with mean 0.5. What is the probability that a given machine has three or more failures in a given week?

A firm owns five of these machines. What is the distribution of the total number of failures per week?

O.N.C.

9.11 The demand for a component is 2 per month, and form a Poisson distribution. Stock is made up at the beginning of each month. What should be the stock level at the beginning of each month so that the probability of a stockout is less than 5%? ($e^{-2} = 0.1353$.)

I.C.A.

9.12   For mean values of 10 or more the Poisson distribution can be approximated by the normal distribution with the same mean and variance. The number of red blood cells per unit volume for a particular animal has the Poisson distribution with mean 15. Find the probability that the number of red cells in a given unit volume exceeds 20.   O.N.C.

9.13   A complex television component has 1000 joints soldered by a machine which is known to produce, on average, one defective joint in forty. The components are examined, and faulty soldering corrected by hand. If components requiring more than 35 corrections are discarded, what proportion of the components will be thrown away?   I.C.M.A.

9.14   (a) Explain what is meant by the 'normal curve' and describe its main characteristics. Illustrate your answer with a suitable graph.
   (b) Show by means of a sketch, suitably labelled, the relationship between the normal curve representing means of samples and the normal curve of the population from which those samples are drawn. What is the chief importance of the distribution of sample means?
   (c) Give a simple numerical example to show how the population mean may be estimated from a sample mean.   O.N.C.

9.15   (a) Explain the meaning of the term standardised normal distribution and illustrate with a simple diagram.
   (b) Records kept by the goods inwards department of a large factory show that the average number of lorries arriving each week is 248. It is known that the distribution approximates to the normal with a standard deviation of 26. If this pattern of arrivals continues, what percentage of weeks can be expected to have a number of arrivals of:

   (i) less than 229 per week?
   (ii) more than 280 per week?   O.N.C.

9.16   The length of rods in a large batch is normally distributed with mean 120 mm and standard deviation 1.5 mm. What percentage of the rods would you expect to measure

   (i) over 122.5 mm;
   (ii) between 116 mm and 124 mm?   O.N.C.

9.17 The mean weight of a consignment of 500 sacks of sugar is 151 lb and the standard deviation 15 lb. Assuming that the weights are normally distributed, find how many sacks weigh:

(a) between 120 and 155 lb,
(b) more than 185 lb, and
(c) less than 128 lb.

Use the abstract from the table of areas under the Normal Curve given below where '*Z*' is the amount of the deviation and '*O*' the appropriate area;

Z	O	Z	O
0.0	0.0000	1.3	0.4031
0.1	0.0398	1.4	0.4192
0.2	0.0793	1.5	0.4332
0.3	0.1179	1.6	0.4452
0.4	0.1554	1.7	0.4554
0.5	0.1915	1.8	0.4641
0.6	0.2258	1.9	0.4713
0.7	0.2580	2.0	0.4772
0.8	0.2881	2.1	0.4821
0.9	0.3159	2.2	0.4861
1.0	0.3413	2.3	0.4893
1.1	0.3643	2.4	0.4918
1.2	0.3849	2.5	0.4938

A.C.A.

9.18 The average number of newspapers purchased by a population of urban households in 1972 was 400, and the standard deviation was 100. Assuming that newspaper purchases were normally distributed, what is the probability that households bought:

(a) between 250 and 500 papers;
(b) less than 250 papers;
(c) between 500 and 600 papers;
(d) more than 500 papers?

Use the abstract from the table of areas under the normal curve given below where Z is the amount of the deviation from the mean and O the appropriate area:

Z	O	Z	O
0.0	0.0000	1.75	0.45994
0.25	0.09871	2.00	0.47725
0.50	0.19146	2.25	0.48778
0.75	0.27337	2.50	0.49379
1.00	0.34134	2.75	0.49702
1.25	0.39435	3.00	0.49865
1.50	0.43319		

A.C.A.

9.19 The thermal efficiency of electricity generating stations in the U.K. in 1969–70 varied from below 10% to over 34% as shown in the table:

Electricity: Output and Efficiency.

Thermal Efficiency of Steam Stations

Thermal Efficiency of Stations (%)	No. of Stations with given Efficiency
34 and over	7
32–34	17
30–32	12
28–30	17
26–28	21
24–26	22
22–24	27
20–22	27
18–20	15
16–18	15
14–16	12
12–14	4
10–12	4
10 and under	3
Total	203

Source: Department of Trade and Industry, Digest of Energy Statistics, 1971.

(a) Calculate
   (i) the average (A.M.) thermal efficiency,
   (ii) the standard deviations.

(b) Assuming the distribution to be nearly normal, what would you expect the range to be, observing that the end classes are 34 *and over* and 10 *and under*?   O.N.C.

9.20   A firm is considering the purchase of a machine to turn ball-bearings. A machine is borrowed for testing purposes, and it is found that 6.68% of ball-bearings have mean diameters greater than 5.03 mm. Assuming the machine to be set at 5 mm, find the standard deviation to which the machine operates. The firm wishes to produce ball-bearings to a design dimension of 5 ± 0.05 mm, and any ball-bearings outside this range would be rejected. Assuming the machine produces 1 million units per month, and each unit rejected costs the firm 1p, find the monthly cost of rejects.

A more accurate machine is available, which costs an additional £100 per month to purchase. If this machine is known to operate with a standard deviation of 0.016 mm, which machine should be purchased?   I.C.A.

9.21   A manufacturer finds that although he promises delivery of a certain item in 7 weeks, the time he takes to deliver to customers is approximately normally distributed with a mean of 6 weeks and a standard deviation of 2 weeks.

Required:

(1) what proportion of customers receive their deliveries late?
(2) what proportion of customers receive deliveries within 4 to 7 weeks?
(3) to what figure should his delivery promise be amended if it is required that only 20% of deliveries should be late?
(4) what proportion of customers will receive deliveries within 5 weeks if the manufacturer reduces the standard deviation of delivery time to 1 week, keeping the mean time at 6 weeks?

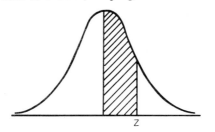

Proportion Lying in Shaded Area of Standard Normal Distribution

Z	0.0	0.1	0.2	0.3	0.4	0.5	0.6	0.7	0.8	0.9
propn.	0.000	0.040	0.079	0.118	0.155	0.192	0.226	0.258	0.288	0.316
Z	1.0	1.1	1.2	1.3	1.4	1.5	1.6	1.7	1.8	1.9
propn.	0.341	0.364	0.385	0.403	0.419	0.433	0.445	0.455	0.464	0.471
Z	2.0	2.1	2.2	2.3	2.4	2.5	2.6	2.7	2.8	2.9
propn.	0.477	0.482	0.486	0.489	0.492	0.494	0.495	0.496	0.497	0.498

A.C.A.

9.22   The heights of 8585 adult males born in the British Isles were measured. The standard deviation and arithmetic mean for this sample were calculated and found to be 2.57 inches and 67.52 inches respectively. Use areas under the normal curve to find the probability that a man taken at random, during the year in which this operation was carried out, would have been (i) over 71 inches, (ii) less than 61 inches, (iii) either taller than 71 inches or shorter than 61 inches, (iv) between 71 inches and 61 inches.   I.C.A.

9.23   A maintenance engineer has established that component XYZ has an operating life of 2500 hours and a standard deviation of 250 hours. Assuming a normal distribution, calculate the probability that any one component XYZ chosen at random would have an operating life of:

(a) less than 2200 hours;
(b) between 2300 and 2700 hours;
(c) between 2300 and 2400 hours;
(d) more than 3000 hours;
(e) between 2000 and 3000 hours.

Normal Curve Areas

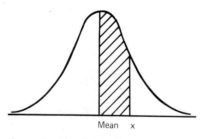

x is the distance the point lies from the mean measured in σ, i.e.

$$\frac{\text{Value} - \text{Mean}}{\sigma}$$

x	Area	x	Area
0.0	0.0000	1.6	0.4452
0.1	0.0398	1.7	0.4554
0.2	0.0793	1.8	0.4641
0.3	0.1179	1.9	0.4713
0.4	0.1554	2.0	0.4772
0.5	0.1915	2.1	0.4821
0.6	0.2257	2.2	0.4861
0.7	0.2580	2.3	0.4893
0.8	0.2881	2.4	0.4918
0.9	0.3159	2.5	0.4938
1.0	0.3413	2.6	0.4953
1.1	0.3643	2.7	0.4965
1.2	0.3849	2.8	0.4974
1.3	0.4032	2.9	0.4981
1.4	0.4192	3.0	0.4987
1.5	0.4332		

A.C.A.

9.24 A machine is packaging nominal 8 oz packets and it has been found that over a long period the actual weight put in the packet has been normally distributed with a standard deviation of 0.05 oz. The company wishes to ensure that no more than 1% of the packets have a weight of less than 8 oz; at what mean weight should the machine be set?

The weekly output of packages averages 2,400,000 and the cost, in pence, of producing a packet of weight w ounces is given by the relationship.

$$c = 6 + 0.5w$$

If, by installation of new machinery, the standard deviation could be reduced to 0.02 oz, and the mean allowed to fall just far enough to give the same percentage below 8 oz as before, determine the average saving in pounds per week.   I.C.A.

Chapter Ten

Sample Design

By the time you begin to read this chapter you already know that most statistical information is obtained, not by examining the whole population, but by obtaining a sample and arguing that the characteristics of the sample are the same as those of the population as a whole. The sample result, obviously, will differ from that we obtain by taking a complete census, and most of later chapters will be concerned with the reliability of the sample results. Our objective here is not to discuss the results of a sample survey, but to explain to you how to select a sample which is truly representative of the population. You would not, for example, expect to obtain a reliable estimate of the heights of men in the United Kingdom if you chose your sample only from men in the Guards regiments; you could not possibly estimate the number of miles people travel by taxi each week if your sample consisted only of taxi-drivers.

Such statements as this are, we think, obvious, but they only tell us how not to select a sample; they give no information about how we should select one. So let us proceed step by step. The basic principle underlying any selection of a sample is that it should be a *random* selection – that is, that every single unit within the population should have an equal chance (or the same probability) of being chosen as a member of the sample. This is, of course, very difficult to achieve. Consider the simple case of drawing a raffle ticket to select the winners of five prizes. Why do you think that after each ticket is drawn the drum containing them is turned? It is, as you will know, to mix up the tickets once again. But would it make any difference if the drum were not turned? In our opinion, it would make a great deal of difference. The person drawing the ticket can easily introduce *bias* into the selection. Consider carefully how you yourself would select the winning tickets. Our observation shows that few people will choose tickets from the top of the drum. They tend rather to plunge into the pile of tickets and select one from near the bottom. Can you see that this sort of behaviour means that tickets near the top of the pile do not have an equal chance of selection with those nearer the bottom? The drum is turned after each ticket is selected

in order to offset this type of bias. We cannot change human behaviour, but we can change the position of the tickets so as to give
each one an equal chance of selection.

To return to sampling proper, in selecting a sample to determine
the average number of miles travelled by taxi each week, the person
who never takes a taxi must have just as much chance of being
selected as have those who use taxis regularly – but no greater chance.
In order to ensure this, statisticians have devised various methods
of selection which, as far as possible, eliminate bias. If we are able
to list the population in some sort of order and number them, we
could determine the members of our sample by drawing numbers
at random, drawing sufficient numbers to include, say, 5% of the total
population. Better still, we could use a table of *random numbers* to
determine who should be included in our sample. You will find an
example of such a table at the end of this book. It is so constructed
that if you select any point at which to start and move through the
table consistently in one direction, horizontally, vertically or diagon-
ally, the digits you read off are randomly chosen and every number
has the same probability of being selected. Suppose that the total
population consisted of 1000 units. These could be numbered from
0 to 999 and you could select those to be included in the sample
by reading off digits from the table of random numbers in groups
of three. If, for example, the first three digits were 294, we would
select the unit numbered 294 as a part of our sample. Similarly if
the first three digits were 004, we would select the unit numbered
4.

If, on the other hand, we were examining industrial output for
faulty units, we could use a form of pseudo-random sampling, by
examining and checking the unit coming off the production line at
predetermined time intervals. Alternatively, we could examine, say,
five units, chosen at random from every carton of output. One way
or another, however, we must ensure that our selection of the sample
is random.

The Sampling Frame

Before we can draw a truly random sample we must be able to define
the total population. The Electoral Register contains the names of
all those entitled to vote in the United Kingdom; enrolment forms
will list the names of all students in your college; business files will
contain all the orders placed in a given financial year. Such lists, files
or card indexes form what is known as a *sampling frame*. They will
give basic details about every member of the population you are concerned with. Now, before drawing a sample, you must carefully ex-

amine the sampling frame to ensure that it is adequate for your purpose. If it is deficient in that a number of units are not included, those
units have no chance of being selected and your sample cannot be
truly random. Let us illustrate such deficiencies by looking at a very
real problem.

It is the habit in Britain for public opinion polls to try to predict
the results of government elections by interviewing a relatively small
number of voters. The sampling frame for such a survey is the Electoral Roll, a list of all those eligible to vote who lived in the area
last November. The list is produced in March each year, so when
it is published it is already four months out of date. By the following
February then, just before a new list is published, it is sixteen months
out of date. Since about 0.5% of the population move into and out
of the district each month (according to a Social Survey report) this
would mean that about 8% of those who are on the Roll no longer
live in the area, while about 8% of those living in the area are not
on the Roll. Add to this the fact that about 4% of those who should
be on the register are omitted because they do not return the necessary forms, and we find that the Electoral Roll is only about 88%
accurate – not a good situation for a sampling frame. It is for this
reason that investigators interview only those who actually go to the
polling booth, or say that they intend to do so.

Systematic Sampling

In practice true random sampling is not possible unless there is a
good sampling frame and the population is fairly small. So, for most
practical work, investigators resort to methods of selection which
are *quasi-random*, or not truly random. One of the most popular is
to choose as a member of the sample every nth item on a list, the
first sample unit being selected by some random method. If, for
example, we wanted a sample consisting of $2\frac{1}{2}\%$ of the population
we would firstly select at random the first unit, say the 29th invoice
in a file, and then every 40th invoice after that – the 69th, 109th and
so on. Can you see why this type of sampling is not truly random?
While the first item is chosen by random methods, every other item
is then preselected. Nevertheless, this method of selection (called systematic sampling) approximates to random sampling sufficiently
well to justify its widespread use. Once again we need a reasonably
good sampling frame, but, in our opinion, having accepted that the
sample is not truly random, it need not be 100% accurate. However,
if we are to use systematic sampling, we must ensure that there are
no 'cyclical' patterns in the sampling frame that match our choice
of items. If, for example, we are taking a survey on a housing estate

to assess the opinion of the residents about the 'open plan' layout, and every tenth house is a corner house, then a 10% systematic sample either always, or never, includes a corner house. Such a pattern as this could substantially affect the results we get.

Now, systematic sampling is useful so long as the population is homogeneous. It is suitable, for example, if accountants are selecting a sample of invoices to check for errors; or if the police are taking a sample of motorists passing a certain point to check that they have a valid driving licence. But you will appreciate that in much statistical work the population is heterogeneous. This is especially true if we are investigating opinions, because in many cases a person's opinions are formed by, or result from, the social class to which he belongs. If we are asking the simple question, 'Do you think that people earning over £10,000 a year pay too much in taxes?' the answer we get will often depend on the income of the person being questioned. Inevitably the rich will answer 'yes', while the poor are more likely to say 'no'.

Stratified Sampling

When the response we get to our questions is likely to depend in this way on the social group to which the person being questioned belongs, we will get far better results if we adopt *stratified sampling*. If we are investigating the social evils of traffic on the roads, it is quite possible that systematic sampling would result in a sample which contained only those who owned cars. The opinions of those who do not own cars would not be represented, and to that extent the sample results will be biassed. Stratified sampling has been designed to ensure that all important views are represented in the sample. In this type of sample each social group is represented in the sample in proportion to the size of that group in the population as a whole. Let us take a simple example to show how stratified samples are constructed. Suppose we are investigating opinions on education of those who are still at school or college. We may decide that these opinions will depend on whether the student is at university, state school, or private school. We know that 20% of students are at university, 10% at private school and 70% at a state school. If we are selecting a sample of 2000 students, our first step is to say that 20% of the sample, or 400 students, must be university students, 200 (10%) from private schools, and 1400 (70%) from state schools. We may now additionally decide that men and women have markedly different opinions, so we will now divide our three groups (or strata) into two sub-groups. If, for example, we know that 15% of university students are women, we would include 30 women among our sample of 200 university students. Each of these sub-groups can be further subdivided, perhaps in relation to age or to parents social class. It does not matter how far groups are subdivided, provided that we are stratifying according to a characteristic which is relevant to the survey. If, for example, we are investigating tele-vision viewing habits there is little point in stratifying the sample according to political affiliations. It is probably completely irrelev-ant. On the other hand, our viewing habits might well be affected by the size of our family, or whether we live in a rural or urban area and we would stratify according to these criteria.

Once we have decided on the number of people in each stratum of our sample, the persons to be included must, of course, now be chosen by some random method.

Now, one peculiarity can arise with this type of sampling. If our strata are many, it may be that an important sub-group of the popu-lation is entitled to be represented by only one or two members. It may be that we feel that we cannot obtain an adequate representation of the opinions of this group if we question one person only, and, if so, we should include more representatives of the group, say four or five. While this may seem reasonable, it means, of course, that members of this group have a far higher probability of being chosen as a part of the sample than have people in other strata. This type of sampling is known as sampling with a *variable sampling fraction*, and in assessing our final results we must make allowance for the difference in the representation of such strata. In many surveys, when samples are drawn from a markedly heterogeneous population the sampling fraction is variable rather than uniform. The principle finds its most important application in the evaluation of stock value by sampling methods. We can afford to take a very small sample of items costing only a few pence, since, if our sample is inaccurate it will make little difference to the total value of stock. But if the items of stock cost a great deal, even a small error may significantly affect our total stock valuation. Thus, in determining total stock value from a sample valuation of stock, accountants almost invariably ensure that high-value items have a greater probability of being selected than do low-value items. We will discuss this point again in a later chapter.

Once again, with stratified sampling, we need a sampling frame which will give us a great deal of information about the social structure. Fortunately nowadays governments undertake so many social surveys and publish so many statistics that there is little diffi-culty in obtaining the necessary information. Hence stratified samp-ling is becoming increasingly popular whenever the objective is to assess people's attitudes or opinions.

Multi-Stage Sampling

One of the problems of simple random sampling is that if the sample selected is widely scattered over the country the interviewer may spend more time in travelling than he does in actually interviewing. Often, then, the cost of taking such a sample can be prohibitive. This is especially true in countries in which urbanisation has not yet developed. You can imagine the problems involved if you were to take a sample of people scattered all over central Canada, Malaysia or West Africa. Interviewers might have to spend weeks in travelling.

It is to overcome this problem that multi-stage sampling has been developed. Rather than spending time in travelling to interview 2000 people scattered all over Malaysia, is it not more convenient to interview say 100 people in each of twenty selected areas. Provided that we can ensure that the sample ultimately selected is representative, a great deal of time and expense can be saved.

In many ways the selection of a multi-stage sample is similar to the selection of a stratified sample, but we select primary groups and sub-groups geographically rather than on the basis of social characteristics. Typically, the first stage is to break down the area under survey into a number of standard regions. These may be areas such as the English county, the Canadian province or any other easily defined administrative area. The sample is then divided among these regions according to their population. The second stage is to select at random a small number of districts, say towns and villages, within the primary region. Once again it is necessary to allocate to each of these districts a number of interviews proportional to its population. Almost certainly at this stage, an element of stratification must appear if the sample is to be representative. Let us suppose that we are selecting six towns at random within each region. If $\frac{1}{3}$ of the population live in cities of over 200,000 people, a further $\frac{1}{3}$ in towns with a population of from 20,000 to 200,000 and the remainder in small towns and villages of under 20,000 inhabitants, it would be desirable to select two areas of each type.

Finally, having selected our towns and villages within each region, the sample in each town or village is chosen by some random method. Again, it may be felt to be desirable to choose a stratified sample within each town. How far this stratification is carried depends, of course, on the purpose of the survey and the homogeneity of the population. If we are examining housing conditions, and the type of housing ranges from one-roomed flats to 25-roomed mansions, some degree of stratification will be necessary. But if all the housing in the area is of an essentially similar type, as it may be in a small village, stratification is probably not necessary.

Every type of sampling discussed so far depends on the existence of a sampling frame. If no such frame exists, random sampling is not possible, and to undertake a census to derive a sampling frame is a very expensive process indeed. Unfortunately, in most under-developed countries, satisfactory sampling frames do not yet exist. Sometimes too, the very cost of conducting a survey may make it necessary to use a different type of sampling. To overcome these problems statisticians have designed two further sampling methods – cluster sampling and quota sampling.

Cluster Sampling

Cluster sampling was devised in the United States of America to try to overcome the problems of cost and the lack of a satisfactory samp-ling frame. Instead of selecting a random sample scattered over a wide area, it is a few geographical areas that are selected at random and every single household in each area is interviewed. Obviously the areas chosen must be relatively small. It is not possible to inter-view every household in cities like London and Singapore. The typi-cal area selected might be three or four streets in a town, or perhaps an apartment block. The great advantage of this type of sampling is the saving in time and cost. Many interviews can take place within a short space of time with a minimum of travelling. Moreover it does not require any knowledge of the population before the survey is undertaken; that is, no sampling frame is necessary.

On the other hand, there is a basic problem with this type of sample. Whilst the population is heterogeneous, those who live in a small area or the same block of flats will tend to be homogeneous. They will tend to have the same opinions, the same characteristics, the same life style. Naturally one cannot be certain of this, but it seems to be highly probable, and since the statistician is selecting only a few such areas there is a great danger that the sample will be biassed. One way of trying to offset this tendency to bias is to increase the number of clusters in the hope that you will then include in your sample every important strata, but every increase in the number of clusters raises the cost of the survey. There comes a time when you will have to weigh the risk of selecting a biassed sample against the cost of avoiding the danger of bias. It is, however, a useful type of sample when you have no sampling frame, or when the cost of taking a random sample is too high.

Quota Sampling

There can be few people who have not been stopped in the street by an interviewer holding a questionnaire, or who at least know someone who has been so stopped. And the immediate reaction seems to be, 'Why did they choose me?'

The essence of this type of sample is that it is not preselected, but is chosen by the interviewer on the spot. He, or more usually she, is given a certain number (a quota) of questionnaires which it is her job to have completed during the course of the week, or month. She has a free choice of whom she asks to answer the questions. This choice, naturally, is subject to some general restrictions. One can imagine a young male interviewer stopping only girls of about his own age whom he thought to be pretty. Free choice does not extend as far as this. The interviewer is told that the completed quota of questionnaires must include a certain number of males and of females; a certain number from specified age groups such as, under 18, 18 to 40, 40 to 65. Controls such as this are easy to implement, but often the quota has to be further subdivided by social class or occupation. This can make quota sampling very difficult as there is no real definition of what constitutes, say, the upper middle class, and certainly you can seldom tell a person's social class by looking at him. Such a requirement necessitates the interviewer being given detailed definitions and descriptions of what the survey body means by each term it uses. Subject, however, to controls such as this, the sample is chosen by the interviewer from people who pass in the street.

Now, obviously, such a technique of sampling can be open to a great deal of abuse and bias. When it was first introduced, many cases were reported of interviewers sitting at home filling in their own questionnaires without ever interviewing anyone. Of course this was soon remedied by the questionnaire asking for names and addresses, and the survey body making a spot check to ensure that such people had actually been interviewed. Deliberate fraud of this nature is very rare now. Much more important is the bias to which the quota survey may be subject. If the interviewer does not start work until, say, ten o'clock, the majority of people she can stop must of necessity be the housewife or the unemployed; if she starts at, say, nine o'clock, the vast majority will be clerical or managerial workers; to start even earlier means that she will probably meet largely manual workers. Thus, the interviewer must be prepared to spread her work throughout the day. It is little use trying to have all the questionnaires completed before the morning coffee-break. A further source of bias is that the people you meet in the street are either going somewhere or doing something: they resent being interrupted and their answers may be hurried and slapdash, given without serious thought. These problems necessitate further controls and advice being given to the interviewer. She may be told at what times to conduct the interviews or even where to conduct them. We would not wish to imply that interviewers are rascals or rogues – far from it – but we must point out that the success of such a survey depends very much on their following their instructions to the letter.

Since the quota sample has these weaknesses, why is it becoming increasingly common? Well, for one thing, it is cheap. It eliminates repeated calls to interview a person who may not be in at home on the first two or three occasions. In fact, it is estimated that each interview in a quota sample costs only about half as much as each interview in a random sample. Then, too, we have in every survey a number of people who do not respond. In a quota sample it does not matter. They are ignored and we pass straight on to the next person with no loss of time and no cost. In other types of sample, a substitute has to be found for each person who does not respond. It might, in fact, be argued that this itself introduces bias into the sample. It may be that the man who is prepared to fill in a questionnaire is some kind of extrovert, and we may be getting the views of only one type of individual.

Nevertheless, given the existence of the controls and checks we have mentioned, all the evidence points to the fact that in skilled hands quota sampling gives reasonably satisfactory results. Statisticians generally accept that it is not a substitute for random sampling statistically, but it is so quick and so cheap a method of carrying out surveys that it is not likely to be replaced for a very long time.

Finally, we must stress that the effectiveness of any sample survey, whatever the method of sampling used, depends to a very large extent on the questions which are asked. If they are ambiguous, so will be our answers; if the interviewer puts the questions with a bias, our results will be biassed. No survey result can be better than the questionnaire on which it is based and this question of questionnaire design is something we must now take up in the next chapter.

Chapter Eleven

Planning a Sample Survey

During every general election newspapers are full of public opinion polls, all of which claim to tell us which way the electors are going to cast their votes. So dogmatic are some of the statements they make that one sometimes wonders if it is really necessary for us to go to the polling booth at all! Then, on voting day, most of those fore-casters who were wrong rapidly disappear, leaving the field to those few who have been reasonably successful. Yet those who have failed need not feel ashamed. No statistician will ever dare hope that his sample results will ever be one hundred per cent accurate, and hours of time are devoted to every sample survey merely to reduce the error to the irreducible minimum. Before we can explain how we do try to avoid errors and bias in our results, we must first look at the poss-ible ways in which the sampling error may arise.

You will have appreciated already that one of the most important factors in any sample survey is the questionnaire – the form which poses the questions which give us the information we want. It is a highly flexible instrument. It can be filled in by the interviewer after a series of oral questions; it can be completed by the person being interviewed in the privacy of his own home; it can be completed on the doorstep, or by telephone, or it can be sent by mail. But in spite of this tremendous flexibility, it lends itself readily to bias and error.

Even before an interview takes place, error may have crept into the survey design. In constructing our questionnaire we may have failed to ask questions which ultimately turn out to be relevant. The field of sampling is littered by experienced researchers who cry, 'If only I had asked that question!' Once we pose our questions sources of error become far more numerous. Questions we ask may be mis-leading or not easily understood; they may mean different things to different people. A question on wages earned last week will be under-stood by some people to mean gross wages; by others to mean net wages; some will include overtime and bonus payments; others will merely state the basic wage; workers paid monthly may merely divide the monthly wage by four, ignoring the fact that in a month, apart from February, there are more than four weeks, and that he really ought to divide his annual salary by 52. Then too there may arise a great deal of bias from the fact that the interviewee does not like to admit to things which he feels may put him in a bad light. If we were to ask, 'How often do you take a bath?', how many people do you think would have the courage to say 'Seldom', or 'Never'? We have a suspicion that the reaction would be something like this. 'Most people bath at least once a week or more. If I admit to less than this I am classifying myself as a dirty person. The investigator will never know anyway, so I will say once or twice a week.' Here, the response is adjusted to present a particular image which the respondent feels is necessary for his own self-esteem.

In the very nature of things, many questions posed in a survey must be personal or intimate questions. There is a very strong rumour that women approaching the age of 40 will remain 39 years old for an indefinite period of time; a man who is a junior clerk in a professional office may well give his occupation as an accountant or lawyer; an unmarried mother may be reluctant to admit that she has children; a man who has not told his wife how much he earns may not be willing to state his true salary. Every one of us has something to hide – something we may not be willing to admit publicly.

Thus, however careful we are, it is not likely that our questionnaire will give us a completely true picture of our sample, and it is always as well to regard the results of a sample survey as, at best, an approximation to reality. Nevertheless, an understanding of the possible sources of error is the first step in reducing the error that may arise in a survey.

Stages in the Sample Survey

Although surveys are designed for an infinite variety of purposes, the basic pattern is the same in every case. The quality of the data we derive depends particularly on three of the stages we will outline. The first is the selection of the sample, since, if this is not representative of the population, no reliable conclusions can be drawn. Secondly, as we have seen, the drafting of the questions to be asked demands very careful thought. Thirdly there is the all-important task of interviewing, since more errors will creep in at this stage than at any other. Most of our discussion in this chapter will centre around these three points. But first:

1. *Define your objectives*
It should be merely common sense to ask right at the beginning what we are trying to find out and how the survey can help us. Yet, all too often, this trite and obvious point is ignored, and as a result the

questionnaire deviates from its objectives, asking questions which are irrelevant to the survey, and failing to ask questions which are essential. It is often useful initially to make a study of any already published statistics to see if it will simplify the survey (or perhaps make it unnecessary). Above all a study of secondary data will help you to clarify your mind as to the type of information which will, or will not, be useful to you. Beyond this, the best advice we can give is to bear in mind constantly *why* you are undertaking the survey. Ask yourself constantly in what way any given piece of information is going to help you to meet your survey objectives. You may still fail to get all the information which, with hindsight, is necessary; but you will be sure that what you do get is relevant.

2. *Decide how the information is to be obtained*

Here you have a choice of two main methods – the postal enquiry, and the survey using personal interviews. The great advantage of the *postal enquiry* is the relatively low cost. It can be sent to a very large number of people relatively cheaply, and so the sample size can be increased considerably without overspending. Additionally there is no risk of bias or mistakes which may occur if the interviewer influences the respondent to give particular answers. But when you get down to it, these apparent advantages are often fictitious. The great weakness of the postal enquiry is that very few people bother to complete and return the questionnaire. On average a response rate of 20% of questionnaires returned without reminders is considered satisfactory, while 40% is exceptionally good. Now, missing data due to non-response can be a major source of error. Unfortunately we cannot ignore those who do not reply and assume that they have the same characteristics as those who do reply. It is very likely that a group who do not bother to return the questionnaire will differ in some important way from those who do take the time and trouble to fill it in. Almost inevitably a postal survey will necessitate sending several reminders, and even then a very high response rate is seldom achieved. Thus, in the final analysis, the cost per completed questionnaire can be quite high.

Often, the response rate can be increased substantially by writing a letter to members of the sample explaining the importance of the survey, what it is hoped may result from it, and requesting their co-operation. Sometimes the promise of a copy of the results might do the trick, especially in business surveys, while, in the case of very important enquiries, it may be necessary to offer a small gift, or even a nominal cash payment. But whatever we do, we are not likely to get a response rate as high as we would like. W. A. Hendricks, in his book *The Mathematical Theory of Sampling*, suggests that it is legitimate to make adjustments to the results of a postal survey to allow for missing data. He quotes a survey undertaken to discover the average number of fruit trees on a particular type of farm. The original questionnaire was mailed, and followed up by two reminders to those who had not yet replied. The response at each stage was noted, and the average number of trees per farm was calculated at each stage. The results were as follows.

No. of Mailings	Response (%)	Ave. No. of Trees per Farm
1	13	456
1 + 2	26	408
1 + 2 + 3	39.4	385

It is obvious that those who replied late were those who had the fewer number of trees, and it could be argued that those who had not replied at all would have fewer trees still on their farms. One way of dealing with this data would be to construct a fully logarithmic graph, showing the relationship between the response rate and the average number of trees per farm. We could then project the trend shown and estimate the average number of trees for a 100% response rate. If we convert all our figures into logarithms, we get the following table.

Logarithm of	
Response Rate	Ave. No. of Trees
1.1139	2.6590
1.4150	2.6107
1.5995	2.5855

These figures can now be graphed and the trend shown projected.

On our diagram the log of the estimated number of fruit trees for a response rate of 100% (log 2.0000) is 2.525, which converts to an estimated average number of fruit trees per farm of 335. In fact the true value was known to be 329. Our estimate is not completely accurate (in fact it is almost 2% in error), but it is still very, very much better than our sample result with a response rate of only 39.4%. The assumption we made here was, in fact, that those who did not respond were similar to those who replied late, and in many surveys replies are divided into groups according to the date of reply in an effort to discover the main characteristics of non-respondents.

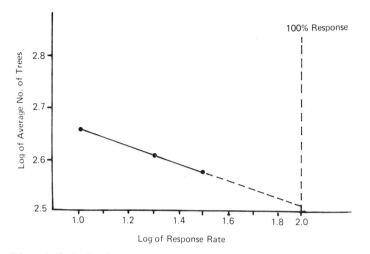

There is little doubt, however, that non-response is a major source of weakness of the postal survey, and the best strategy of all is to arouse and maintain interest in the survey so as to secure as high an initial response as possible. The experience of the British Social Survey points to the fact that response rates of 80% *can* be achieved, if the respondent's co-operation is secured, if the idea can be put over that the survey is of importance to him personally, and if the questionnaire is short and simple. But in spite of their limited success, the hard fact of the matter is that a self-selecting group who decide to return the questionnaire is not representative of the population as a whole. The only way in which non-response can be completely overcome is to make the return of the forms compulsory, and even then there is no guarantee that they are filled in accurately. Since only the government can exercise compulsion, they are the main users of this type of survey.

Perhaps the most widely used method of conducting the sample survey is the *personal interview*. Here a third party, the interviewer, acts as a communications link between the investigator and the members of the sample. He, or she, is responsible for contacting the respondent, for asking questions and for recording the responses. So important is the interviewer that it can well be argued that the representativeness of the sample depends on their ability to persuade their subject to co-operate in filling in the questionnaire, and the accuracy of the sample depends on their skill in extracting and recording information.

Unfortunately, it is all too easy for the interviewer to introduce bias. His tone of voice, even facial expression, and any tendency for him to indicate his own views may all lead to the interviewee express-ing opinions which are those of the interviewer and not his own. There are times when, however simply a question is worded, it will be misunderstood and will have to be 'interpreted' by the interviewer. In this interpretation the precise meaning that was intended may well be lost. Then too, faced with a hesitant or tongue-tied member of the public, even the skilled interviewer may prompt, or even put answers into her mouth. Less than 48 hours before writing this, one of your authors was stopped, in a quota sample, and asked if he had recently seen a television advertisement for a particular brand of after-shave lotion. Since he was preoccupied thinking about this chapter he hesitated to collect his thoughts; to his horror, before he could speak, the young interviewer said, 'Perhaps you haven't seen it,' and underlined that phrase on the questionnaire. Can you see what went wrong? Busy people, stopped on their way to work, need a few minutes to collect their thoughts before questions are put; the interviewer suggested the response instead of waiting; and, worst of all, she then accepted her own suggestion. In fact, your author not only *has* seen the advertisement in question, but actually uses that brand of after-shave lotion. We hate to think of the bias that will appear in that particular survey and can only hope that it was a prac-tice survey carried out by students of statistics.

In spite of these problems, the personal interview does have a large number of advantages over the postal questionnaire. Non-response is minimised. In fact a response rate as high as 80% is not at all un-usual. Inevitably, there will be some non-response as a few people may be out every single time the interviewer calls; they may be on holiday, or have left the district, or merely refuse to answer. We would distrust any interviewer who claimed to have a 100% response, but would not dispute a claim of 90% from a trained investigator. Then too, more questions (and more complicated questions) can be asked in an interview than can be asked in a postal questionnaire; questions can be asked of people who could not complete a written questionnaire – the very young, the very old, or the illiterates; often mere visual observation will enable the interviewer to check whether the answers are likely to be correct. Finally, in a personal interview, the order in which the questions are put is under control, whereas in a postal survey there is no control over the order in which they are answered. As we will see later, this can be a crucial factor in elimi-nating bias.

Nevertheless, some surprising things occur. Just after the Second World War, in a survey to ascertain how many people would claim campaign medals, it was found that the age of the female interviewer affected the response of the ex-servicemen. The younger, and perhaps prettier, the interviewer was, the greater was the percentage of her interviewees who denied that they would claim their medals.

Obviously training can do a great deal to eliminate interviewer bias. But, however well your team may be trained, mistakes will still occur. It is not the obvious mistakes that matter. When we edit the schedules we will soon pick up the fact that John William Smith is a man, and not a woman as marked on his form. It is the small mistakes which we cannot detect which are important. It is very easy to misunderstand an answer, especially if it cannot be answered by a simple 'yes' or 'no'. It is just as easy to classify an answer wrongly, underlining *Never* for example, instead of *Infrequently*. The only way in which mistakes of this nature can be detected is if a sub-sample of an interviewer's respondents are interviewed a second time by the most highly skilled interviewers available. In fact, many bodies do this to check the potential accuracy of the completed questionnaires as a matter of course. It is, however, expensive, and in the long run the best solution may well be to give each interviewer as detailed instructions as are possible, and as much training and experience as can be afforded. Some investigators argue that tests have shown that on a normal sample survey, the trained interviewer is no more accurate than the amateur; but there is little doubt that in the modern 'in-depth' surveys the trained interviewer can elicit responses that the amateur can never hope to elicit.

3. *The preparation of the questionnaire*
We have stressed repeatedly that a badly designed questionnaire may ruin an otherwise well-planned survey. Essentially, questions and answers are the means of communication between the investigator and his subject. If you think about it, in this process there are five possible sources of error for every question. Firstly the question itself may not be phrased to enquire about what the investigator wishes to know; secondly the question may not be heard correctly; thirdly what is heard may be misunderstood; fourthly the reply may be misheard by the interviewer; and fifthly the reply may be misunderstood by the interviewer. Is it not obvious that what we need are short, unambiguous questions which allow of a limited number of unambiguous replies? Unfortunately, this is not always possible. If we desire questions which allow only of the simple answer 'yes' or 'no', there can be no misunderstanding of the answer, even if the question itself is ambiguous. But there is always the need for the third alternative answer, 'Don't know', and such questions are difficult to devise. Suppose we asked the simple question, 'Do you think that garages should give trading stamps and free gifts with sales of petrol?' Let us consider

just how 'simple' this question is. Apart from the obvious replies, 'yes', 'no', and 'I don't know', some people may think that it depends on the number of trading stamps given with each gallon or on the nature of the free gift. Others may wish to say 'yes' to gifts and 'no' to trading stamps, or vice versa. Are we to assume in our answer that if the garages ceases to give gifts or stamps that the price of petrol will be reduced, or will it remain the same? So you see, the question is not so simple, and considerable skill is called for in constructing questions to which the answer is a categorical 'yes' or 'no'. Usually this kind of question is confined to purely factual matters such as, 'Do you own a car?'

The second type of question is what we have come to know as a multiple-choice question. Here the respondent is asked a question such as, 'Why did you take your holiday in Spain last year?', and the question is followed by a number of possible reasons, one of which is to be underlined. The problem with this type of question is that the list of reasons must be limited, and of necessity we must include a category 'other reasons', leaving the respondent to reply as he wishes. Once again we have opened the door to ambiguity. A further problem is the implication in such a question that only one of the reasons given is important. Two or three, or perhaps all, the reasons may be equally important, or perhaps none are of importance. Here the order of the alternatives can be of importance. Experiments in varying their order show that there is a marked tendency to choose alternatives at the top and bottom of the list, ignoring those in the middle.

The final type of question is open-ended, leaving the reply entirely to the respondent. 'Why do you drink this particular brand of beer?' This is a very useful kind of question to obtain qualitative information, but it is the most open of all to ambiguity. If it is summarised by the interviewer what we are recording is what the interviewer thought the respondent meant. If the reply is quoted in full it may be rambling, incoherent and open to many interpretations, and this is just as dangerous.

In order to help us get over this problem of communicating with our sample, there are a number of rules we must follow when we are constructing the questions to ask. The problem is to devise questions which everyone understands, which mean the same thing to everyone, and which ask what they are meant to ask.

(i) Firstly, keep the questions short. Not only is a short question easier to understand, but also there is nothing more confusing to a person being interviewed than to forget the beginning of a question before the end is reached. The ideal type of question from this point of view is the extremely simple, 'What is your age?' As a general rule it is better to break down a more complicated question into two or three shorter ones. Consider the following question which you could be asked if you were filling in a car accident report form for an insurance company. 'If you were driving your own car give the reference number of your insurance policy; if not, state the owner's name, whether his insurance cover is comprehensive or third party only, and give the name of his insurance company.'

Such an example is of course grossly exaggerated. No one but an amateur (or perhaps a civil servant) would produce such a question, and in practice it would appear in this form:

1. a. Were you driving your own car?　　Yes/No
   b. What is the number of your insurance policy?　　7K/.....
2. If your answer to question 1a is NO
   a. Give the name of the owner　　Mr/Mrs/Miss
   b. What type of insurance cover does he/she have?
   　　　　　　　　　　　　Comprehensive/Third Party
   c. What is the name of his/her insurance company?　　......

You will see that each of these short questions concentrates on one thing at once and is not likely to confuse the person filling in the form.

(ii) Use simple language. In any sample there is likely to be a very wide variety of ability in the use of language, and we must make sure that everyone understands what we mean. It is not a question of underrating the intelligence of the members of the sample but of trying to ensure that the interviewer does not have to explain the question in his own words which may introduce some bias into the answer. In any case we feel it is better to say, 'Are you telling a lie?', rather than, 'Are you perpetrating a terminological inexactitude?' Simplicity has been the keynote of every great speech in history, from Julius Caesar's 'I came, I saw, I conquered', to Winston Churchill's great wartime speeches. They were great because everyone understood them. Follow the same policy in drafting your own questions.

(iii) Avoid questions which lead to a particular answer. It is far better to ask, 'What do you consider to be the best brand of toothpaste?', than to ask 'Do you consider White Shine to be the best brand of toothpaste?' The mere mention of a name is often enough to cause a particular response. Equally we must try to avoid emotive words. Socialist and Tory arouse more passion than do Conservative and Labour. At the beginning of the last war when a survey of people's attitudes in America was being taken, it was found that almost twice as many people claimed to be anti-Nazi than claimed to be anti-

German. Try at all costs to avoid implying in your question that you would like a particular answer.

(iv) Make sure that the respondent has the information. It is of little use asking people in Central Africa what type of central heating they prefer. Even if the question is a simple one, the informant may not know the answer. A housewife may never have been told her husband's salary; or she may have forgotten when she last bought biscuits. Often she has to be led up to such things step by step. Firstly she should be asked if she has ever bought Brand X biscuits. If she replies 'yes', she can then be asked if she has bought them in the last year, then the last month, then in the last fortnight and so on until she remembers clearly. The approach may seem cumbersome, but experience has taught us that we should not rely too much on people's memory.

(v) Consider if a respondent would be willing to tell the truth. He may know the answer, but be unwilling to reveal it, since certain answers may appear (to him) to lower his prestige in the eyes of the interviewer. Television viewers may claim to prefer the more serious programmes to the more frivolous ones; readers may claim to read classical novels when in fact they read cowboy stories. We can, of course, always insert test questions to check if these answers are truthful. We could, for example, ask them to summarise the content of two serious television programmes they have seen in the last week, or give the author and title of a couple of serious novels they have read. In 1960, when one of your authors was helping to undertake a survey, one housewife gave her age as 41, and then when asked for her date of birth, gave it as 1911, which, of course, made her age 49. Such a situation calls for a great deal of tact on the part of the interviewer. More interesting is a further American survey[1] in which the following questions were asked:

Question	% Replying Yes
1. Have you ever heard of the word 'afrohetin'?	8
2. Do you recall voting last December in the special election for your state representatives?	33
3. Have you ever heard of the famous writer John Voolson?	16
4. Have you heard of the *Midwestern Life Magazine*?	25
5. Have you heard of the Taft–Johnson–Pepper Bill on veterans' housing?	53

[1] Quoted in Elliot and Christopher, *Research Methods in Marketing*.

The interesting thing about this survey is that none of the things mentioned in fact ever existed, yet so many people said they had heard of them. Those who said 'yes' probably did so because they felt that if they had taken more interest in current affairs they *would* have heard of them.

(vi) Consider the order of the questions. Here, two things are important. The person being interviewed must not feel that the questionnaire is going to be too difficult to complete, or pry too much into his private life. The early questions should be easy and general, and only as confidence builds up should searching questions be introduced. Equally, wait until the interviewer has been able to build up some sort of friendship with the respondent before you introduce, slowly and carefully, questions on his private life. And if your questions are really personal, such as, 'Have you ever been unfaithful to your wife?', do stress that the survey is absolutely confidential. A question such as this would, of course, have been preceded by more general questions as to whether the respondent believed that fidelity in marriage was of great importance, or usual.

(vii) Finally, try to ensure that the answers given are capable of being interpreted in one way only. A very common category of answer is 'Don't know'. This, however, could mean, 'I do not understand the question', or 'I do not have the information', or 'I have the information, but cannot decide between alternatives', or 'I have the information, but am not going to tell you'.

It is important that interviewers should indicate which of these alternatives is meant, rather than lumping together such diverse information under one general heading.

4. *Select the sample*
Since we have already dealt with the many different types of sampling in the last chapter, we will merely stress here that the sample must be chosen to be of such a size and composition that it will yield the best possible results consistent with the expenditure you are permitted.

5. *Undertake a pilot survey*
However careful you have been so far, what you have done still remains to be tested in the field. It may be that the questionnaire we have designed will be unsatisfactory in practice. To test what we have done so far, we usually undertake a small pilot survey. How many people we interview does not matter so long as they are chosen at random; the results themselves are not as important as the lessons

we learn. We may find, for example, that a question we thought to be simple and self-explanatory is misunderstood by most people, and will have to be altered. It may be that one section of the questionnaire results in replies so vague that it becomes obvious that we are asking questions about which few of our respondents have any knowledge. It would be better to leave it out altogether.

At this stage it is our work we are testing, and experience of the pilot survey will yield valuable information about the difficulties we are likely to meet in the field, and will save us from making serious mistakes in the much more costly survey proper.

6. *Brief the interviewers*
Before the fieldwork proper starts, all interviewers should hold a final meeting. They will already have a copy of their instructions, and great care should be taken to ensure that they understand them. The lessons learned, and the difficulties met with in the pilot survey should be carefully examined and a course of action determined to meet circumstances that may arise. We will never be able to foresee all the difficulties of every single interviewer, but we must ensure that every single one of them has every scrap of information which is available and knows exactly what he is about to do.

Now, finally, we do not pretend that if you follow all the above advice and rules you will produce the perfect sample survey. There will still be mistakes, but we hope that you will have avoided the worst. Nor will we claim that your sample results will be one hundred per cent accurate. Such a sample has yet to be devised. But you will have avoided some of the major sources of error.

Error there will be, however. If you have done your job well, it will be small. The next two chapters will show you how to estimate the magnitude of the error that may remain; those that follow will show you how to assess the significance of your sample results and take decisions on them.

EXERCISES TO CHAPTERS 10 AND 11
11.1 Statistical data may be collected by sample or census inquiry. Describe both methods and explain why sample inquiry is more frequently used than census inquiry. A.C.A.

11.2 Describe three of the more important methods of sampling used in conjunction with statistical surveys. Suggest methods which may be employed in statistical surveys to validate the sample information obtained. I.C.S.A.

11.3   Explain what is meant by (a) stratified, (b) quota sampling, illustrating by a brief example in each case how samples are selected. Comment on the main advantage(s) and disadvantage(s) of each method.   A.C.A.

11.4   Distinguish between random sampling and quota sampling. Indicate the advantages and disadvantages of each method, and state how non-response would be dealt with in the use of each procedure.
                                                                     I.C.S.A.

11.5   Describe carefully how FOUR of the following types of sample are taken: simple random, stratified random, multi-stage random, systematic, quota.   O.N.C.

11.6   Identify the relative advantages and disadvantages of different techniques of sampling such as random, systematic, stratified, multi-stage and quota. Select the technique which you think would be most appropriate for a motor-car manufacturing company seeking information from car owners to enable the company to design 'the most popular family saloon car'. Support your selection with a reasoned argument.   O.N.C.

11.7   (a) Why are samples used?
       (b) Describe in detail two methods of selecting samples.
       (c) What kind of errors arise in sampling?   O.N.C.

11.8   Explain what is meant by (a) random sampling, (b) quota sampling. What are the principal arguments in favour of using some form of random sampling rather than a quota sample?   O.N.C.

11.9   What is the object of sampling? Discuss the problems involved in selecting from a large population samples which typify these populations.   O.N.C.

11.10   What is the object of 'sampling'? Explain briefly the principles on which sampling is based and discuss the problems involved in obtaining from large human populations samples which characterise them adequately.   O.N.C.

11.11   Describe the following types of samples:
       (a) random;
       (b) stratified;
       (c) systematic;
       (d) multi-stage.

State the conditions under which each would be used and the advantages to be gained.   O.N.C.

11.12   (a) What is meant by the term *sampling frame*? Give two examples of a sampling frame from which a human population could be sampled.

(b) Define each of the following and describe the advantages of each type of sample:

(i) stratified;
(ii) multi-stage;
(iii) quota.   O.N.C.

11.13   (a) An inquiry is to be carried out among a population which has the following characteristics:

Proportion of bus travellers to travellers by other means   4:8
Proportion travelling less than five miles to that
     travelling five miles and over:

(i) bus travellers   7:3
(ii) travellers by other means   ,   2:3

If each interviewer is to question a quota of sixty people, how many of each class of person should be selected per quota?

(b) What chief advantage has the quota method of sample selection when compared with other methods? What are its disadvantages?

(c) What advantages are derived from the use of statistical samples?   O.N.C.

11.14   Discuss the sampling methods which you consider should be employed to obtain the following information:

(a) Public opinion on the Common Market.
(b) Weights of workers (male, female and juvenile) employed in a very large factory.
(c) Heights of Canadian-born persons resident in the U.K.
(d) Health details relating to office workers employed by local authorities in the U.K.   O.N.C.

11.15

(i) In what ways does quota sampling differ from random sampling?
(ii) What are the considerations involved in deciding whether the information which is usually derived from the population census should be obtained by a random sample of all households?   O.N.C.

11.16 (a) Postal questionnaires and interviews are two methods of collecting data. List the advantages of each method.

(b) One of the main defects of surveys by interview is the problem of interviewer bias. What is interviewer bias and how can the problem be minimised?

(c) What are the main points to be considered in the design of a postal questionnaire? I.C.M.A.

11.17 (a) What rules should be observed in constructing a questionnaire for collecting statistical information?

(b) What are the advantages and disadvantages of using questionnaires for collecting data? O.N.C.

11.18 Describe the main methods which are used in the collection of statistical data, and comment on the problems associated with each method. O.N.C.

11.19 Discuss the problems involved in using questionnaires for the collection of statistical data. O.N.C.

11.20 Give an account of the principles to be considered when drawing up questionnaires. O.N.C.

11.21 List, and then describe carefully with examples, general rules which should be followed when designing a questionnaire for a statistical survey.

A local authority is considering whether or not to construct a sports centre and intends to send to a sample of residents a short postal questionnaire in order to ascertain their views. Design a suitable questionnaire. O.N.C.

11.22 (a) What is meant by a *sample*? Describe briefly the following:

(i) random sampling;
(ii) multi-stage sampling;
(iii) stratified sampling.

(b) Describe briefly the ways in which bias may arise in response to each of the following questions when directed by an interviewer at members of the class of people indicated.

(i) Do you sympathise with Communism? (general public)
(ii) Do you use 'X' (a washing-up liquid)? (housewives)
(iii) How many people are there in your family? (general public)
O.N.C.

11.23   Describe carefully the way in which you would select a sample for an investigation into:

(a) the journeys made by car and lorry drivers through a town;
(b) the brands of pipe tobacco smoked by men in a particular residential suburb.   O.N.C.

11.24   As the Personnel Officer of a factory employing 10,000 workers at three locations of approximately equal labour strength, you wish to carry out an inquiry among all the employees to find their views on a rearrangement of holidays. It has already been agreed that the present fourteen days per annum with six additional days at bank holidays should be increased to a total of twenty-seven days per annum. The inquiry is to find out how the workers prefer the new total to be distributed through the year.

(a) Discuss the suitability of a postal questionnaire for this purpose, comparing this method with other possible methods. State your final choice of method and give your reasons.
(b) Draft in general outline a questionnaire to be used with the method upon which you have decided.   O.N.C.

11.25   (i) What are the advantages and disadvantages of employing random sampling methods instead of non-random sampling methods when carrying out a nationwide sample survey?

(ii) Describe *in detail* how you would obtain a random sample of adults from a town of approximately 50,000 inhabitants. What are the main factors affecting the sample size? How would you deal with the problem of non-responders?   O.N.C.

11.26   A large local authority with approximately 100,000 residents proposes to conduct a survey to obtain some idea of the expected use of a proposed new sports centre. Explain briefly:

(a) the advantages of employing random sampling methods instead of non-random sampling methods;
(b) the principal factors affecting sample size;
(c) how you would deal with the problem of non-responders;
(d) how you would stratify the population if it was decided to employ a stratified random sample.   O.N.C.

11.27   (a) State the main points which should be observed when designing a questionnaire.

(b) Draft a questionnaire (of about 8 questions), to be completed by a sample of motorists using a large firm's car service department, which will provide information regarding the views of those motorists on the organisation of the service department. (Technical questions are *not* required.) O.N.C.

11.28 You have been asked to conduct a survey on wages within a large company. Explain in detail how you would go about the designing, carrying out and reporting on the results of your survey. O.N.C.

11.29 Distinguish clearly between stratified random sampling, multi-stage random sampling, quota sampling and the deliberate selection of a sample. Explain the circumstances in which each would be advantageous. Discuss the problems involved in the use of sampling frames. O.N.C.

11.30 What do you understand by the term *sampling frame*? Give an example, in each case, of a sampling frame suitable for sampling from

(i) adults in the United Kingdom,
(ii) students in technical colleges.

You have been asked to advise on the design of a random sample of about 10,000 addresses in Great Britain. Describe how you would select your sample if you are to employ a multi-stage stratified sample. Pay particular attention to your sampling units and to your stratification. O.N.C.

11.31 (a) Outline the principles of questionnaire design.
(b) Draw up a questionnaire of about eight questions either

(i) to discover from part-time students in a technical college information relating to the course they are pursuing and its relevance to their future job prospects, or
(ii) to test public opinion on the proposal to set up a Welsh parliament. O.N.C.

11.32 (a) Give *two* occasions when the selection of a pure random sample would not be feasible. What types of sampling would overcome the difficulties?
(b) A manufacturer of electrical appliances wishes to carry out a survey of households in a given smokeless fuel zone to assess the sales potential for an electric central heating system. Answer the following questions, giving reasons for each answer.

(i) What would determine the size of the sample chosen?
(ii) What information may be used to provide a sampling frame?

(iii) Should the manufacturer use postal questionnaires or carry out door-to-door interviews?

(iv) Should questions be 'open-ended' or require a pre-printed answer to be ticked?   O.N.C.

11.33   Either

(a) Explain what is meant by a pilot survey and justify its place in the planning of a social survey, or

(b) Explain what is meant by cluster sampling, illustrating your answer with an example.   O.N.C.

11.34   Outline the steps involved in planning a statistical survey. Discuss three of them in detail.   O.N.C.

11.35   (a) Describe how *bias* occurs in a statistical investigation. Which sampling technique would be used to obtain an unbiassed sample of:

(i) ages of West Indian-born males resident in the United Kingdom;

(ii) weights of male, female and juvenile employees in a large factory;

(iii) health details of councillors in English district councils?

(b) Explain briefly the following:

(i) sampling frame;

(ii) quota sampling;

(iii) systematic sampling.

Chapter Twelve

Sampling Theory

You will remember that in discussing the concept of dispersion we introduced you to the idea of Z scores and the Normal Curve – the perfectly symmetrical bell-shaped curve. Later, we extended this concept, pointing out that the normal curve represented, in fact, one particular type of probability distribution, the Normal Distribution. If, for example, we construct a frequency distribution showing the length of life of telegraph poles in the United Kingdom (which does give a nearly perfect normal distribution), we can use this to state the probability of a telegraph pole lasting more than 15, more than 17, or more than y years before it needs replacing, and also the probability of its life being more than x years but less than y years, or any other range you wish. You will appreciate that here we are concerned with a continuous distribution of the form:

Poles Lasting	Number of Poles
Under 5 years	x
5 years and under 10 years	y
10 years and under 15 years	z
and so on	

Suppose we have a total population of telegraph poles of 40,000, and that 6432 of them have a life of less than 25 years. We can say that the probability of a pole chosen at random needing replacement during the first 25 years of its life is $\frac{6432}{40000}$ or 0.1608. But, as you know, if we wanted to calculate the probability of that pole having a life of over 25 but less than 50 years, we will have to use Z scores – and for this we will need both the arithmetic mean and the standard deviation. From here onwards we will have to differentiate between the mean and standard deviation of the population and of the sample. If we are talking of the *population*

the arithmetic mean is designated by μ (mu)
the standard deviation is designated by σ (sigma)

If we are talking of the *sample*

> the arithmetic mean is designated by $\bar{x}$
> the standard deviation is designated by s

In this case we are talking of the entire population of telegraph poles so we will calculate our Z scores as $\frac{x-\mu}{\sigma}$ Suppose that $\mu = 35$ and that $\sigma = 15$, and that we wish to estimate the probability that a pole will have a life of between 50 and 65 years. The relevant Z scores are $\frac{(50-35)}{15}$ and $\frac{(65-35)}{15}$, that is, 1.0 and 2.0. What we are really asking is, what proportion of the area under the normal curve lies between these two Z values?

From our tables we find that 97.725% of the area under the curve falls below a Z score of 2.0, and 84.13% below a Z score of 1.0. Thus,

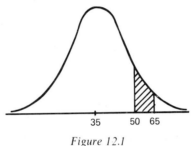

Figure 12.1

13.595% falls between these two values, and the probability we require is 0.13595 or 0.136.

The time has now come to extend these ideas still further in order to develop the basic principles of sampling. Before we begin, let us stress one or two assumptions that we make in order to do this. We have to assume, of course, that the sample taken is a good sample, and representative of the parent population. The previous two chapters have outlined the problems of selecting a sample, and, if we have overcome these problems, the only error left in our results will be the error which may result merely because we are examining a sample and not the whole population. As we will see, this error can be estimated statistically. Secondly we will assume that the population we are sampling is large, so that sampling without replacement does not create problems. Thirdly, in this chapter, we will discuss only those circumstances in which the sample itself is large. The use of small samples creates problems which will be taken up in later chapters.

Sampling Distribution of Sample Means

Let us suppose now that we are selecting a sample from a large parent population. The work we have done already will tell you that there are a very large number of different ways in which the sample may be selected. Even if there are only 50 items in our total population there are 2,118,760 different ways in which a sample of five can be selected. Can you imagine in how many ways we could select a sample of 50 items from a population of 100,000? We will suppose further that we are drawing the sample in order to discover the average weekly consumption of sugar per head. It is very unlikely that if we were to draw two samples only, both would show the same average consumption. If, in fact, we had the time (and the patience) to examine every possible sample, we would have millions of averages, ranging from zero consumption for some samples to a very high intake of sugar for other samples, and we could construct a frequency distribution based on these results. Such a frequency distribution might begin something like this:

Weekly Average Consumption of Sugar per Head

Consumption (ounces)	No. of Samples
0	37
1	94
2	365
3	1246
4	7384

and so on until we have a complete frequency distribution. We have constructed what we call a *sampling distribution of sample means*. Now, if the population itself is normally distributed, you would expect such a distribution also to be normal, but the strange thing is that even if the parent population is not normally distributed, the sampling distribution of sample means still turns out to be normally distributed as long as the sample is reasonably large. The algebraic proof of this is complicated, but you can perform a simple experiment yourself which will show that this is so. If we take the ten different digits 0 to 9, then each number can occur just once, so each has

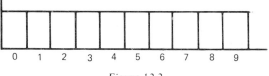

Figure 12.2

the same probability of being chosen if we select one at random. The distribution is by no means normal – it is a rectangular distribution graphed as in Fig. 12.2.

Now select a sample of three items. It will, of course, have to be sampling with replacement. There is only one way in which you can select a sample with an average of 0 – if you select as your sample of three digits nought on each occasion. But there are three ways in which you can select a sample with a total of 1 and a sample average of $\frac{1}{3}$ – that is, samples comprising 1 0 0; 0 1 0; and 0 0 1. Similarly there are six ways in which you can select a sample of three digits with a total of 2 and a sample average of $\frac{2}{3}$ – 2 0 0; 0 2 0; 0 0 2; 1 1 0; 1 0 1; and 0 1 1. If you continue like this until all possible samples have been taken (it is cumbersome as there are 1000 samples), and graph the frequency distribution of the sample means, you will find that the distribution of sample means that you have constructed approaches the shape of a normal distribution as in the graph.

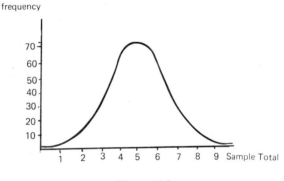

Figure 12.3

The greater the number of items in the sample, the closer does the distribution fit the normal curve, and if the sample is large, the fit becomes almost perfect. Thus, anything we can find out about this distribution will tell us something about our sample averages.

Let us look firstly at the standard deviation of a distribution such as this. In sampling theory the standard deviation of a sampling distribution is called the *standard error*, but it is still designated by s. The first thing to notice is that, unless we draw samples of one item, s must be less than σ. This is because, in taking a sample of many items, the extreme values must be offset by less extreme values, and may even be offset completely by an extreme value in the opposite direction. Thus, if we again consider the numbers 0 to 9, and take a random sample of one item, the range of our sample results is still from 0 to 9. But if we take a sample of two items (without replacement) the range of our sample averages is reduced to $\frac{(0+1)}{2}$ to $\frac{(8+9)}{2}$, i.e. 0.5 to 8.5. If we take a sample of three numbers the range is further reduced to $\frac{(0+1+2)}{3}$ to $\frac{(7+8+9)}{3}$ or from 1 to 8. The larger the size of the sample the smaller is the range of the sample averages and hence the smaller is the standard error of the sample means. The problem is to determine by how much to reduce the standard deviation of the population. Since the size of the standard error obviously depends on the size of the sample you will not be surprised to know that:

$$\text{Standard error of } \bar{x} = \frac{\sigma}{\sqrt{n}} \quad {}^{1}$$

This presumes that the standard deviation of the population is known, but if it is not, σ can be replaced by s without serious error if the size of the sample is large. We will discuss later just how large is a 'large sample'.

The Central Limit Theorem

We can now state one of the most important theorems in the whole of sampling theory, known as the Central Limit Theorem. This states that if a random sample of size n is drawn from a population with a mean μ and a variance of σ^2, then as n increases the distribution of

$$\frac{\bar{x} - \mu}{\sigma / \sqrt{n}}$$

approaches the standard normal distribution. In words, this means that the Z scores of our distribution of sample means are normally distributed, or, even more simply, that our sample distribution of sample means is normally distributed.

The importance of this theorem lies in the fact that in estimating the error which may arise in a sample, we assume that the distribution of the sample means is normal, i.e. that the Central Limit Theorem is true.

EXAMPLE

Suppose a confectioner produces cakes which he packs in cartons of 100 for the catering trade. He prints on the carton: 'average weight per cake not less than 95.5 grams'. If cakes have a mean weight of

---

[1] For a formal proof of this and of later theorems see *Modern Analytical Techniques*, Owen and Jones, Chapter 6 (Polytech).

100 grams and a standard deviation of 20 grams, what proportion of batches contravene the Trade Descriptions Act?

Every time the confectioner packs a carton, this is equivalent to selecting a sample of 100 cakes. We can consider, then, that the average weights of cartons forms a sampling distribution of sample means. Using the theorem examined earlier, the mean of these sample means will be 100, and the standard error $\frac{20}{\sqrt{100}} = 2$. We wish to know the proportion of cartons with mean weight of cakes less than 95.5. Diagrammatically, the situation looks like this:

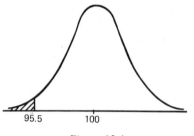

Figure 12.4

The Z score for 95.5 is

$$\frac{95.5 - 100}{2} = -2.25$$

and consulting the tables we would conclude that $100 - 98.778 = 1.222\%$ of cartons would contravene the Act.

Sums and Differences

The sampling distribution discussed so far was constructed from sample means. Let us now form a sampling distribution by taking sums and differences. Now this seems peculiar, so let us explain precisely what we mean.

As you know, a great deal of modern industry is based, not on 'making something', but on assembling components that have been made in a number of different factories. Let us take the simplest possible case and imagine that we are joining together two straight metal bars produced in two separate workshops. The first workshop aims to produce a bar 20 cm long, but of course there will be minute differences in the lengths of the bars produced. We will assume that the lengths of the bars are normally distributed about an average of 20 cm, and the distribution has a standard deviation of 0.05 cm. In statistical terms we have a normal distribution $N(20\,\text{cm};$

0.0025 cm). This is merely a shorthand way of saying 'the distribution is normal and has an arithmetic mean of 20 cm and a *variance* of 0.0025 cm'. You will remember that about 99.95% of items fall within the range arithmetic mean ± 3.5 standard deviations. Thus we can say that this batch of rods varies in length from 20 cm + 0.175 cm to 20 cm − 0.175 cm, i.e. from 20.175 to 19.825 cm.

Similarly, the second workshop aims to produce rods 10 cm long, and here we have a normal distribution $N(10 \text{ cm}; 0.0016 \text{ cm})$. Can you see that the output of this workshop will vary in length from 10 + 0.14 to 10 − 0.14 cm, i.e. from 10.14 to 9.86 cm?

When a workman picks up two rods for joining he selects them at random. If he chooses the longest rod from each pile he will produce a finished article (20.175 + 10.14) cm long = 30.315 cm. He might equally well choose the two shortest rods, in which case his finished rod would be only (19.825 + 9.86) cm long = 29.685 cm. Thus, the completed rod would vary in length from 30.315 to 29.685 cm, and we thus obtain a distribution of sums. Naturally you would expect a high proportion of the rods to be in the vicinity of 30 cm long and only a very small proportion to be at either of the extreme lengths. We can expect, that is, that the distribution of the sums would be normal, especially as the two parent populations are normally distributed.

Now what can we say about such a distribution? Firstly our expectation about the majority of the output having a length about 30 cm proves to be correct if we consider the first two theorems:

1. If the parent populations are normally distributed so will be the distribution of sample sums.
2. The mean of the sample sums is the sum of the means of the populations from which they were drawn.

If you now look at the range over which the lengths of the joined rods can vary you can see that it is far greater than the range over which either single rod can vary. The single rods vary over a range of 0.35 cm to 0.28 cm respectively; the combined rods cover a range of 0.63 cm, which is in fact, as you might expect, the sum of the two individual ranges. This leads to the third proposition relating to the distribution of sample sums:

3. The variance of the sample sums is the sum of the variances of the populations from which they were formed.

Let us take an example to show the way in which these theorems can be applied. A manufacturer produces two types of metal rods. Type A has lengths distributed as $N(3.5 \text{ cm}; 0.0009 \text{cm})$ and type B as $N(4.5 \text{ cm}; 0.0016 \text{ cm})$. A rod of each type is selected, joined together, and fitted into a channel 8.1 cm long. What proportion of rods will not fit?

Initially we require the distribution of the lengths of the combined rods. Firstly, our theorems tell us that the distribution is normal. Secondly, we know that the average length of the combined rods is equal to the sum of the individual averages, $3.5 + 4.5 = 8$ cm. Thirdly the variance is equal to the sum of the individual variances, $0.0009 + 0.0016 = 0.0025$. Thus the distribution we require is $N(8 \text{ cm}; 0.0025 \text{ cm})$. This distribution is illustrated as:

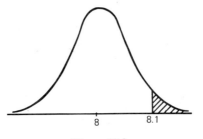

Figure 12.5

We wish to know the proportion of combined rods that will not fit the channel into which they must be placed, that is, what proportion is longer than 8.1 cm; or what proportion fall within the shaded area. To do this we must calculate the Z score for 8.1 cm, which you will remember is

$$\frac{x - \bar{x}}{s} = \frac{8.1 - 8}{\sqrt{0.0025}} = \frac{0.1}{0.05} = 2$$

From our tables we can see that 97.725% of our rods have a Z score less than 2 and it follows that 2.275% have a Z score greater than 2 and will not fit.

Turning now to a distribution of sample differences, one can visualise this situation arising when we are estimating the weight of food in a container by subtracting the weight of the empty container from that of a full container. Suppose that the average weight of a full packet of rice is 225 grams, and the average weight of the box is 7 grams, naturally we are able to say that the average weight of the contents is 218 grams. This is easy enough to see, but it leads to our next proposition that the mean of the sample differences is equal to the difference between the means of the populations from which they were drawn.

It may seem strange at first sight, but when we pass on to consider the variance of the sample differences, we meet the same proposition that we met earlier: the variance of the sample differences is equal to the *sum* of the variances of the populations from which they were drawn. Why should this be so? If again we consider the possible range of the weight of the contents, surely it is possible in the packing of the rice to pack the minimum weight of rice in the maximum weight of container, or vice versa, and the range of the weight of contents (the difference) will then be greater than the range of the weights of either the empty boxes or of full boxes? An example will make this clear.

Suppose the weights of full boxes is distributed as $N(225; 2.25)$ and the containers in which we are packing the rice as $N(7; 0.0025)$. Again taking the range mean ± 3.5 standard deviations as covering all but a negligible part of the population, the range of weights of the full containers is $225 \pm 3.5\sqrt{2.25}$, or from $225 + 5.25$ to $225 - 5.25$; a range of 230.25 to 219.75 or 10.5 grams. Similarly, the range of weights of the containers is $7 \pm 3.5\sqrt{0.0025}$ or from $7 + 0.175$ to $7 - 0.175$; or a range of 7.175 to $6.825 = 0.35$ grams. Thus the minimum weight of contents would be found if we took a full container of 219.75 grams and found that the empty container weighed 7.175 grams – the contents would in fact weigh 212.575 grams. The maximum weight of contents is found when we select a packet weighing 230.25 grams and the empty container weighs only 6.825 grams – the contents weigh 223.425 grams. The range of weights of the contents is from 223.425 to 212.575 grams – a range of 10.85 grams; equal to the sum of the individual ranges. Can you see now why we add the individual variances to obtain the variance of the differences? Our new distribution of the weights of the contents would be

$$N(225 - 7; 2.25 + 0.0025) = N(218; 2.2525)$$

Suppose the firm now printed on its packet 'minimum net weight of contents 214 grams'. What is the probability that a Weights and Measures Inspector would choose a sample packet which contained less rice than this?

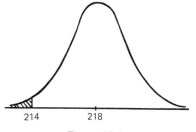

Figure 12.6

Here we wish to calculate the probability that the weight of the packet chosen will fall within the shaded area. Again, we must calculate the Z score,

$$\frac{214-218}{\sqrt{2.2525}} = -2.665$$

The table tells us that there is a probability of 0.996 that the weight of the rice will exceed this value, so the probability of a packet having a net weight below 214 grams is only 0.004 – a very low probability indeed.

Standard Error of a Proportion

There is an increasing tendency in recent years to give the results of a sample survey in the form of a percentage figure. A manufacturer says that not more than 3% of his output develops any defect within the first year of use; public opinion surveys say that a given percentage of the population prefers filter tip cigarettes to plain cigarettes; or that 48.6% of the population will vote for Mr. Smith in the next election. Now the trouble is, of course, that when opinions are being expressed there is no question of the sample means being calculated and no chance of calculating the standard deviation. Yet, if we are to go much further we must be able to calculate Z scores and for this we need at least the standard error. When we are dealing with percentages we have just three facts available – the percentage expressing an opinion (which we will call P); the percentage who do not express that opinion $(100 - P)$; and the number in the sample (n). On the basis of these three quantities statisticians have devised a formula for the standard error of the proportion (or percentage)

$$\text{s.e. of the percentage} = \sqrt{\frac{P(100-P)}{n}}\%$$

The main difference between a proportion and a percentage is that the percentage figure gives the 'number out of a hundred', e.g. 47%, while the proportion gives us the 'number out of one', e.g. 0.47.

Suppose in a survey of voting habits 800 people were interviewed, and the result indicated that 47% of the votes cast would in fact go to Mr. Smith. On the surface, then, his opponent seems sure to be elected, but what is the probability that Mr. Smith will in fact be chosen? If Mr. Smith gets over 50% of the votes he will be elected, so let us calculate the Z score corresponding to 50%.

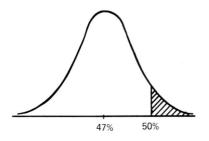

Figure 12.7

$$\text{s.e.} = \sqrt{\frac{47 \times 53}{800}} = 1.765.$$

Hence our Z score becomes

$$\frac{50 - 47}{1.765} = 1.7$$

Our tables tell us that there is a probability of 0.9554 that the votes cast for Mr. Smith will be less than 50% and that he has therefore a probability of being elected of 0.0446. Mr. Smith would probably prefer to say that he has a $4\frac{1}{2}\%$ chance of being elected.

Chapter Thirteen

Estimation and Confidence Limits

In the last three chapters we have said a great deal about samples and introduced a great deal of theory. All this has been essential, but the time has now come to use our knowledge in order to analyse the sample results we have obtained. It will help you to follow the analysis if you bear in mind the fundamental questions that arise when we look at the results of a sample survey. Inevitably, the first thing that you will ask is 'What confidence can we have in the results of our sample survey?' After all, we have taken one sample only out of millions of possible alternatives, and it is conceivable that we have chosen a sample that is not representative of the population. Even if we dismiss such doubts, there is still the fact to be reckoned with that the results we have obtained are sample results, and it would be strange indeed if a sample mean were to be exactly equal to the population mean. How do we know what the population mean is likely to be when we only have a sample mean to work from? Let us first look at the question of confidence.

Confidence Limits

Suppose we draw a sample of 100 items from a population which is normally distributed as $N(5; 0.01)$. The standard error of such a sample is $\frac{\sigma}{\sqrt{n}}$ or $\frac{\sqrt{0.01}}{\sqrt{100}} = \frac{0.1}{10} = 0.01$. If we drew many such samples we would obtain a sampling distribution of sample means distributed as $N(5; 0.0001)$.

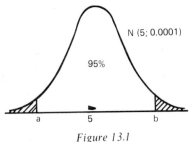

Figure 13.1

Let us now ask ourselves between what limits we would expect the central 95% of our sample means to lie. We are excluding the 2.5% of means at the top of our distribution and the 2.5% at the bottom. We will, then, require the Z scores for points *a* and *b*. Considering point '*b*', the relevant Z score is that which tells us that 97.5% of means falls *below* this value, and in looking at our tables we find this to be 1.96. When we consider point '*a*' we require the Z score that tells us that 97.5% of means lie above this value. Even without looking again at the table we know this to be − 1.96.

Thus, we can say that 95% of our sample means will fall within the range

$$\mu \pm 1.96 \times \text{standard error} = 5 \pm 1.96\sqrt{0.0001} = 5 \pm 0.0196$$

Thus 95% of our sample means fall within the range 4.9804 to 5.0196. Such limits are known as confidence limits and the one we have calculated is the 95% confidence limit. We can say that we are 95% sure that any sample we choose will give us a sample mean lying between 4.9804 and 5.0196.

There is still, of course, the possibility (a 5% possibility) that the mean of the sample we do choose will fall outside this range, and, if the matter is important, you may be dissatisfied with this. Let us now go further and ask if you would be satisfied if only 1% of the sample means you choose would fall outside the range we quote.

Here we wish to find the range covered by the central 99% of sample means, excluding only 0.5% at the top and 0.5% at the bottom. From our tables we can see that the relevant Z scores are ± 2.576 and we would say that:

We are 99% confident that the mean of the sample we choose will lie between

$$5 + 2.576 \text{ s.e. and } 5 - 2.576 \text{ s.e.} = 5 \pm 0.02576 = 5.02576 \text{ and } 4.97424$$

The range of possible values of course has to be increased as our degree of accuracy goes up, but this is natural and inevitable.

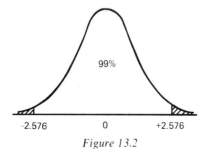

Figure 13.2

Finally, if we want to be even more confident than this, we could calculate the range of possible values within which 99.99% of sample means will lie. We find the relevant Z score to be ± 3.9, and the 99.99% confidence limits to be $5 + 0.039$ and $5 - 0.039 = 5.039$ to 4.961.

Summarising what we have done so far we find that the

> 95% confidence limits are given by $\mu \pm 1.96$ s.e.
> 99% confidence limits are given by $\mu \pm 2.576$ s.e.
> 99.99% confidence limits are given by $\mu \pm 3.9$ s.e.

This seems very straightforward, but a great deal of care has to be exercised in assessing confidence limits. You see, so far we have been taking a central range of sample means, but occasions might arise when we wish to assess how confident we are that a sample mean will not be greater than a given value. In medicine for example it is often important that the dose of medicine does not contain more than a certain amount of a drug. No harmful effects occur if the patient takes less, but he must not take more. Let us examine a distribution of means of large samples, and ask ourselves what is the value below which we would expect a randomly chosen sample mean to fall, with 95% confidence.

Here, of course, we are still looking at 95% of the possible sample means, but we are excluding the 5% at the top rather than $2\frac{1}{2}$% at each end. Reference to our tables tells us that a Z score of 1.645 is

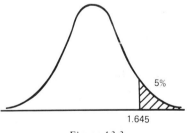

5%

1.645

Figure 13.3

the value below which 95% of sample means will lie, and we can now say that we are 95% confident that any sample mean chosen at random will have a value less than $\mu + 1.645$ s.e. Similarly, we can be 99% confident that the value of the sample mean we select will fall below $\mu + 2.33$ s.e., and 99.9% confident that it will be less than $\mu + 3.09$ s.e.

So we have two types of confidence limits – how do we decide which type to use? As we will see in the next chapter, it is vitally important that we make the right choice. The best advice we can give you is that before you calculate the Z score to determine any particular confidence limits, you should draw a simple diagram and determine exactly what part of the distribution of sample means you are excluding, and exactly what it is you wish to know. Also, we must stress that confidence limits calculated in this way are applicable only to large samples. Their calculation in the case of small samples is somewhat different and will be considered in another chapter.

Estimating the Population Variance

Suppose we draw a sample of 100 items with a mean $\bar{x}$ and a variance s^2, but have no information at all about the population. To estimate the confidence limits for our sample we need to know the population variance σ^2. How should we proceed in a situation such as this, which is usual when we are engaged in sampling? It has been established that the variance of any sample we take tends to understate the population variance so we can take as a starting point that $\sigma^2 > s^2$. Can you see why this is so? Surely, we are more likely to obtain items in our sample which are relatively close to the mean. This will be specially so if the population is roughly normal, and the sample is relatively small. As the sample size increases, then its distribution will resemble the population more closely, and s^2 and σ^2 will become more alike. The problem is to determine the adjustment we must make to s^2 to obtain the best estimate of σ^2. You may take it that for any sample the best unbiassed estimate of the variance of the population from which it was drawn is

$$\hat{\sigma}^2 = \frac{s^2 n}{n - 1}$$

where n is the number of items in the sample. The 'hat' placed over the symbol for the variance shows that it is an estimate. Consider carefully the factor $\frac{n}{(n-1)}$. As the size of the sample increases $\frac{n}{(n-1)}$ approaches 1.0, and if the sample is large there will be very little difference between $\frac{n}{(n-1)}$ and 1.0. So, as we would expect, hardly any adjustment would be necessary to the sample variance. Figure 13.4 shows this approach to 1.0 as the sample size increases.

Suppose however that the sample we take is small, say 10 items. $\frac{n}{(n-1)}$ now becomes $\frac{10}{(10-1)} = 1.11$ and it is probable that the dif-

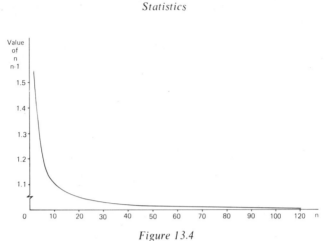

Figure 13.4

ference between $\hat{\sigma}^2$ and s^2 will be important. An example will make this clear.

A manufacturer takes samples of 100 light bulbs and burns them continuously until they fail. He finds that they have an average life of 215 hours with a variance of 144 hours. Since the sample is large we argue that $\hat{\sigma}^2 = s^2 = 144$ and hence $\hat{\sigma} = 12$. But let us see precisely what would happen if we applied the conversion factor. Now

$$\hat{\sigma}^2 = \frac{n}{n-1} s^2 = \frac{100 \times 144}{99} = 145.4545 \text{ and } \hat{\sigma} = 12.0604$$

You must agree that the difference arising when we multiply by $\frac{n}{(n-1)}$ is of negligible proportions. But suppose we had a much smaller sample, say 10 items only, which gives us the same variance. Now

$$\hat{\sigma}^2 = \frac{10 \times 144}{9} = 160 \text{ and } \hat{\sigma} = 12.649$$

We cannot now argue that s^2 is a good approximation for σ^2.

So important is this question of large and small samples that the expression $\frac{n}{(n-1)}$ gives us a working scale which enables us to define a large sample. A sample is large when $\frac{n}{(n-1)}$ is approximately equal to one, and there is a general agreement that this occurs when $n > 30$. We will, then, use the expression 'large sample' to mean a sample in which $n > 30$.

All our examples so far have been concerned with a single sample but in later chapters we will meet many examples in which we are considering not one, but two or more samples. We may be considering whether the apparent differences between sample results are caused merely by random sampling errors, or whether, in fact, the characteristics of the population have changed. Here we meet the problem of how to combine the variances of the two samples so as to obtain an unbiassed estimate of the population variance.

If we consider two samples drawn from the same population we may find that the first sample of n_1 items has a variance $s_1{}^2$. From this sample we would estimate the population variance to be

$$\frac{s_1{}^2 n_1}{(n_1 - 1)}$$

Suppose now that we draw a second sample of n_2 items with a variance $s_2{}^2$, the estimated population variance from this sample is

$$\frac{s_2{}^2 n_2}{(n_2 - 1)}$$

Now it seems logical to argue that we can get a better estimate of the population variance by pooling the results of both samples than we could from either sample alone. Pooling our variances we get

$$\hat{\sigma}^2 = \frac{s_1{}^2 n_1 + s_2{}^2 n_2}{n_1 + n_2 - 2} \quad \text{and} \quad \hat{\sigma} = \sqrt{\frac{s_1{}^2 n_1 + s_2{}^2 n_2}{n_1 + n_2 - 2}}$$

Once again, if our samples are large we need not include the correction -2 in the denominator as the difference in our results will be negligible. Suppose we draw a sample of 100 items with a variance of 90, and a second sample of 144 with a variance of 84. Our estimate of the population variance then becomes

$$\hat{\sigma}^2 = \frac{90 \times 100 + 84 \times 144}{100 + 144} = \frac{21096}{244} = 86.459, \text{ and } \hat{\sigma} = 9.298$$

Incorporating the adjustment

$$\hat{\sigma}^2 = \frac{21096}{242} = 87.173 \text{ and } \hat{\sigma} = 9.337$$

and the difference is negligible. But if the samples were small, say, 10 and 16 items respectively

$$\hat{\sigma}^2 = \frac{90 \times 10 + 84 \times 16}{26 - 2} = 93.5 \quad \text{and} \quad \hat{\sigma} = 9.67$$

If we were to forget to incorporate the -2 adjustment our result would have been

$$\hat{\sigma}^2 = \frac{90 \times 10 + 84 \times 16}{26} = 86.31 \quad \text{and} \quad \hat{\sigma} = 9.29$$

The difference is alarming and serves as a warning not to ignore the necessary adjustment when we are dealing with small samples.

Estimating the Population Mean

Earlier, we stated that we are 95% confident that a sample mean will be in the range $\mu \pm 1.96$ s.e. Let us now examine this a little more closely. Do we mean by this that if we draw a single sample then the probability that it lies in this range is 0.95? Surely, we cannot mean this – the sample mean will either lie within this range or it will not; i.e. the probability will be either one or zero! In other words, for a single sample mean, we can only evaluate the probability of it being within the range *after the sample has been drawn*. What, then, is the meaning of the 95% confidence limits? Surely, they do not refer to a single sample, but to the means of many samples. The probability that a single sample mean lies within the range $\mu \pm 1.96$ s.e. is either one or zero but *if we draw many samples then we would expect 95% of their means to lie within this range.*

Many of you will have realised by now that the calculations we have performed in this chapter are not of the type you would meet in practice. Given the population mean and variance, we have set up confidence limits for sample means; i.e. we used knowledge of the population to predict something about samples. However, we will not usually know the population mean and variance – and it will be more usual to use sample data to learn something about the population. Let us suppose that a sample has a mean $\bar{x}$ and a variance s^2, and the sample is large. Hence we know that

$$\hat{\mu} = \bar{x}$$
$$\text{and} \quad \hat{\sigma}^2 = s^2$$

We can set up a 95% confidence for the population mean like this:

$$\hat{\mu} \pm \frac{1.96\hat{\sigma}}{\sqrt{n}}$$

Now let us ask what this means. It does *not* mean that we are 95% sure that the population mean lies within these limits – after all it either will or will not, so once again the probability is either one or zero. A 95% confidence limit for the population mean means that if we make 100 estimates from 100 samples, and set up confidence limits for each, then we would expect the population mean to lie within 95 of these confidence limits.

Let us now return to our manufacturer who takes samples of 100 light bulbs and burns them continuously until they fail. The object of the exercise is to discover the average life of his output. He finds that the average life of bulbs in his sample is 215 hours with a variance of 144 hours. We can now set up a 95% confidence limit for the mean life of all bulbs he produces.

$$\hat{\mu} \pm \frac{1.96\hat{\sigma}}{\sqrt{n}} = 215 \pm \frac{1.96 \times 12}{\sqrt{100}} = 215 \pm 2.352$$

Now we cannot believe that any student will find much difficulty in mastering this simple principle if the question asks only for a confidence limit of the population mean. But the technique is capable of alternative applications and you must learn to recognise when it is relevant.

EXAMPLE

A company makes a product to order and wishes to state with some degree of certainty the time between the placing of an order and the delivery of the product. A sample check of 81 orders shows that the average delivery time was 25 days with a standard deviation of 6 days. What should it quote to its customers about delivery dates?

Assuming a normal distribution of sample means the standard error of the sample of 81 items $= \frac{s}{\sqrt{n}} = \frac{6}{9} = 0.66$. We can use our Z scores to ascertain that 95% of deliveries will take place within

$$25 \pm 1.96 \times 0.66 = 25 \pm 1.3 \text{ days}$$

99.8% of deliveries will take place within

$$25 \pm 3.09 \times 0.66 = 25 \pm 2.04 \text{ days}$$

Thus we could quote a delivery date of between 23 and 27 days with a confidence level better than 99%.

Estimating Proportions

You will remember that when we discussed the Binomial Distribution we argued that if we drew a sample of n items from a population in which the probability that an item was defective was p, then the probability of there being 0, 1, 2, 3, ... n defectives in the sample is given by the expansion of $(q + p)^n$. Now suppose that instead of considering the actual number of defective items, we consider instead the proportion of items defective. So, instead of talking of two items being defective in a sample of five, we consider $\frac{2}{5}$ of the sample as being defective. Our distribution gives us the probability of 0, $\frac{1}{n}$, $\frac{2}{n}$, $\frac{3}{n}$, ... 1 of the sample being defective.

To obtain this distribution of the proportion defective, we have reduced the distribution of defectives by the factor $\frac{1}{n}$, and it follows that we must reduce the mean and the standard deviation (or standard error) of our sample by the same amount. Now we already know that the mean of the binomial distribution is np, so the mean proportion defective is $\frac{1}{n} \times np = p$, which is the probability that a single item in the population is defective. Similarly, the standard error of the proportion defective is

$$\frac{1}{n} \times \sqrt{npq} = \sqrt{\frac{pq}{n}} = \sqrt{\frac{p(1-p)}{n}}$$

If n is large the proportion of defectives in the sample will be normally distributed, and, as before, we can set confidence limits to our sample result.

EXAMPLE
In a public opinion poll taken a few weeks before an election, a survey of 1000 voters showed that 56% intended to vote for Mr Jones. How confident can Mr. Jones be that he will be elected?

As with all large samples, it is important initially to calculate relevant Z scores. Now Jones will be elected if he obtains more than 50% of the votes, so the relevant Z score in this case is

$$Z = \frac{0.5 - 0.56}{\sqrt{\dfrac{0.56(1 - 0.56)}{1000}}} = \frac{-0.06}{\sqrt{0.01569}} = -3.82$$

Our tables tell us that 99.993% of all items lie above this Z score, and the probability of Mr. Jones not being elected is only 0.007%. He can be 99.99% confident of a favourable result.

EXAMPLE
In a survey undertaken by the carpet industry, a random sample of 2500 families was taken, and 498 indicated that they were intending to buy a new carpet within the next year. What is the proportion of families likely to buy a new carpet within the next 12 months?

The survey shows that $\frac{498}{2500}$ or 19.92% of the families surveyed intend to buy a new carpet. Thus our standard error is

$$\text{s.e.} = \sqrt{\frac{0.1992 \times 0.8008}{2500}} = 0.00799$$

Setting up 95% confidence limits we can be 95% confident that the proportion intending to buy a new carpet is

$$0.1992 \pm 0.00799 \times 1.96 = 0.1992 \pm 0.0157$$

Similarly, we can be 99% confident that the proportion intending to buy a new carpet is

$$0.1992 \pm 0.00799 \times 2.576 = 0.1992 \pm 0.02$$

In percentage terms we can say that we are 99% confident that $19.92\% \pm 2\%$ of families will be buying a new carpet in the next year.

Moderately Large Samples

In both the above examples we were concerned with sample sizes which were unequivocally large. Often, however, surveys of this nature are undertaken on the basis of samples which are large according to statistical definition ($n > 30$), but which are still small enough to leave a nagging doubt in one's mind about the validity of the results, especially when opinions are being asked for. Samples in the range of about 50 to 100 interviews fall within this category. They are too large to use the small sample methods we introduce later, but still they are not large enough to quell all our doubts. What can we do about this? One way is to accept more conventional figures which slightly understate the range when setting up confidence limits. Thus we set

95% confidence limits at $p \pm 2 \times$ standard error
99% confidence limits at $p \pm 2.6 \times$ standard error
99.8% confidence limits at $p \pm 3 \times$ standard error

Even though the limits are widened, the difference is marginal, and many people argue that, for samples of this size, it is better to be conservative and quote the maximum width of confidence limits; that is, calculate the confidence limits based on the maximum possible standard error. Now this occurs when

$$\sqrt{\frac{p(1-p)}{n}}$$

is a maximum, and for all results it cannot be greater than

$$\sqrt{\frac{0.25}{n}}$$

You can easily see from Fig. 13.5 that $p(1-p)$ cannot be greater than 0.25. Using this technique we could give our 95% confidence limits as

$$p \pm \sqrt{\frac{0.25}{n}} \times 1.96 = p \pm \frac{0.98}{\sqrt{n}}$$

and our 99% confidence limits as

$$p \pm \sqrt{\frac{0.25}{n}} \times 2.576 = p \pm \frac{1.288}{\sqrt{n}}$$

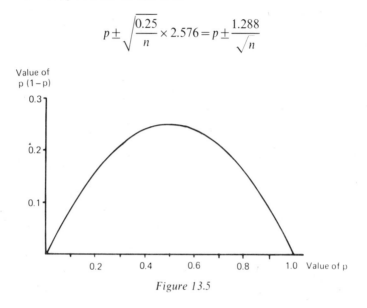

Figure 13.5

Determining the Sample Size

In the examples we have considered so far, we have calculated confidence limits with prior knowledge of the sample size. Now suppose we reverse the procedure – given the confidence limits, can we calculate the sample size? Suppose we wish to estimate a population mean and we want to be 95% sure that our estimate is within $\pm r$ of the true value of the mean – what size sample must we examine? Well, we know that the 95% confidence limits are given by

$$\hat{\mu} \pm \frac{1.96 \hat{\sigma}}{\sqrt{n}}$$

now if we require $\hat{\mu}$ to be within $\pm r$ of the true value μ, then

$$r = \frac{1.96 \hat{\sigma}}{\sqrt{n}} \text{ and } \sqrt{n} = \frac{1.96 \hat{\sigma}}{r}$$

so

$$n = \left(\frac{1.96 \hat{\sigma}}{r} \right)^2$$

Notice that before we can calculate the sample size n we must have some estimate of the population standard deviation $\hat{\sigma}$.

EXAMPLE

A manufacturer wishes to estimate the mean dimension of a certain component. He would be satisfied if he obtained an estimate within ± 0.01 cm of the true mean, and was 95% confident of his result. An initial sample has a standard deviation of 0.2 cm. What size sample should be examined?

Here we have $\hat{\sigma} = 0.2$ and $r = 0.01$, so

$$n = \left(\frac{1.96 \times 0.2}{0.01}\right)^2 = 1537$$

Of course, if we wanted to be 99% confident, then we would substitute 2.576 for 1.96 in our formula for n.

Using a similar analysis, we can obtain an expression for the sample size n necessary to get within $\pm r$% of the true population percentage p% for a stated degree of confidence. The 95% confidence limits are

$$p \pm 1.96 \sqrt{\frac{p(1-p)}{n}}$$

and as we wish the confidence limit to be $\pm r$, it follows that

$$r = 1.96 \sqrt{\frac{p(1-p)}{n}} \quad \text{and} \quad n = \frac{1.96^2 p(1-p)}{r^2}$$

Again, we need some idea of the population proportion p before we can calculate n.

EXAMPLE

Your sales manager informs you that he has conducted a survey of competitors' customers, and that 5% intend to switch to your product on the next purchase. Before investing in new equipment to take advantage of this you must be 99% certain that his estimate is correct to within $\pm \frac{1}{2}$%. What size sample should be examined to check the sales manager's claim?

As we wish to be 99% sure, we write 2.576 instead of 1.96 in the formula above.

$$n = \frac{2.576^2 \times (0.05 \times 0.95)}{(0.005)^2} = 12608$$

Such an exceptionally large sample would cost quite a lot of money!

Finally, before using any of the methods outlined in this chapter, please make sure that you are dealing with large samples. If small samples are used, then the distribution of sample means and the distribution of proportions will not be normal, and the analysis we have used will be inappropriate.

EXERCISES TO CHAPTERS 12 AND 13

13.1   (a) Calculate the mean and standard deviation of the life of the entire batch of electric bulbs whose pattern of duration is given below.

Hours of Life (hundreds)	Number of Bulbs
0–5	10
5–10	20
10–20	76
20–40	72
40 and over	30

(b) Discuss how your results are affected by the manner in which you treat the open class interval 40 and over.

(c) The variance of X_1 is defined as

$$\sum_{x_1 = 1}^{n} \frac{(X_1 - \bar{X})^2}{n - 1}$$

where $\bar{X}$ is the mean and n is the number of observations. Why are the deviations squared? Why is the divisor $n-1$ rather than n?

C.I.P.F.A.

13.2   (a) Explain what is meant by:

(i) sample mean;
(ii) sampling distribution of the mean;
(iii) standard error of the mean.

(b) From a random sample taken over the period of a year a shop-keeper calculated his average daily sales to be £218 and the standard deviation of the sample to be £18. The number of days' sales in the sample was thirty.

(i) Estimate the mean daily sales for the year at the 99.8% level of confidence.
(ii) On the assumption that the shopkeeper would be unable to obtain any further stock for another twenty-four hours, estimate the value of stock he should hold in order to be 95% sure that his stock would last for twenty-four hours. State any other assumptions you would find necessary to make in order to calculate your estimate.   O.N.C.

13.3   (a) What do you understand by a sampling distribution of the means? How is it obtained?

(b) For a random sample of 400 typists drawn from a population of 8000 typists, the mean monthly salary is £135 and the standard deviation is £20.

You are required to:

(i) calculate the standard error of the mean, and
(ii) explain the use of this measure in relation to typists' average monthly salaries. A.C.A.

13.4 A machine is cutting metal rods to a specified length of 2 inches, and it is known that the machine operates with a standard deviation of 0.02 inches. The quality control department test the output of the machine to ensure that the setting does not 'drift'. A sample of 100 rods gave a mean length of 2.005 inches. Does this suggest that the setting of the machine has drifted upwards?

13.5 (a) What is meant by simple random sampling?

(b) A random sample of 1000 manufactured items is inspected and 250 are found to contain defects. What is the likely range of the proportion defective in the population of items (use 95% confidence limits)? I.C.S.A.

13.6 An auditor checks the petty cash withdrawals made by a firm over 300 randomly chosen days, recording his results in a frequency distribution.

Withdrawals (£)	0–20	20–40	40–60	60–80	80–100	100–120	120–140	140–160
frequency	7	25	54	80	70	50	10	4

Find the mean and standard deviation.

Assuming that withdrawals are Normally Distributed, find the cash float that would be sufficient on 95% of occasions. I.C.A.

13.7 An auditor selects 100 invoices *at random* and checks for error in calculation. Errors in the firm's favour he marks with a plus and errors in the supplier's favour he marks with a minus. He tabulates his results as follows:

Error (£)	Frequency
−40 to −30	1
−30 to −20	2
−20 to −10	16
−10 to 0	49
0 to 10	23
10 to 20	6
20 to 30	2
30 to 40	1

Find the mean and standard deviation.

Assuming a Normal Distribution estimate limits within which you would expect the mean error on all invoices to be. Assuming the firm handles 10,000 invoices per annum, estimate the most likely, most favourable and least favourable errors for one year.   I.C.A.

13.8   A population of sales invoices is to be sampled so that the mean value per sale can be estimated. One hundred sales invoices are selected at random from this population and classified by value as shown in the following frequency distribution. Use the sample information to construct an interval estimate for the population mean at the 95% and 99% confidence levels.

Value (£)	Number of Sales Invoices
0– 50	10
50–100	9
100–150	15
150–200	22
200–250	13
250–300	7
300–350	9
350–400	5
400–450	6
450–500	4
	—
	100

I.C.A.

13.9   (i) Explain the statistical term 'standard error of the sample mean', and further describe the relationship between sample size, confidence level and precision in developing confidence intervals for population parameters.

(ii) Ordit and Partners are carrying out a study of three independent paperback book retail firms that each have a large number of shops around the country. From samples taken from shops of each firm, the following information was determined:

Firm	Sample Size	Sample Average Selling Price (£)	Sample Standard Deviation Selling Price (£)
A	81	0.85	0.20
B	49	0.76	0.18
C	36	0.87	0.08

(a) Ordit wish to estimate the average selling price of paperbacks for each of the three firms. Use the data given to set up a confidence interval estimate for the true average paperback selling price of each of the three firms, using a confidence level of 90%. Comment on your results.

(b) If, for all three firms, Ordit wished to be within £0.05 of the true average price of paperbacks with 90% confidence, what size of sample should they have taken from the shops of each firm?

(c) In the light of your answer to (b) comment on the appropriateness of the data originally collected for the purpose as given in (a).

Percentage Points of the Normal Distribution

α is the probability that Z_α, the value of the standardised normal variate, is exceeded (α is the probability in the extreme right-hand tail of the distribution).

α	0.10	0.05	0.025	0.02	0.01	0.005
Z_α	1.282	1.645	1.96	2.05	2.33	2.58

A.I.A.

13.10   Now you will have to think about this one! Part of the assembly of a machine involves placing a metal rod into a slot. The lengths of metal rods have the distribution $N(16, 0.03^2)$, and the lengths of slots have the distribution $N(16.1, 0.04^2)$. Find the distribution of the clearance between the bar and the slot. If a clearance of under 0.2 inches is satisfactory find the proportion of assemblies that fail to meet this requirement.

13.11   A random sample of 1000 people shows that at the next election 550 will support A. Is it certain that A will be elected, and if not, what proportion of the voters would you expect him to obtain?

13.12   (a) Explain what you understand by the standard error of a proportion and its purpose.

(b) An analysis of a random sample of 1000 married women revealed that 480 had part-time jobs.

You are required to:

(i) estimate the population proportion at the 95% confidence level, and
(ii) explain your answer.

$$Note: \left(\text{Use the formula } \sigma_{prop.} \sqrt{\frac{pq}{n}} \right)$$

A.C.A.

13.13   (a) What is the standard error of a proportion?

(b) In a sample of 500 beer drinkers, 50 were women. You are required to estimate the population proportion at the 95% confidence level, and explain your answer.

$$\left(\text{Use the formula } \sigma_{\text{prop.}} \sqrt{\frac{pq}{n}}\right)$$

A.C.A.

13.14   Let us examine a little more closely the assertion that only 30% of those of us who are drivers regularly wear seat belts. Such an assertion (unless it is mere guesswork) can be made only as a result of asking a number of people chosen at random. Suppose 100 people were chosen: estimate the proportion wearing seat belts with 95% confidence. How many people would have to be interviewed if we wished to fix the proportion within $\pm 1\%$ with 95% confidence?

13.15   (i) What do you understand by the term *standard error of the mean*?
   Explain the relationship of the standard error to the reliability of an estimate of the population mean, given the mean and standard deviation of a sample of known size taken from a very large (infinite) population.
   (ii) A random sample of 400 men in an industry in 1970 had an average weekly wage of £28.60 with a standard deviation of £3.60.

(1) Estimate, using 95% confidence limits, the mean wage.
(2) Given the same mean and standard deviation estimate how large your sample would have to be if the confidence interval for the population mean was £28.60±0.18.   O.N.C.

13.16   In a random sample of 200 garages it was found that 79 sold car batteries at prices below those recommended by the manufacturer.

(i) What is a random sample? Describe briefly how one can be selected.
(ii) Estimate the percentage of all garages selling below list price.
(iii) Calculate 95% and 99% confidence limits for this estimate and explain what these mean.
(iv) What size sample would have to be taken in order to be 95% certain that the population parameter could be estimated to within 2%?
(v) What sample size is necessary in order to be completely certain that the percentage could be estimated to within 2%? Explain.   I.C.A.

13.17 A manufacturer wishes to estimate the mean weight of sacks of carbon black. He would be satisfied if his estimate was within ± 5 lb of the true mean weight and be 99% sure of his estimate. An initial sample gives a S.D. of 15 lb. What size sample yields the required estimate?

13.18 The total value of an inventory of 21,000 items has been estimated as £420,000 by taking a sample of 200 items and finding the average value to be £20. Given that the standard deviation of the population is £5:

(a) give a 95% confidence interval estimate of the mean and thus the total value;
(b) if there was an accepted error of £10,000 for the total, with 95% confidence, what size of sample should be taken?

I.C.A.

13.19 In 1966, a simple random sample of 100 sales invoices was taken from a very large population of sales invoices. The average value for sale was found to be £18.5 with a standard deviation of £6.0. Obtain the 95% confidence interval for the true average value per sale.

How large a simple random sample would have been required so as to be 95% confident that the sample mean did not differ from the true mean by more than £0.5? I.C.A.

13.20 A bulk supplier of steel beams is required to quote the average breaking strength of each batch he produces and delivers. His estimate must be within ± 10 lb weight of the true mean with 99% probability. From past experience, he knows that breaking strengths have a standard deviation of 30 lb. What size sample would yield the required estimate?

13.21 A manufacturer produces metal rods, and the distribution of breaking strengths are $N(60, 5^2)$ lb. He wishes to pack the rods in bundles and guarantee that the average breaking strength of rods exceeds 59 lb, with 95% probability. How many rods should be in each bundle?

13.22 A local election is being held and there are two candidates, Smith and Jones, for one vacancy. The total electorate is 2000. A random sample of the electorate reveals that 55% of them will vote for Smith. How confident can you be that Smith will be elected if the size of the sample is 100? How large a sample would be needed

for the 55% sample result for Smith to make you 99% confident of
a win for him?   C.I.P.F.A.

13.23   Your sales manager excitedly informs you that he has conducted a survey of competitors' customers, and has discovered that
5% intend to switch to your product on the next purchase. He advises
you to invest now to take advantage of this increase. The sales
manager interviewed 100 people. What would you tell him? To be
sure that it is worthwhile to expand capacity, you must be convinced
within $\pm\frac{1}{2}\%$ of your sales increase. What size sample should be examined? What would you conclude?

Chapter Fourteen

Statistical Decisions

We are all experts in taking decisions. Does this surprise you? Well, throughout your life you have had many decisions to take, and the fact that you are alive today, reading this book, indicates that you have taken many decisions correctly. Take a simple problem – the need to get to the other side of a busy road. You have to decide when it is safe to cross. The fact that you have so far taken the correct decision proves that you have carefully weighed up the evidence, and interpreted this evidence correctly. Sometimes the decision will be easy to take: the road might be completely empty and you can cross with safety; and at other times the road will be so busy that to attempt to cross would be suicidal. In other words, we have all the necessary information available to make the correct decision every time. A cautious (and according to Road Safety Officers a sensible) person would obey the following decision rule: only cross the road when no traffic is in sight. If we obey this rule, then we will always cross the road safely (unless we fall down an uncovered manhole!). Unfortunately, however, it is not always possible to obey this rule, as there are many roads that are so busy that we could never cross. With normal city centre roads we will seldom find a situation where they are completely empty of traffic, and we must use our judgement to decide when it is safe to cross.

Basically, there are two problems involved in the decision-taking process. Firstly, there is the problem that even when all the information is available, it is possible that an incorrect interpretation would be put on this data. Consider the case of the vehicle that has its left-hand indicator flashing. A reasonable interpretation of this data would be that the vehicle intends to turn left: you decide to cross the road and are run over. You made the wrong decision – why? You interpreted the data to mean that the vehicle would turn left – you should have interpreted it to mean that the self-cancelling device had failed to work following the last left turn (or that the driver was so bad that all signals should be ignored).

A second problem involved in the decision-taking process is that often we do not have all the information necessary to guarantee that we make the correct decision. Moreover, it is possible that we could not obtain all the information we need – it might, for example, be too expensive to obtain it. We will have to resort to sampling to give us some idea of the information we need. Now as you already know, we cannot be completely sure of sample results, so if we base our decisions on sample evidence, it is quite conceivable that we make the wrong choice. It is a major task of statistics to evaluate the probability of making an incorrect decision, and to keep this probability to a minimum.

Type I Errors

We will now discuss a problem that faces many manufacturers: how to control the quality of the output. Let us suppose that the manufacturer produces woodscrews by a completely automatic process. One of the problems with the automatic process is that occasionally a screw misses the threading stage, so such screws should be rejected. Now there is little that can be done about this, and the manufacturer has installed machinery that would automatically remove such rejects. From past experience it is known that about 5% of output would be rejected by this machine. Now, although there is not much chance of bettering this rate, machine malfunction can cause the rate to worsen considerably. The problem experienced so far is that it has been difficult to detect just when the rate of rejects has increased because the quantity of output is so great. Obviously, the manufacturer wants to keep the rate as near to 5% as possible – after all, rejects cost money! What he decides to do is to install an automatic sampling device which randomly selects 1000 screws per hour, sorts them, and counts the number of rejects.

The purpose of drawing these samples is, of course, to detect when the reject rate has worsened, and do something about it. Taking remedial action involves stopping the process, and this will be expensive as output will be lost. So if remedial action is to be taken, the manufacturer wants to be pretty sure that the reject rate has worsened. What he wants is some *decision rule* to determine when to stop the process and make the necessary adjustments. Now as 5% of the output is rejected, the manufacturer can expect, on average, 50 rejects in each sample. Suppose he errs on the cautious side, and takes as his decision rule – 'stop the process if the number of defectives exceeds 60'.

Unfortunately, this rule does not exclude the possibility of taking the wrong decision; i.e. stopping the machine when the reject rate has not increased. Using our knowledge of the binomial distribution, we should be able to calculate the probability of taking the wrong decision. It will be the wrong decision if the number of defectives exceeds 60, but the reject rate is still 5%. The appropriate binomial distribution is $(0.95+0.05)^{1000}$ and the probability we require is $P_{(61)}+P_{(62)}+P_{(63)}+\ldots+P_{(1000)}$. Now obviously it would be advisable to use the normal approximation to the binomial distribution. Firstly, we require the standard deviation

$$\sigma = \sqrt{npq}$$
$$n = 1000, \quad p = 0.05, \quad q = 0.95$$
$$\sigma = \sqrt{1000 \times 0.05 \times 0.95}$$
$$= 6.89$$

The probability that the sample contains more than 60 defects is shown in the diagram by the shaded area (remember that we must

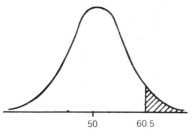

Figure 14.1

make a 0.5 adjustment when using a normal approximation to the binomial distribution). The Z score is

$$\frac{60.5 - 50}{6.89} = 1.52$$

Consulting the normal distribution tables, the probability we require is 6.43%. So if the manufacturer decides to stop the process if the number of defectives in the sample exceeds 60, on the assumption that the reject rate has risen above 5%, then the probability that he has made the wrong decision is 6.43%.

Is this, then, an acceptable risk? Well, this is really a decision that only the manufacturer can take. To decide whether this risk is too high, he must weigh up what is at stake. Can you see how the manufacturer can reduce the risk of taking the wrong decision? All that he need do is to alter his decision rule, taking a number of defectives greater than 60 as the borderline. If, for example, his decision rule was to stop the process if the number of rejects in the sample exceeds 65, then the Z score would be

$$\frac{65.5 - 50}{6.89} = 2.25$$

and the probability of making the wrong decision would be 1.22%.

The relationship between the probability of taking the wrong decision and the number of defectives in the decision rule is something we will examine in more detail later. What we shall now do is express the problem in statistical jargon. The manufacturer formulates the *hypothesis* that the overall number of rejects is 5%. He uses the following decision rule: if the number of rejects in a sample exceeds 60, reject the hypothesis and stop the process, otherwise accept the hypothesis. Notice that we have not altered the philosophy of his decision rule – all that we have done is to introduce the word 'hypothesis'. Now we have seen that there is a danger of making the wrong decision and needlessly stopping the process. Using statistical jargon, there is a danger of *rejecting the hypothesis when it should be accepted.* Statisticians refer to this risk as a *Type I error.* We have seen that the risk of a Type I error will vary according to the number of rejects quoted in the decision rule. We can quantify this risk by calculating the Z score for each number of rejects quoted in the decision rule.

No. of Rejects Quoted in the Decision Rule	Z Score	Probability of a Type I Error
52	0.36	0.3594
54	0.65	0.2578
56	0.94	0.1736
58	1.23	0.1093
60	1.52	0.0643
62	1.81	0.0351
64	2.10	0.0179
66	2.39	0.0084
68	2.69	0.0036
70	2.98	0.0014

It is useful to draw a graph of this data, and this is done in Fig. 14.2. The manufacturer can see at a glance the risk of incurring a Type I error as he varies the number of defectives in the decision rule. Of course, it is quite possible to state the degree of risk of a Type I error that would be acceptable, and read off from the graph the number of defectives in the decision rule that would yield this degree of risk. Suppose, for example, he would consider as acceptable a 5% chance of a Type I error, then consulting the graph we see that

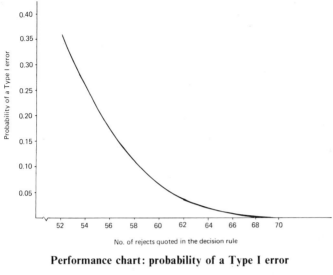

Performance chart: probability of a Type I error

Figure 14.2

the decision rule should be 'stop the process if the number of defectives exceeds 63'. Using statistical jargon, we say that the graph is the *performance chart* for Type I errors in our decision rule. Notice that as we increase the number of defectives in our decision rule, the probability of a Type I error decreases.

Type II Errors

Let us summarise what we have done so far. We have formulated the hypothesis that the number of rejects is 5%, and we use as a decision rule that if the number of defectives in a sample exceeds a certain number n, then we would reject the hypothesis and stop the process, otherwise we accept the hypothesis and allow the process to continue. We have seen that in operating this decision rule there is a danger of rejecting the hypothesis when it should be accepted – so we would needlessly stop the process. This is because it may be possible that the number of rejects in the sample exceeds n even though the overall number of defectives is still 5%. We call this a Type I error, and the performance chart shows how the risk of a Type I error varies with the size of n in our decision rule.

Now the Type I error is not the only risk the manufacturer runs when operating the decision rule. Originally, he operated the rule:

stop the process if the number of defectives exceeds 60, otherwise allow the process to continue. The philosophy underlying this rule is that if the number of defectives is 60 or less, then the overall number of defectives produced is 5%. Now it is quite possible for the overall rate of defectives to rise above 5%, but the sample he draws will contain 60 defectives or less. Should this be the case, then he will be allowing the process to continue when really he should stop the process and make the necessary adjustments. Returning to statistical jargon, there is a danger of *accepting a hypothesis that should be rejected.* Such risks are referred to as *Type II errors*, and we should be able to calculate the probability of such errors.

Suppose the overall rate of rejects produced rose to 7%. For samples of 1000, we have $n = 1000$, $p = 0.07$ and $q = 0.93$. So the appropriate binomial distribution is $(0.93 + 0.07)^{1000}$.

$$\text{mean} = np = 1000 \times 0.07 = 70$$
$$\text{standard deviation} = \sqrt{npq} = \sqrt{1000 \times 0.07 \times 0.93} = 8.07$$

We can now use the normal approximation to the binomial distribution to obtain the probability of obtaining 60 or less defectives in a sample of 1000 items.

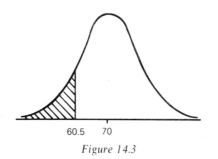

60.5   70

Figure 14.3

The Z score is

$$\frac{60.5 - 70}{8.07} = -1.18$$

and consulting the normal tables we see that the probability of a Type II error is 0.119. In other words, there is an 11.9% chance that the decision rule will fail to detect a rise in the overall rate of defectives to 7%, i.e. there is an 11.9% chance that the manufacturer makes the wrong decision.

The probability of making a Type II error will depend on the actual rate of defectives produced by the process. So if we list all possible reject rates, we can calculate the appropriate probabilities of Type II errors.

Proportion of Rejects Produced by the Process	Mean (np)	S.d. $\sqrt{(npq)}$	Z Score	Probability of Type II Error
0.055	55	7.21	0.76	0.7764
0.060	60	7.51	0.07	0.5279
0.065	65	7.80	-0.58	0.2810
0.070	70	8.07	-1.18	0.1190
0.075	75	8.33	-1.74	0.0409
0.080	80	8.58	-2.27	0.0116
0.085	85	8.82	-2.78	0.0027
0.090	90	9.05	-3.26	0.0004
0.095	95	9.27	-3.72	0.0001
0.100	100	9.49	-4.16	0.0000

Figure 14.4 shows this information graphically. Notice as the percentage of defectives produced by the process increases, the smaller is the probability of making a Type II error. Notice also that to calculate the probability of making a Type II error we must make an assumption about the value of the overall rate of defectives produced by the system. For Type I errors, this was not necessary, so it is easier to calculate the performance chart for Type I errors. Also, the performance chart for Type II errors is not in a very convenient form – it does not show the manufacturer how he can lessen the probability of a Type II error.

Earlier, we calculated that if the overall rate of defectives produced by the process was 7%, then the probability of a Type II error, given our decision rule, is 11.9%. Suppose we changed the decision rule to read: 'stop the process if a sample contains more than 55 defectives'. Now if the overall rate of defectives is 7% and a sample contains 55 defectives or less, then the process will not be stopped when it should be, and the probability of this happening can again be calculated.

$$Z = \frac{55.5 - 70}{8.07} = -1.80$$

and from the normal tables, the probability of taking the wrong decision is 3.59%. So if we reduce the number of defectives in our decision rule, this decreases the probability of a Type II error. Unfortunately, this action would automatically increase the probability of a Type I error!

Summarising, then, a Type I error occurs when we reject a hypothesis that should be accepted, and a Type II error occurs when we

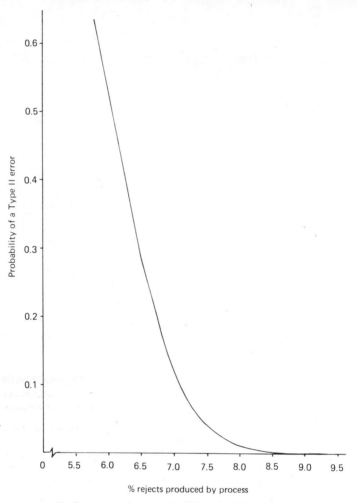

Performance chart: probability of a Type II error

Figure 14.4

accept a hypothesis that should be rejected. Many statisticians summarise the distinction in a table like this:

		Decision	
		Accept	Reject
Hypothesis is	True	Correct decision	Type I error
	False	Type II error	Correct decision

If we state our hypothesis and decision rule, we can immediately calculate the probability of a Type I error, but we cannot calculate the probability of a Type II error without introducing other assumptions. In other words, to calculate the probability of Type I errors, we keep the hypothesis constant and vary the decision rule; but to calculate the probability of Type II errors, we keep the decision rule constant and vary the hypothesis. We can reduce the probability of a Type I error by increasing the number of rejects in our decision rule, but unfortunately this would increase the probability of a Type II error. Now this is quite a problem, and in the next section we will try to reconcile this problem.

Significance Testing

In the last section we found no difficulty at all in calculating the probability of a Type I error. The reason for this was the form taken by our hypothesis: that the overall rate of rejects was 5%. So we could put $p = 0.05$ into the binomial distribution and calculate the probability of a Type I error with ease. Notice that in applying this hypothesis, we are assuming that the reject rate found in the past has continued; i.e. that the reject rate has not changed. We have done this despite the fact that the purpose of our investigation is to detect when the reject rate worsens. Because our hypothesis assumes that 'nothing has happened', it is called a *null hypothesis* and we use the symbol H_0 to stand for a null hypothesis. Now you may object that this seems rather strange – the purpose of sampling is to detect when the reject rate worsens, so we should be testing the hypothesis that the reject rate is greater than 5%. Now this is all very well, but it will mean that we are unable to calculate the probability of a Type I error without stating by *how much* the reject rate has worsened. In other words, stating that $p > 0.05$ means that we do not have a value for p to insert in the binomial distribution, and so we will be unable to calculate the probability of a Type I error. It is for this reason that we will ensure that from now on all the hypotheses we test will be null hypotheses.

The testing of null hypotheses has two implications that we must now examine. Firstly, the null hypothesis involves stating the complete opposite to what you are trying to detect. In the example we have been considering so far, we were trying to detect whether the reject rate had worsened, but the null hypothesis is that the reject rate is still 5%. Again, suppose we are trying to test for bias in a coin – the appropriate null hypothesis would be that the coin is unbiassed. It would follow from this that the probability of a head is 0.5, so we could then calculate the probability of a Type I error. We

can now state a rule for formulating null hypotheses – if you are trying to detect change, then the appropriate null hypothesis is that no
change has occurred.

The second implication of formulating a null hypothesis is that
it is no help to us whatsoever in calculating the probability of a Type
II error. To do this we must state an *alternative hypothesis*. This is
precisely what we did when calculating the probabilities of a Type
II error in the last section. In fact, we stated a number of alternative
hypotheses ($p = 5.5\%$, $p = 6\%$, $p = 6.5\%$, etc.). Now obviously there is
a problem here: if we reject the null hypothesis it would seem reasonable to accept the alternative hypothesis: but which alternative hypothesis should we accept?

Let us now see if we can find a way round this problem. We incur
Type II errors if we accept a hypothesis that should be rejected –
so if we never accept a hypothesis we cannot make a Type II error!
Let us restate the problem we have so far been considering in order
to investigate this situation more closely. We know from past experience that the process is, on average, rejecting 5% of all screws produced. Now suppose we know that this reject rate can change either
way; i.e. improve or get worse, and we wish to sample to detect such
changes. The reason for this is that perhaps we can then account
for fluctuations in reject rates – they may depend on the quality of
steel used, or which shift is operating the machinery. In any case,
we will adopt the null hypothesis that the reject rate is 5%, and operate the decision rule 'reject the null hypothesis if the number of defectives in the sample is greater than 60 or less than 40, otherwise *reserve
judgement*'. Notice that we never accept the null hypothesis, and in
many statistics textbooks you will come across the conclusion 'no
reason to reject the null hypothesis' – which of course doesn't mean
that it should be accepted! The philosophy behind this argument is
that samples which contain between 40 and 60 defectives do not show
a *significant* departure from the expected 50 defectives. In other words,
the range 40–60 can be attributed to chance or sampling fluctuations.
However, defectives outside this range cannot be attributed to chance,
the *sample result is significant* and we must reject the null hypothesis.
Notice the use of the word 'significant' – many statisticians give the
title *significance testing* to the methods we have been describing.

So you see it is possible to avoid making Type II errors altogether.
However, you may complain that the reasoning behind this is very
suspect. Initially, we were trying to detect when the overall reject
rate rose so that we could do something about it. Our null hypothesis
was that the overall reject rate was 5%, and our decision rule was
'stop the process if the number of defectives exceeds 60'; i.e. reject
the null hypothesis. Now suppose that the number of rejects was 60

or less, and that this would induce us to conclude that there is no reason to reject the null hypothesis. Now think carefully about this! If the number of defectives in the sample exceeds 60, we stop the process; if the number does not exceed 60 we reserve judgement. But can we reserve judgement? If we try to do this, we will allow the process to continue – which is tantamount to accepting the null hypothesis! In such circumstances, then, we cannot avoid the risk of a Type II error!

Let us now see if we can devise an acceptable methodology for significance testing. Firstly, we will formulate a null hypothesis (H_0) in such a way that we can calculate the probability of a Type I error. Also, we will formulate an alternative hypothesis (H_1) so that rejection of H_0 automatically involves the acceptance of H_1. We will then specify the probability of a Type I error that we would be prepared to consider an acceptable risk. We call this probability the *level of significance*, and it is usual to specify probabilities of 5% and 1%. We then construct a decision rule based on the hypothesis and level of significance we have chosen. Whenever possible we word the alternative hypothesis in such a way that if we do not reject the null hypothesis we reserve judgement. If this is not possible, then the wording of the alternative hypothesis is such that the alternative to rejecting the null hypothesis is accepting it. In this latter case, we keep our fingers crossed that the probability of a Type II error is not too large. If Type II errors would be really serious, then we must examine the performance chart to see how likely they are.

One-sided and Two-sided Tests

We will now apply this methodology to the problem we have so far been considering. Firstly, we specify the hypotheses

H_0: $p = 0.05$, i.e. the overall reject rate is 5%
H_1: $p > 0.05$, i.e. the overall reject rate is greater than 5%
Level of significance $= 0.05$, i.e. the risk of a Type I error is 5%.

Consulting the performance chart for Type I errors, we see that for a 5% probability we must quote 61 defectives in our decision rule, so our decision rule is 'reject H_0 if the number of defectives in the sample exceeds 61, otherwise accept H_0'. We could represent this situation diagrammatically as in Fig. 14.5.

Summarising this situation, then, we can say that on the basis of our null hypothesis we expect, on average, 50 defectives in samples of 1000. If the number of defectives is 61 or less, then we can say that the deviation from 50 can be attributed to chance. But if the number

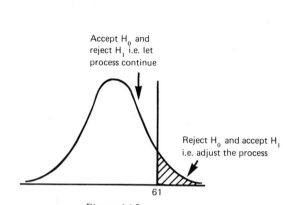

Figure 14.5

of defectives exceeds 61 we cannot attribute this to chance; i.e. the result is significant, and we reject the null hypothesis concluding that the reject rate is greater than 5%. We realise that in using this decision rule we run a 5% risk of making a Type I error.

In this example, we are interested in detecting shifts in the reject rate in one direction only. If the reject rate increases, then we must take some action. But if it decreases – so much the better. Tests to detect changes in one direction only are called *one-sided tests* or *one-tail tests*, and a glance at Fig. 14.5 will explain why this is so. However, there will be many cases when it will be more meaningful to detect changes in either direction. To take an example, suppose we know that 40% of the electorate vote Socialist, and we wish to detect changes in the Socialist vote by sampling. It will be of equal interest to know whether the Socialist vote has increased or decreased. The appropriate hypotheses here would be

$$H_0: p = 0.4$$
$$H_1: p \neq 0.4$$

Notice that in this case the alternative hypothesis is stated in a 'not equal to' form. Without going into the mechanics of this problem

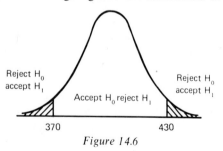

Figure 14.6

(we will do this in the next chapter) suppose the decision rule was: 'in a sample of 1000, if the number voting Socialist is between 370 and 430 accept H_0 and reject H_1, otherwise accept H_1 and reject H_0'. Diagrammatically, the decision rule could be represented as in Fig. 14.6.

Tests such as this are called *two-sided* or *two-tail tests*, again for obvious reasons. So if you wish to test for a change in an *unspecified direction* you should use a two-sided test, but if you wish to test for a change in a *specified direction* you would use a one-sided test. The type of test used will be reflected in the formation of the alternative hypothesis. Which type of test is appropriate will depend on the problem under consideration. There is no hard-and-fast rule to follow: as we shall see in the next chapter the choice is really a matter of common sense.

Chapter Fifteen

Statistical Significance

In the last chapter, we indicated how statistics can help us come to the right decision. The methodology we used was as follows. We formulated two hypotheses: a null hypothesis and an alternative hypothesis, in such a way that rejecting one meant accepting the other. The wording we chose for the null hypothesis enabled us to calculate the probability of a Type I error. We then stated a decision rule, for example 'reject the null hypothesis and accept the alternative hypothesis if the number of defectives in the sample exceeds x'. If we rejected the null hypothesis, we then calculated the probability of a Type I error, and we called this probability the level of significance. This, then, is the methodology of the statistical technique called *significance testing*. In this chapter, we will move from methodology to the technique itself. In particular, we will be dealing with tests involving sample means and sample proportions. Before we do this, however, we must examine the choice of an appropriate level of significance.

We saw in the last chapter that when we altered our decision rule in such a way that we reject the null hypothesis only if the number of defectives is greater than previously stated, we then reduced the probability of a Type I error. We must now decide on the risk of a Type I error that we could consider acceptable. Now, of course, the acceptable level of risk is a personal choice, and it will vary with the problem we are considering. We would want, for example, a lower level of risk if we were testing the efficacy of a new drug than we would want if we were testing a marksman for bias in shooting. Despite this essentially subjective nature of the level of risk, statisticians do apply conventions. They consider a 5% probability of a Type I error as being acceptable, and construct their decision rules accordingly. If the hypothesis is rejected on the basis of this decision rule, we state that the sample result is *significant at the 5% level*. In other words, we do not think that the sample result can be attributed to chance, and our probability of making a Type I error is 5%. Also, it is usual to construct a second decision rule based on the probability of a Type I error being 1%, so if the null hypothesis is rejected on the basis of this rule, we state that the sample result is *significant at the 1% level*. So applying our decision rules to sample results, there are four possible conclusions we could reach:

(a) Accept the null hypothesis and reject the alternative hypothesis. In this case, we are saying that the sample results can be attributed to chance. However, as we saw in the last chapter, reaching this conclusion leaves us wide open to Type II errors, and the only way to avoid them is to conclude that

(b) there is insufficient reason to reject the null hypothesis – a conclusion that does not conclude anything and suggests the necessity for further sampling. However, if anything useful is to be achieved, then sooner or later we must risk the possibility of a Type II error and come to some definite conclusion.

(c) Reject the null hypothesis and accept the alternative hypothesis at the 5% level, but not at the 1% level. Here we are stating that the occurrence of the sample results cannot be attributed to chance, and the probability of a Type I error is less than 5% but greater than 1%.

(d) Reject the null hypothesis (and so accept the alternative hypothesis) at the 1% level. In this situation we are taking a less than 1% chance of incurring a Type I error.

Now let us look at the actual wording of the decision rule. We have implied that the decision rule will be stated in terms of the sample statistic, for example 'reject the null hypothesis if the proportion defective exceeds x'. Now it is much more useful to state the decision rule, not in terms of the sample statistic, but in terms of its Z score. This will enable us to state a few simple decision rules that will cover a wide range of different significance tests. To see how we can do this, let us suppose that we have a population with a certain parameter (mean, proportion, etc.) of P, and we want to test whether this parameter has increased. We will do this by examining a sample statistic S. We can formulate the null hypothesis and alternative hypothesis as follows.

$$H_0: S = P$$
$$H_1: S > P$$

Notice carefully that this is a *one-sided test*: we are interested in movements in the population parameter in one direction only. Now suppose we calculate the Z score of the sample statistic (we will discuss how this is done later in the chapter): if we assume that the sample statistic is normally distributed, then we can use the normal tables to find the probable values of Z. We can see that

$$P(Z > 1.645) = 5\%$$
and
$$P(Z > 2.33) = 1\%$$

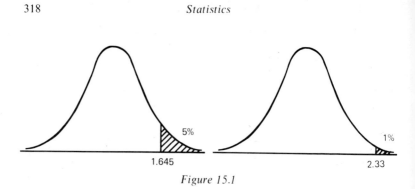

Figure 15.1

We can now restate our conclusions using Z scores rather than the sample statistic itself. If –

1(a) $Z < 1.645$, either accept the null hypothesis or reserve judgement

1(b) $1.645 < Z < 2.33$, reject the null hypothesis at the 5% level but not at the 1% level

1(c) $Z > 2.33$, reject the null hypothesis at the 1% level.

Suppose on the other hand that we were testing for a decrease in the population parameter rather than an increase, then

$$H_0: S = P$$
$$H_1: S < P$$

So, of course, the test would still be one-sided, but in this case we would be interested in the other tail of the distribution. As the normal distribution is symmetrical, the Z scores would have the same numerical value as previously, but they would be negative rather than positive. It would seem sensible, then, when calculating the Z score for a one-sided test to ignore the sign of the Z score, this will enable us always to be able to apply the decision rules 1(a), 1(b) and 1(c) above.

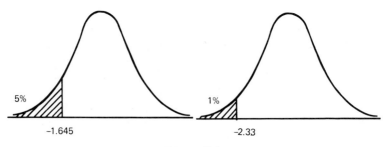

Figure 15.2

Finally, suppose we are attempting to detect a change in the population parameter without stating the direction of the change. We now have

$$H_0: S = P$$
$$H_1: S \neq P$$

In this case we are performing a *two-sided test*, and again assuming that the sample statistic is normally distributed, we can obtain the probable values for Z.

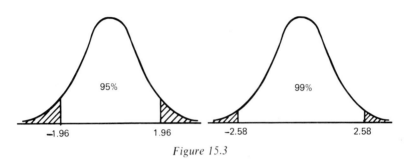

Figure 15.3

If, as before, we ignore the sign of the sample statistic's Z score, we can obtain decision rules for a two-sided test based on the Z score of the sample statistic. If

2(a) $Z < 1.96$, either accept the null hypothesis or reserve judgement

2(b) $1.96 < Z < 2.58$, reject the null hypothesis at the 5% level but not at the 1% level

2(c) $Z > 2.58$, reject the null hypothesis at the 1% level.

When we use Z scores in this fashion, i.e. for significance testing, they are often referred to as the *critical values* of the sample statistic.

Notice the relationship between the decision rules for a two-sided test and confidence limits. We could, in fact, restate the decision rules in terms of confidence limits: if the Z score is within the 95% confidence limits, the sample statistic is not significant. If the Z score is between the 95% and 99% confidence limits, the sample statistic is significant at the 5% level, but not at the 1% level. If the Z score of the sample statistic is outside the 99% confidence limits, the sample statistic is significant at the 1% level.

Let us now summarise what we have done. We have examined carefully the philosophy underlying significance testing, and we have devised decision rules based on the Z score of the sample statistic.

The application of the decision rules hinges on our ability to calculate the Z score of the sample statistic, and also hinges on our assumption that the sample statistic is normally distributed. To obtain techniques of significance testing, we must now turn our attention to these latter points

Tests of Sample Means (Large Samples)

EXAMPLE 1

A sugar refiner packs sugar into bags weighing, on average, 1 kilogram. Now the setting of the machine filling the bags tends to 'drift', i.e. the average weight of bags filled by the machine sometimes increases and sometimes decreases. If the mean weight of bags increases, then in effect he is actually giving away some sugar. If the mean weight decreases then he may find himself in trouble with the Weights and Measures Inspector. So it is really important that he controls the average weight of bags of sugar. He wishes to detect shifts in the mean weight of bags as quickly as possible, and reset the machine. In order to detect shifts in the mean weight, he will periodically select a sample of 100 bags, weigh them, and calculate the sample mean.

In effect, the refiner is performing a significance test, adopting as his null hypothesis that there is no shift in the average weight (μ) of bags of sugar.

$$H_0: \mu = 1$$

Now shifts of the mean weight in either direction are important, so a two-sided test is appropriate here. The alternative hypothesis must be

$$H_1: \mu \neq 1$$

What other information do we need to know? Clearly, we need to know the variance of the weights of bags of sugar – suppose this is 0.01 kg. Applying the central limit theorem, we can calculate the standard error of the means of samples of 100 bags.

$$\text{s.e.} = \frac{\sigma}{\sqrt{n}} = \frac{0.1}{\sqrt{100}} = 0.01 \text{ kg}$$

If the sample drawn has a mean 1.03 kg, then we could represent the situation diagrammatically as in Fig. 15.4.

The Z score of the sample statistic is

$$Z = \frac{1.03 - 1}{0.01} = 3$$

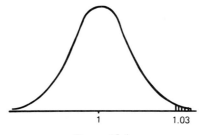

Figure 15.4

and consulting our decision rules for two-sided tests we would have to conclude that the sample statistic is significant at the 1% level ($Z > 2.58$). We would reject H_0 and accept H_1: the sample mean does provide evidence that the machine setting has drifted.

Let us now move from the particular to the general. If we wished to test the significance of a sample mean, then we could calculate the Z score like this

$$Z = \frac{\frac{|\mu - \bar{x}|}{\sigma}}{\sqrt{n}}$$

$$= \frac{|\mu - \bar{x}|\sqrt{n}}{\sigma}$$

Remember that the vertical lines enclosing $\mu - \bar{x}$ mean that we should take the *absolute value* of the difference, i.e. ignore the sign of the difference. Let us now apply this to a second example.

EXAMPLE 2

A certain highway in a city centre has been investigated in the past for noise pollution by vehicles. As a result of many measurements it has been found that between 16.30 and 17.30 on any weekday the average noise level is 130 decibels, with a standard deviation of 20 decibels. The residents are convinced that the noise level is getting worse, and having taken 50 readings, obtain an average of 134 decibels. Is their claim justified?

Clearly, this is a one-sided test, so we can formulate

$$H_0: \mu = 130$$
$$H_1: \mu > 130.$$

and the Z score for the sample statistic is

$$Z = \frac{|130 - 134|\sqrt{50}}{20}$$
$$= 1.41$$

Consulting our decision rules for one-sided tests, we see that for our sample statistic $Z < 1.645$, so the sample mean is not significant. We would reject the alternative hypothesis and accept the null hypothesis – the difference between the sample mean and the population mean can be ascribed to chance factors, and we cannot conclude that noise levels on this highway have increased.

The two examples we have considered so far assume that we have a prior knowledge of the population – in particular they assume that the population mean and standard deviation are known. Had we not known the population standard deviation, we could have estimated it using s, the sample standard deviation. No adjustment to s^2 would have been necessary because in both cases we had large samples. Now of course, it will not always be the case that we know the population mean, and if we cannot compare a sample with a population then we must compare a sample with a sample. Tests of this nature come under the general heading of the *significance of the difference between the means of two samples*. Let us see how this test works by considering an example.

EXAMPLE 3

The authors of this book agree on most matters, be they academic, social or cultural. They are both keen supporters of association football. However, on one thing they will never agree – which is the best team in the English Football League. One of the authors (the misguided one) is convinced that the finest team is Manchester United, but the other author (the one you must agree with) is, of course, a Liverpool F.C. supporter. To settle this argument once and for all, the authors agreed to apply statistical analysis to this problem. They will examine a sample of football matches, count up the number of attacking moves made per match, and so obtain a mean and standard deviation of the number of attacking moves made per match for both teams. Now we have a real problem here – is this test one-sided or two-sided? Suppose that μ_1 is the mean number of attacking moves made by Manchester United, and μ_2 is the mean number of attacking moves made by Liverpool. The appropriate null hypothesis would be that there is no difference in the mean number of attacking moves, i.e.

$$H_0: \mu_1 = \mu_2 \text{ or}$$
$$H_0: \mu_1 - \mu_2 = 0$$

Now the Manchester United supporter is convinced that his team is the better, so the appropriate alternative hypothesis that he wishes to test is

$$H_1: \mu_1 > \mu_2$$

i.e. a one-sided test. Likewise, the Liverpool supporter would wish to test the alternative hypothesis

$$H_1: \mu_2 > \mu_1$$

Again a one-sided test. But what of you, the unbiassed reader? (at least, we will assume that you are unbiassed). You really don't know what to expect, so the appropriate alternative hypothesis from your viewpoint would be

$$H_1: \mu_1 \neq \mu_2$$

i.e. a two-sided test! For the purposes of this problem, we will adopt the two-sided alternative hypothesis.

Let us suppose that sampling from the matches played we have

	Number of Attacking Moves		Number of Matches
	Mean	Standard Deviation	
Manchester United	$30 = x_1$	$6 = s_1$	$50 = n_1$
Liverpool	$32 = x_2$	$5 = s_2$	$60 = n_2$

Now the standard error of the mean for Manchester United is

$$\frac{s_1}{\sqrt{n_1}} = \frac{6}{\sqrt{50}} = 0.849$$

and the standard error of the mean for Liverpool is

$$\frac{s_2}{\sqrt{n_2}} = \frac{5}{\sqrt{60}} = 0.645$$

In making these calculations, we assume that the sample results for Manchester United come from a population with a standard deviation of 6, and the sample results for Liverpool come from a population with a standard deviation of 5. We can now use the sample difference theorem to calculate the standard error of the difference between the means, i.e.

$$\text{Standard error of the difference} = \sqrt{\left(\frac{s_1}{\sqrt{n_1}}\right)^2 + \left(\frac{s_2}{\sqrt{n_2}}\right)^2}$$

$$= \sqrt{\frac{s_1^2}{n_1} + \frac{s_2^2}{n_2}}$$

$$= \sqrt{(0.849)^2 + (0.645)^2}$$

$$= 1.066$$

Now the actual difference between the means is $|\bar{x}_1 - \bar{x}_2| = 2$, but if the null hypothesis is correct, then the difference does not deviate significantly from zero. In other words, we can consider the difference of 2 as coming from a population of sample mean differences, with a mean zero and a standard error 1.066. So the Z score of the sample mean difference is

$$\frac{2-0}{1.066} = 1.876$$

Consulting our decision rules for two-sided tests, we see that the Z score is not significant. We must accept the null hypothesis that there is no difference in the mean number of attacking moves made.

Notice that in the last example we stated the general expression for the standard error of the difference between the sample means, so if we wish to test for a difference between the means of two large samples, we test the significance of the Z score

$$Z = \frac{|\bar{x}_1 - \bar{x}_2| - 0}{\sqrt{\dfrac{s_1{}^2}{n_1} + \dfrac{s_2{}^2}{n_2}}}$$

We must state, though, that to use this method of significance testing, the samples must be *independent*, i.e. both samples are assumed to have come from the same population, and the selection of the first sample in no way affects the selection of the second. This method, then, could not be used for 'before and after' types of experiments, i.e. when the sample is considered under different conditions. Later we will show you how to deal with samples that are not independent (statisticians call them *paired samples*).

The t-Distribution

The examples we have considered so far have been concerned with large samples ($n > 30$), and if we are to test the significance of small samples then the method we have used will not be valid. Why is this? Well, our method depends upon the essential feature of the Central Limit Theorem – that sample means are normally distributed. Now as you know, the Central Limit Theorem is dependent on the samples considered being large. So if we perform significance tests on the means of small samples, and if we use the methods of the last section, we will be assuming normally distributed sample means – and we have no right to assume this. If we are going to test the means of small samples, then, we must know their probability distribution.

This problem was investigated by W. S. Gosset, who was a statistician employed by Guinness Breweries. He wrote under the pen name

'A Student'. Gosset realised that the means of small samples would show a greater spread than those of large samples – the probability distribution would be similar in shape to a normal distribution, but would be flatter. He gave the name '*t*-distribution' to this probability distribution. Now the derivation of the *t*-distribution is way beyond the scope of an elementary statistics text, but we can state that as the size of the sample increases then the *t*-distribution becomes more like the normal distribution. Just as with the normal distribution, Gosset produced a table of areas under the *t*-distribution, and we will concentrate on showing you how to use this table for significance testing.

Firstly, let us consider what is meant by the statistic *t*. You are by now well used to calculating Z scores, and you know that calculating a Z score implies a normal distribution. Now if we calculate the Z score for the mean of a small sample, then this will imply that the sample mean is normally distributed – and we know that this is not the case. To avoid any confusion, then, we will call the Z score of the mean of a small sample a *t* score – implying it has a *t*-distribution.

Secondly, we stated that as the sample size increases, the *t*-distribution becomes more like the normal distribution. *This implies that for each different sample size, there will be a different t-distribution*, so if we are going to find the probability for a *t* score, then we must be certain that we are using the right *t*-distribution. When we use the normal distribution tables, we can find probabilities as long as we know the Z score; but when we are using the *t*-distribution, we need to know not only the *t* score but also the sample size. So the normal table is a one-variable table (there is only one standard normal distribution), but the *t*-distribution is a two-variable table as there are many standard *t*-distributions. Turn now to the *t* table at the end of this book. You will immediately notice a difference between this table and the standard normal table. With a normal table the probabilities are printed in the main body of the table. The table is so designed that you enter it knowing the Z score, and then determine the appropriate probability. But a *t* table is not designed in this way. It is designed so that we enter it knowing the probability (they are printed across the top) and then determine the appropriate *t* score.

Look at the diagram at the top of the table and you will realise that there is a second important difference between the *t* table and the normal table. The normal table is concerned with the area to the left of a given Z score – but the *t* table is concerned with the area to the right. How, then, do we use this table? Suppose that we wanted to find the *t* score that would be *exceeded* by 5% of sample means.

The value we require is one of those in the column headed $P = 5$. Well, which one should we select? It all depends on the sample size, i.e. which t-distribution is appropriate to the problem. You have probably already guessed that the numbers on the left-hand side of the table (headed v) represent the size of the sample. Unfortunately, you would be quite wrong to assume this – v represents not the sample size but the number of *degrees of freedom*. Now we will return to what this means in a minute, but for the moment take it to be one less than the sample size. So, for samples of 5, $v = 4$, and we would expect 5% of the means of such samples to have t scores greater than 2.132.

Now let us see what effect the t-distribution has on confidence limits of sample means. Clearly, as the means of small samples are not normally distributed, we can no longer state that the 95% confidence limit is always

$$\bar{x} \pm 1.96 \text{ s.e.}$$

After all, 1.96 is a Z score, and this must now be replaced with a t score. For example, suppose a sample of 10 items has a mean of 12 and a variance 2. As this sample is small, the estimated population variance would be

$$2 \times \frac{10}{9} = 2.22$$

and the standard error of the sample means is

$$\frac{\sqrt{2.22}}{\sqrt{10}} = 0.471$$

To obtain a 95% confidence interval for the sample mean, we enter the t table with $P = 2.5$, and $v = 10 - 1 = 9$, finding that $t = 2.262$. So the 95% confidence interval for the sample mean is

$$12 \pm 2.262 \times 0.471$$
$$= 12 \pm 1.065$$

While we are looking at the column headed $P = 2.5$, we can verify a fact that we already know – that as the sample size increases, the t-distribution approaches the normal distribution. If the sample size increases, then the degrees of freedom must increase, and the value of t in the 2.5% column approaches 1.96.

Degrees of Freedom

Now let us discuss what is meant by degrees of freedom, and try to give reasons why the t-distribution is tabulated against degrees of freedom rather than the sample size. The point is that the Central Limit Theorem states that sample means will be normally distributed as long as the samples are large *and as long as we know the population variance*. Now, of course, there will be many cases where we do not know the population variance, and we must estimate it by using the sample variance. We saw in an earlier chapter that an unbiased estimate of the population variance was given by

$$\hat{\sigma}^2 = \frac{ns^2}{n-1}$$

Now by doing this we have introduced the possibility of another error in our test – the fact that $\hat{\sigma}^2$ can vary as well as $\hat{\mu}$. So the t-distribution is a sampling distribution that takes into account not just variations in $\bar{x}$, but also variations in $\hat{\sigma}^2$. The extent of the variations in $\hat{\sigma}^2$ from sample to sample depends on the number of degrees of freedom we use in calculating $\hat{\sigma}^2$.

Suppose, then, we set about estimating a population variance by sampling, and we draw a sample of one item. Obviously, a sample of one item tells us nothing about the variance at all, as a single number cannot show any dispersion. However, if we draw a second item in our sample, we can make some estimate of the variance. So can you see that as the first item sampled tells us nothing about the variance, then if we have a sample of n items, then only $n-1$ of them gives us the estimate of the population variance? So in a sample of n items, we have $n-1$ degrees of freedom in estimating the population variance.

This description does not tell us why we use the word 'freedom'. Well, think of it this way. It is a well-known fact that you cannot obtain a quart out of a pint pot: similarly in sampling, there is a limited amount of information that can be obtained from a sample. Now the degrees of freedom prevent you from drawing more information from a sample than it contains. Suppose, for example, there is a sample of 5 numbers – well, we are free to give the numbers any value we like, and we have 5 degrees of freedom. But suppose we agree that the mean of the sample must be 6 – this means that the sample total must be 30. We are no longer free to assign any value to the 5 numbers – if for example, we make the first 4 numbers 10, 1, 5 and 7, then the last number *must* be $30-(10+1+5+7)=7$. We have used up one of the degrees of freedom by stating the sample mean – and so there would be only 4 degrees of freedom left.

So we have seen that in estimating a population variance from a sample of n items, we have $n-1$ degrees of freedom. In fact, the divisor used in estimating the population variance is the number of degrees of freedom. Earlier, we learnt that to estimate the population variance from two samples, we use the formula

$$\frac{n_1 s_1{}^2 + n_2 s_2{}^2}{n_1 + n_2 - 2}$$

so in making this estimate we have $n_1 + n_2 - 2$ degrees of freedom.

One-sided and Two-sided Tables

Now as we stated earlier, the t table at the end of this book gives the areas to the right of a given value of t. Now if we are going to use the t-distribution for significance testing, then we must be absolutely sure that we know how to use this table. Suppose we draw samples of 12 items from a normal distribution, and find the t scores of the sample means. Here, we have 11 degrees of freedom, and the appropriate part of the table is reproduced below.

$P =$	5	2.5	1	0.05
$v = 11$	1.796	2.201	2.718	3.106

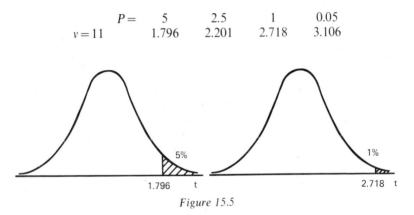

Figure 15.5

Reading from this table, we can see that 5% of sample means can be expected to have t scores greater than 1.796, and 1% of sample means can be expected to have t scores greater than 2.718. Clearly, then, if we wish to perform a one-sided significance test on the means of samples of 12 items, then 1.796 and 2.718 would be the 'critical values' that would appear in our decision rules. But suppose we wished to undertake a two-sided significance test – then these values would not be appropriate. If we wanted to undertake a two-sided test, then we would be interested in the t values that are excluded by all but 5% and all but 1% of the sample means. Consulting the table, the critical values would be 2.201 and 3.106. So if we are interested in one-sided tests, the critical values would be given in the 5% and

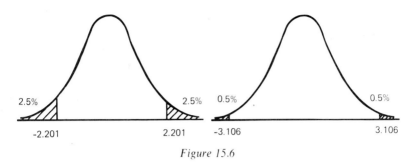

Figure 15.6

1% column, but if we are interested in two-sided tests, then the critical values would be given in the 2.5% and 0.5% columns.

The table we use in this book gives the areas in one tail of the *t*-distribution only, and consequently is called a one-sided table. Unfortunately, some tables give areas in both tails like this –

Figure 15.7

Consequently, the table would occur in a different form. It would look like this:

$P=$	10	5	2	1
$v = 11$	1.796	2.201	2.718	3.106

So if you want to test (one-sided) for significance at the 5% level, the figure in the column headed 10% is appropriate (can you see why? 10% in both tails is equivalent to 5% in one tail). Likewise, if you want to test (two-sided) for significance at the 5% level, the figure in the column headed 5% is appropriate.

You are probably complaining that this is all rather confusing. Life would be much simpler if statisticians made up their mind on one uniform format for the table and stuck to it. We couldn't agree more with this view, and we wish here and now to plead for uniformity in statistical tables. Certainly, one problem faced by many students is how to decide whether a table is one-sided or two-sided.

The way to decide this is to examine the row where $v = \infty$, because the areas in this row will be identical to those of the normal distribution. Look along this row until you find 1.96. If this figure is in the column headed 5%, then the table is two-sided, but if it is in the column headed 2.5%, then it is a one-sided table.

Tests of Sample Means (Small Samples)

Let us now apply our knowledge of the t-distribution for testing means of small samples. We cannot construct decision rules for one-sided and two-sided tests using the t-distribution, because the appropriate t-distribution will depend upon the number of degrees of freedom. Before we examine some examples, however, we would like to issue a word of warning – the use of the t-distribution in significance testing assumes that the sample was drawn from a normally distributed population. This assumption was not called for with tests of means of large samples, and this in itself is a good enough reason for using large samples wherever possible.

EXAMPLE 4

The expected lifetime of electric light bulbs produced by a given process was 1500 hours. To test a new batch a sample of 10 was taken which showed a mean lifetime of 1410 hours. The standard deviation is 90 hours. Test the hypothesis that the mean lifetime of the electric light bulbs has not changed, using a level of significance of

(a) 0.05
(b) 0.01   (I.C.M.A.)

This question asks us to test that the mean has not changed, so we must employ a two-sided test.

$$H_0: \mu = 1500$$
$$H_1: \mu \neq 1500$$

Now the number of degrees of freedom in this example is $10 - 1 = 9$, so entering the t table for $v = 9$, we can obtain decision rules for 5% and 1% levels of significance. As our table is one-sided, but the test is two-sided, our critical values for t will be obtained from the columns headed $P = 2.5$ and $P = 0.5$. So our decision rules are

(a) Accept H_0 and reject H_1 if $t < 2.262$
(b) Reject H_0 and accept H_1 if $2.262 < t < 3.25$ (5% level of significance)
(c) Reject H_0 and accept H_1 if $t > 3.25$ (1% level of significance)

In this example, we do not know the population standard deviation, so we must estimate it using the sample standard deviation. In an earlier chapter we saw that

$$\hat{\sigma}^2 = \frac{ns^2}{n-1}$$

So the estimated population variance is

$$\frac{10 \times 90^2}{9} = 9000$$

and the estimated standard deviation is

$$\sqrt{9000} = 94.87$$

So the t score for a sample mean of 1410 is

$$\frac{|1410 - 1500|\sqrt{10}}{94.87} = 2.999$$

Consulting our decision rules, we see that the result is significant at the 5% level but not at the 1% level. We reject H_0 and accept H_1, and conclude that there is some evidence to suggest that the mean lifetime has changed.

EXAMPLE 5

After treatment with a standard fertiliser, the average yield per hectare is 4.2 tonnes of wheat. A super fertiliser is developed and administered to 10 hectares. The yields from the 10 hectares were 4.3, 6.0, 4.9, 6.1, 6.2, 5.4, 4.1, 4.2, 3.8 and 3.9 tonnes. Does this fertiliser give a higher yield?

Firstly, we should notice that in this case a one-sided test is appropriate, so we have

$$H_0 : \mu = 4.2$$
$$H_1 : \mu > 4.2$$

and consulting the tables for $t = 9$, we can obtain the decision rules. As the test is one-sided, the critical values for t will be given in the columns headed 5% and 1%.

(a) Accept H_0 and reject H_1 if $t < 1.833$
(b) Reject H_0 and accept H_1 if $1.833 < t < 2.821$ (5% level of significance)
(c) Reject H_0 and accept H_1 if $t > 2.821$ (1% level of significance)

We now need the sample mean and variance

x	x^2
4.3	18.49
6.0	36.00
4.9	24.01
6.1	37.21
6.2	38.44
5.4	29.16
4.1	16.81
4.2	17.64
3.8	14.44
3.9	15.21
48.9	247.41

$$\bar{x} = \frac{\Sigma fx}{\Sigma f} = \frac{48.9}{10} = 4.89$$

$$s^2 = \frac{\Sigma x^2}{n} - \left(\frac{\Sigma x}{n}\right)^2$$

$$= \frac{247.41}{10} - (4.89)^2$$

$$= 0.8289$$

The estimated population variance is

$$\frac{10 \times 0.8289}{9} = 0.921$$

and the estimated population standard deviation is

$$\sqrt{0.921} = 0.9597$$

The t score for the sample mean is

$$\frac{|4.89 - 4.2|\sqrt{10}}{0.9597} = 2.27$$

So we conclude that the sample mean is significant at the 5% level but not at the 1% level. We reject H_0 and accept H_1, concluding that there is evidence to suggest that the super fertiliser is effective.

When we dealt with large samples, we found it was possible to test the significance of the difference between the means of two samples. Using the t-distribution, we can also do this for small samples. In some cases, it is possible to test the mean difference by calculating the difference between the items in the sample. For us to be able to do this, the samples must be 'paired', i.e. the same item must appear in both samples, though treated under different conditions. We would use this method for the 'before and after' type of statistics so favoured by advertising agencies (i.e. the samples are not independent).

EXAMPLE 6

Before coaching, five candidates scored 38, 41, 52, 27 and 18% respectively in a statistics examination. After coaching, they scored 40, 45, 49, 30 and 24% respectively. Does this evidence suggest that coaching is effective?

Subtracting the scores, we obtain the change following coaching.

$$x = 2, 4, -3, 3, 6 \quad \bar{x} = 2.4 \quad \sigma^2 = 9.04$$

Suppose we adopt as our null hypothesis that coaching is ineffective: then the mean difference $\bar{x}$ does not differ significantly from $\mu = 0$. We can regard the mark differences as coming from a normal distribution, mean zero and variance

$$\frac{9.04 \times 5}{4} = 11.3$$

So the standard deviation of this population must be $\sqrt{11.3} = 3.36$. If we assume that the mean of this population is zero, our null hypothesis is

$$H_0 : \mu = 0$$

We are asked to test whether coaching is effective, i.e. increases the marks gained by students, so a one-sided test is appropriate and the alternative hypothesis is

$$H_1 : \mu > 0$$

In this example, $v = 4$, so consulting the t table we obtain the following decision rules

(a) Accept H_0 and reject H_1 if $t < 2.132$
(b) Reject H_0 and accept H_1 if $2.132 < t < 3.747$ (5% level of significance)
(c) Reject H_0 and accept H_1 if $t > 3.747$ (1% level of significance)

The t score for the mean difference is

$$\frac{|2.4 - 0| \sqrt{5}}{3.36} = 1.6$$

so the t score is not significant, and we accept the null hypothesis that there is insufficient evidence to suggest that coaching is effective.

In most cases, samples will be independent rather than paired, and if we want to test the significance of the difference between their means, we must use the method employed earlier in this chapter. Suppose we have two samples, the details of which are as follows:

	Sample Size	Mean	Variance
First sample	n_1	$\bar{x}_1$	s_1^2
Second sample	n_2	$\bar{x}_2$	s_2^2

Suppose we adopt the null hypothesis that both samples were drawn from the same population: we have a variance for each sample, and using the methods of the chapter on estimation and confidence limits, we can pool the variances of the samples to estimate the variance of the population, i.e.

$$\hat{\sigma}^2 = \frac{n_1 s_1^2 + n_2 s_2^2}{n_1 + n_2 - 2}$$

Having estimated the variance of the population, we can now estimate the standard error of the difference between two independent means to be

$$\sqrt{\frac{\hat{\sigma}^2}{n_1} + \frac{\hat{\sigma}^2}{n_2}}$$

So the null hypothesis is

$$H_0: \mu_1 = \mu_2 \text{ or}$$
$$H_0: \mu_1 - \mu_2 = 0$$

i.e. the difference between the sample means will not differ significantly from zero. So the t score we must test is:

$$t = \frac{|\bar{x}_1 - \bar{x}_2| - 0}{\sqrt{\frac{\hat{\sigma}^2}{n_1} + \frac{\hat{\sigma}^2}{n_2}}}$$

Before examining an example, we must now ask how many degrees of freedom are associated with this test. There are $(n_1 - 1)$ degrees of freedom associated with the first sample, and $(n_2 - 1)$ associated with the second sample. Now as we are pooling both samples, there are $n_1 + n_2 - 2$ degrees of freedom associated with estimating the population variance.

EXAMPLE 7

Lumo Ltd. manufacture electric light bulbs, and claim that on average their lamps last longer than the lamps of their competitor Brighto Ltd. A random sample of ten lamps made by Lumo had the following lives (in hours) before failing.

$$x_1 = 200 \quad 210 \quad 190 \quad 200 \quad 190 \quad 200 \quad 180 \quad 200 \quad 200 \quad 210$$

and a random sample of eight lamps made by Brighto yielded

$$x_2 = 190 \quad 200 \quad 210 \quad 190 \quad 180 \quad 190 \quad 200 \quad 190$$

Does this evidence substantiate Lumo's claim?

Firstly, we use suitable short-cut methods to calculate the mean and variance for each sample.

x_1	$\dfrac{x_1 - 200}{10}$	$\left(\dfrac{x_1 - 200}{10}\right)^2$	x_2	$\dfrac{x_2 - 200}{10}$	$\left(\dfrac{x_2 - 200}{10}\right)^2$
200	0	0	190	−1	1
210	1	1	200	0	0
190	−1	1	210	1	1
200	0	0	190	−1	1
190	−1	1	180	−2	4
200	0	0	190	−1	1
180	−2	4	200	0	0
200	0	0	190	−1	1
200	0	0		−5	9
210	1	1			
	−2	8			

$$\bar{x}_1 = 200 + \frac{-2 \times 10}{10} = 198 \text{ hrs} \qquad \bar{x}_2 = 200 + \frac{-5 \times 10}{8} = 193.75 \text{ hrs}$$

$$s_1^2 = 100 \times \left[\frac{8}{10} - \left(\frac{-2}{10}\right)^2 \right] \qquad s_2^2 = 100 \times \left[\frac{9}{8} - \left(\frac{-5}{8}\right)^2 \right]$$

$$= 76 \text{ hrs} \qquad\qquad\qquad = 73.44 \text{ hrs}$$

We will test the null hypothesis that there is no difference between the mean lengths of lives of lamps, against the alternative hypothesis that Lumo's lamps last longer than Brighto's lamps, i.e.

$$H_0 : \mu_1 - \mu_2 = 0$$
$$H_1 : \mu_1 > \mu_2$$

As we are in fact assuming that both samples could have been drawn from the same population, the estimated variance of this population is

$$\hat{\sigma}^2 = \frac{n_1 s_1{}^2 + n_2 s_2{}^2}{n_1 + n_2 - 2}$$

$$= \frac{10 \times 76 + 8 \times 73.44}{10 + 8 - 2}$$

$$= 84.22 \text{ hrs, with 16 degrees of freedom}$$

The test is one-sided, so entering the t table with $v = 16$ we can obtain decision rules for this one-sided test

(a) Accept H_0 and reject H_1 if $t < 1.746$
(b) Reject H_0 and accept H_1 if $1.746 < t < 2.583$ (5% level of significance)
(c) Reject H_0 and accept H_1 if $t > 2.583$ (1% level of significance)

$$t = \frac{|198 - 193.75| - 0}{\sqrt{\dfrac{84.22}{10} + \dfrac{84.22}{8}}}$$

$$= 0.976$$

Consulting our decision rules we see that the difference between the means is not significant. We accept the null hypothesis: there is insufficient evidence to suggest that Lumo's lamps last longer.

Tests of Sample Proportions

Tests involving sample proportions are extremely important in practice. In the last chapter, we saw the basis of such a test applied to quality control. Again, many market researchers express their results in terms of proportions, e.g. '40% of the population clean their teeth with Gritto'. It will be useful to design tests that will detect changes in proportions. As you can imagine, the binomial distribution forms the basis of such tests. Let us first examine how we can test the significance of the proportion of a small sample.

EXAMPLE 8

Suppose it is claimed that in a very large batch of components, about 10% of items contain some form of defect. It is proposed to check whether this proportion has increased, and this will be done by drawing a sample of 20 components. Adopting our null hypothesis in the usual way we have

$$H_0: p = 0.1$$
$$H_1: p > 0.1$$

where p is the proportion defective in the sample. Assuming that H_0 is true, then we can calculate the probability distribution for samples of 20 components like this:

$$(0.9)^{20} + {}^{20}C_1(0.9)^{19}(0.1) + {}^{20}C_2(0.9)^{18}(0.1)^2 + {}^{20}C_3(0.9)^{17}(0.1)^3 + \ldots$$

Evaluating this expression, we have

No. of Defectives	Probability	Cumulative Probability
0	0.1215	0.1215
1	0.2700	0.3915
2	0.2850	0.6765
3	0.1900	0.8665
4	0.0897	0.9562
5	0.0319	0.9881
6	0.0089	0.9970
7	0.0020	0.9990
8	0.0004	0.9994
9	0.0001	0.9995

Examining this table, we see that the probability of obtaining more than 4 defectives is $1 - 0.9562 = 4.38\%$, and the probability of obtaining more than 6 defectives is $1 - 0.9970 = 0.3\%$. So if we obtain more than 4 defectives in a sample, we can reject the null hypothesis at the 4.38% level of significance, and if it contains more than 6 defectives we can reject at the 0.3% level of significance.

Now calculations involving the binomial distribution are very tedious. The way to avoid them is to draw a large sample, and we can then use the normal approximation. Suppose that in the last example a sample of 150 contained 20 defectives – would this indicate that the proportion defective had increased? Again, we have

$$H_0: p = 0.1$$
$$H_1: p > 0.1$$

And on the basis of our null hypothesis

$$\text{mean} = np = 0.1 \times 150 = 15 \text{ defectives per sample}$$
$$\sigma = \sqrt{npq} = \sqrt{150 \times 0.1 \times 0.9} = 3.67$$

The Z score for 20 defectives is

$$\frac{20 - 15}{3.67} = 1.36$$

and using our decision rules for one-sided tests involving the normal distribution we would conclude that the proportion defective is not significant, and we could accept the hypothesis that the proportion defective is 0.1.

EXAMPLE 9

Finally, let us examine how we could investigate the significance of the difference between two proportions in two samples. Suppose that in a sample of 300 people from Liverpool, 220 cleaned their teeth with Gritto, and in Manchester 240 out of 350 use Gritto. We wish to determine whether there is any difference between the proportions using Gritto. Clearly, this is a two-sided test, so we have

$$H_0: p_1 = p_2 \quad \text{or} \quad p_1 - p_2 = 0$$
$$H_1: p_1 \neq p_2$$

The proportion using Gritto in Liverpool is $\frac{220}{300} = 0.733$, and the proportion using Gritto in Manchester is $\frac{240}{350} = 0.686$. If the null hypothesis is true, then we can regard both samples as coming from the same population. The best estimate we have of the proportion using Gritto in this population is

$$\frac{220 + 240}{300 + 350} = \frac{460}{650} = 0.708$$

In an earlier chapter, we saw that the variance of the proportion of a sample of n items is

$$\frac{pq}{n}$$

where p is the proportion in the population with the desired characteristic. So the variance of the proportion of samples of 300 is

$$\frac{0.708 \times 0.292}{300}$$

and the variance of the proportion of samples of 350 is

$$\frac{0.708 \times 0.292}{350}$$

Using the theorem of sample differences, the variance of the differences between these proportions is

$$\frac{0.708 \times 0.292}{300} + \frac{0.708 \times 0.292}{350}$$
$$= 0.708 \times 0.292 \left(\frac{1}{300} + \frac{1}{350} \right)$$
$$= 0.00128$$

and the standard error of the difference is $\sqrt{0.00128} = 0.0358$. Now if the null hypothesis is true, then the difference between the proportions in the sample could well be zero. So the Z score for this difference in proportions is

$$\frac{|0.733 - 0.686| - 0}{0.0358} = 1.31$$

and consulting our decision rules for two-sided tests, we would accept the null hypothesis that the proportion using Gritto in Liverpool and Manchester could well be the same.

As you can see, there are a wide variety of significance tests for testing means and proportions. Certainly, there are more than those mentioned in this chapter – there are tests, for example, for testing several means and proportions. However, the tests covered in this chapter will take you quite a long way in statistical analysis. Before we finish this chapter, let us stress again the importance of the sample size. You will have noticed that large samples impose fewer restrictions on testing, and their results will be much more reliable. It is for this reason that you should use large samples wherever possible.

EXERCISES TO CHAPTERS 14 AND 15

15.1 Discuss briefly the following statements:

(i) in hypothesis testing it is more important to minimise the Type I error than to worry about the Type II error;

(ii) in hypothesis testing it is essential that the decision to use either a one- or a two-tailed test should be taken before the sample is drawn. C.I.P.F.A.

15.2 From past experience it has been found that 5% of a certain output is rejected. To test the null hypothesis $H_0: p = 5\%$, a sample of 400 items are drawn. Form decision rules for testing H_0 at the 1% level if (a) the alternative hypothesis is one-sided and (b) the alternative hypothesis is two-sided.

15.3 Suppose that in 15.2 we adopt the one-sided alternative hypothesis, and the true reject rate rises to 7%. What is the probability of a Type II error?

15.4 Metal plugs are turned to a mean diameter of 5 cm, standard deviation 0.01 cm. We wish to test for change in the mean diameter at the 5% level of significance by drawing a sample of 100 plugs. Devise an appropriate decision rule. What would your decision rule have been if we wished to detect increases in the mean diameter?

15.5   A manufacturer produces cables with a mean breaking strength of 2000 lb and a standard deviation of 100 lb. By using a new technique the manufacturer claims that the breaking strength can be increased. To test this claim, a sample of 50 cables produced by the new technique is tested, and the mean breaking strength found to be 2050 lb. Can the manufacturer's claim be supported at a 0.01 level of significance?   I.C.M.A.

15.6   In a certain country, men have a mean height of 5 ft 6 in, standard deviation 3 in, and women have a mean height of 5 ft 3 in, standard deviation 2 in. In a random sample of 100 married couples, the average height difference between husband and wife was 2 in. Does this suggest that height of partner affects the decision to propose marriage?

15.7   A survey has provided data on the television watching habits of ten-year-old children of different social classes. A sample of 220 children in social class five were found to watch for a mean period of 3.8 hours per day with a standard deviation of 0.5 hours, while a sample of 63 children in social classes one/two watched for a mean period of 3.2 hours with a standard deviation of 0.42 hours. Test, at the 1% level, whether children in social class five spend more time watching television than do those in classes one/two.   O.N.C.

15.8   Two drugs, A and B, were tested for a certain effect on laboratory mice. Two samples, each of fifty mice, were chosen randomly, one drug administered to each, and a measure, x, of the effect, obtained. The results were as follows:

$$Drug\ A \quad \Sigma x = 1750 \qquad \Sigma x^2 = 62{,}520$$
$$Drug\ B \quad \Sigma x = 1980 \qquad \Sigma x^2 = 85{,}610$$

Test, at the 1% level of significance, the hypothesis that the two drugs have the same mean effect against the alternative hypothesis that drug B has a higher mean effect. You may assume that the effect on mice, of each drug, is normally distributed.   O.N.C.

15.9   What is meant by 'standardising' a normal distribution and how is it done?
   A company samples the products of two suppliers of light bulbs. The 80 bulbs in the batch from supplier A are shown to have a mean life of 503 hours with a standard deviation of 43 hours. The 110 bulbs from supplier B have a mean life of 488 hours with a standard devia-

tion of 39 hours. Test the hypothesis that there is no difference between the mean lives of bulbs from the two suppliers at the 10%, 5% and 1% levels of significance.

(The relevant test is based on the fact that the statistic

$$Z = \frac{m_1 - m_2}{\sqrt{\dfrac{s_1{}^2}{n_1} + \dfrac{s_2{}^2}{n_2}}}$$

has a standard normal distribution. The n_1, n_2 are the numbers in the samples, the m_1, m_2 are the sample means, and the S_1, S_2 are the sample standard deviations.) H.N.C.

15.10 The following table gives incomes after tax for the U.K. for 1962 and 1963.

Income (£)	1962		1963	
	No. in thousands	Income after Tax (£m)	No. in thousands	Income after Tax (£m)
50–249	5,100	1,000	4,500	900
250–499	6,600	2,500	6,800	2,600
500–749	6,200	3,800	6,000	3,800
750–999	4,800	4,200	4,900	4,300
1,000–1,999	4,100	5,100	4,600	5,800
2,000–3,999	300	900	400	1,000
4,000 and over	100	400	100	500
Totals	27,200	17,900	27,300	18,900

Source: National Income and Expenditure.

(a) Plot the Lorenz curves for income after tax in 1962 and 1963 and comment on your findings.
(b) Test the hypothesis that the mean income has not changed between 1962 and 1963. C.I.P.F.A.

15.11 Data produced by the Family Expenditure Survey show that the percentage distribution of households by income in 1965–7 for two standard regions was as follows:

Weekly Income	% of all Households	
	Yorkshire and Humberside	Northern Ireland
Under £6	6	8
£6 but under £10	9	11
£10 but under £15	12	12
£15 but under £20	14	18
£20 but under £25	17	17
£25 but under £30	13	12

Weekly Income	% of all Households	
	Yorkshire and Humberside	Northern Ireland
£30 but under £35	9	11
£35 but under £40	6	3
£40 but under £50	8	5
£50 or more	6	3

(a) Is there a significant difference between the mean percentage income in the two regions?

(b) Explain as carefully as you can the purpose of hypothesis testing. C.I.P.F.A.

15.12 Suppose that a survey of a number of firms in two regions of a country shows that their investment in a given year was as follows:

Investment (£000's)

	24–	28–	32–	36–	40–	44–48

Number of Firms

	24–	28–	32–	36–	40–	44–48
Region A	8	41	77	90	58	26
Region B	19	36	47	58	27	13

Is there any evidence of a difference in average investment between the two regions? C.I.P.F.A.

15.13 The table below gives distributions of earnings for samples of workers taken from two firms:

Earnings (£)

	20–	22–	24–	26–	28–	30–32
Number of workers in Firm A	11	23	42	40	28	14
Number of workers in Firm B	12	26	54	62	44	38

What evidence is there of a difference between average earnings in the two firms? C.I.P.F.A.

15.14 Permanent Houses Completed in the U.K. (including flats, each flat being counted as one unit)

Year	For Private Owners (thousands)	For Local Housing Authorities (thousands)
1963	177.8	123.9
1964	221.3	154.7
1965	217.2	165.0
1966	208.6	176.9
1967	204.2	199.7
1968	226.0	188.0
1969	186.0	180.9

Year	For Private Owners (thousands)	For Local Housing Authorities (thousands)
1970	174.3	177.0
1971	196.3	154.8
1972	200.6	120.4
1973	190.6	102.6

Source: Annual Abstract of Statistics.

Is there a significant difference in the average number of permanent houses completed in the two groups between 1963 and 1973?

C.I.P.F.A.

15.15   In conducting a survey of food prices, two samples of prices of a given food item were collected. Sample A came from a congested city area, and Sample B was obtained in the suburbs. The results were as follows:

	Sample A	Sample B
n	14	18
$\sum_{i=1}^{n} p_i$	12.60	14.96
$\sum_{i=1}^{n} (p_i - \bar{p})^2$	1.68	1.96

where p_i = price recorded in the ith store. Test the hypothesis that there is no difference between the mean price of the particular food item in the two areas. (Use 5% level of significance.)   C.I.P.F.A.

15.16   A machine has been operating at 60% efficiency. After adjustment, nine test runs produced the following efficiencies:

64,   59,   71,   63,   68,   61,   62,   61,   63

Test, at the 5% level, whether efficiency has improved.   O.N.C.

15.17   In order to test the effectiveness of a drying agent in paint, the following experiment was carried out. Each of six samples of material was cut in two halves. One half of each was covered with paint containing the agent and the other half with paint without the agent. Then all twelve samples were left to dry. The time taken to dry was as follows:

Drying Time (hours)

	Sample Number					
	1	2	3	4	5	6
Paint with the agent	3.4	3.8	4.2	4.1	3.5	4.7
Paint without the agent	3.6	3.8	4.3	4.3	3.6	4.6

Required: Carry out a '*t*'-test to determine whether the drying agent is effective, giving your reasons for choosing a one-tailed or two-tailed test. Carefully explain your conclusions.

Selected Values of $t_{0.05}$

Degrees of Freedom

	4	5	6	7	8	9	10	11	12	13
One-tailed test	2.13	2.02	1.94	1.90	1.86	1.83	1.81	1.80	1.78	1.77
Two-tailed test	2.78	2.57	2.45	2.36	2.31	2.26	2.23	2.20	2.18	2.16

A.C.A.

15.18 (a) What do you understand by the *t*-distribution?

(b) From a random sample of 9 machine components an average life of fifteen months is expected with a standard deviation of two months.

(i) Calculate the limits between which the actual average life of the components could vary, based on this sample, at 95% and 99% confidence limits.

(ii) Considering that the components are expected to be of high quality, what comments would you make on the results?

I.C.M.A.

15.19 Ten pairs of identical twins had the following birthweights in kilograms:

Pair	1	2	3	4	5	6	7	8	9	10
First-born	3.95	3.41	3.73	4.13	3.48	4.28	3.98	4.18	4.04	3.73
Second-born	3.93	3.35	3.72	4.18	3.44	4.15	3.89	4.20	4.00	3.72

(i) Stating any assumptions which you make, test, at the 5% significance level, the hypothesis that there is no difference in weight between first-born and second-born twins.

(ii) If the data had been collected to test the hypothesis that the first-born are heavier, what conclusion would you reach?

O.N.C.

15.20 A group of 10 students scored the following marks in a test:

Candidate	A	B	C	D	E	F	G	H	I	J
Score	53	60	61	47	40	56	75	46	82	61

After coaching, their marks were

Candidate	A	B	C	D	E	F	G	H	I	J
Score	60	58	67	51	60	72	71	48	94	76

Did coaching improve their marks?

15.21 Define the standard error of a mean of samples of *n* observations and use the concept to explain briefly why one has more confidence in the mean of a large sample than in the mean of a small one.

Show why it is unlikely that a sample of 64 observations with a mean of 5.2 was drawn from a population with a mean of 5.5 and a standard deviation of 0.8. Would your answer be the same if the sample contained 16 items? A.C.A.

15.22 The internal auditor of your company has reported to you as management accountant as follows:

'From 1000 sample postings made before metrication 210 errors were discovered whereas 250 errors were found in 1000 sample postings made after metrication. It would appear that although the staff has not changed, the postings before metrication were more accurate than they are after. Special steps would be taken to regain the accuracy previously enjoyed.'

(a) What statistical hypothesis does this statement imply?
(b) Evaluate this hypothesis and state if it should influence you as management accountant in your decision on whether to take special action. I.C.M.A.

15.23 A market research company wishing to determine whether it is more usual in the North for working men to come home to a midday meal than in the South interviews two random samples each of 500 men. In the sample from the North 330 men come home midday compared with 280 in the sample from the South. Is the difference significant? I.C.M.A.

15.24 Two groups, A and B, each consist of 100 people who have a disease. A serum is given to group A but not to group B; otherwise, the two groups are treated identically. It is found that in groups A and B, 75 and 65 people, respectively, recover from the disease. Does this result support the hypothesis that the serum helps to cure the disease? I.C.M.A.

15.25 A company selling a prestige product carries out market research surveys in two consecutive years on heads of households with income in excess of £10,000 per year. The survey results were:

	1973	1974
Sample size	1300	1000
No. possessing product	351	240

Assuming the rejection area to be outside 2.33 S.D., does the 1974 survey suggest that the product's sales are declining? I.C.M.A.

15.26   Family Expenditure Survey: Household expenditure on commodities and services 1967–8.

	North (£ per week)	South-west (£ per week)
Housing, etc	3.77	4.86
Food	6.17	6.18
Drink and tobacco	2.46	1.87
Clothing and footwear	2.07	1.79
Durables and other goods	2.79	3.50
Transport and services	4.54	5.53
Total	21.80	23.73
Number of households in sample	1000	1000

Do households in the North spend a significantly greater proportion of their total expenditure on drink and tobacco than those in the South-west? Explain fully the theoretical basis for the test you have applied.   C.I.P.F.A.

15.27   A motor-car manufacturer purchases gear assemblies from a sub-contractor who undertakes to ensure that not more than 5% of his supplies will be defective. In order to provide a check on the quality of incoming supplies a random sample of 200 assemblies is selected of which 17 are found to be defective.
  (a) Does the sample evidence indicate that the sub-contractor is not maintaining the quality of his supplies at the agreed level? Use the significance levels of 0.05 and 0.01.
  (b) Construct an interval estimate for the proportion of all the sub-contractors supplies that are defective. Use a confidence level of 95%.
  (c) What is the minimum sample size required to estimate the proportion in part (b) of the question to within $\pm 0.5\%$ at the 95% confidence level.
  (d) As the result of a board decision the firm now purchases gear assemblies from a second sub-contractor. A random sample of 500 gear assemblies from his supplies reveals that 20 units are defective. Test the hypothesis that there is a significant difference in quality between the two sub-contractors' supplies. Use significance levels of 0.01 and 0.05.

15.28   In a public opinion poll of 500 people, 70% favoured a certain policy. In another district 60% of the 500 interviewed favoured the policy. Is there a significant difference of opinion?

15.29   For question 15.28, what is the minimum sample size that would make a difference between 60% and 70% significant?

Chapter Sixteen

The Chi-Square Distribution

If you think carefully, you will realise that the significance tests we have considered all depend, to a greater or lesser extent, on the presence of the normal distribution. When considering large samples, the Central Limit Theorem supplied us with evidence that the sample statistic was normally distributed, and we constructed significance tests on this basis. With small samples, we could assume that the sample statistic had a t-distribution, as long as the sample was drawn from a normal population. But suppose it is only possible to draw a small sample, and suppose that we cannot guarantee that the population from which we draw this sample is normally distributed? Under such circumstances we would not, according to statistical theory, be justified in using a t-test. But as you must also realise, we will seldom be able to give the guarantees demanded by the t-test. Now this news must be very annoying to you – we have spent a lot of time mastering the t-test, and now we find that the conditions necessary for its use will seldom be met in practice! Take heart – things are not as bleak as they sound. A number of empirical studies have been made into the effect of using the t-test on samples drawn from non-normal populations (such studies are called *sensitivity analysis*). Generally, these studies tend to support the view that the t-test tends to be rather insensitive to movements away from the normal distribution when testing null hypotheses of sample means. So long as the population does not depart too much from a normal distribution, you will be safe in applying the t-test.

A second point is that the tests we have considered so far have been concerned with *parameters* – namely the population mean and proportion. Now, earlier in this book, we emphasised the importance of using all the information that is available to us. Do you remember that one of the strongest criticisms we levelled against the median and range was that they did not use all the information that was available? Now here we are again – testing sample means and proportions and ignoring the individual items in the sample! What we should, perhaps, be doing is to examine the importance of how the individual items in the sample are distributed – we should be applying a so-called *non-parametric test*. Now there are many such tests, but we shall concentrate our efforts on just one of them: the Chi-square Test (pronounce it 'kye square' and use the symbol χ^2). Certainly, of all the significance tests, this is the most widely used and applied.

Observed and Expected Frequencies

Suppose you have been given the task of assessing consumer preference with respect to five washing powders – Zip, Whito, Acme, Blanco and Bleacho. You supply a small quantity of each powder in boxes marked A, B, C, D and E to 1000 housewives, and ask them to test the powders and state which powder they prefer. The result of your enquiry is as follows:

Washing powder	Zip	Whito	Acme	Blanco	Bleacho
No. preferring that powder	187	221	193	204	195

Now you suspect that housewives are unable to distinguish between washing powders. Any preference that they have will be influenced not by the powder's characteristics, but by the persuasive powers of the advertisements promoting the powder, and by the attractiveness of the packet. For this reason, the housewives do not know which powder they are using (remember they are labelled A, B, C, D and E, and each powder is packed in a plain white box). Returning to statistical jargon, we have formulated the null hypothesis that housewives are unable to distinguish between the powders, and we will use the sample evidence to test the validity of this hypothesis. Of course, the appropriate alternative hypothesis is that housewives can distinguish between the powders.

Earlier in this book, we implied that the null hypothesis to be tested should always be formulated in such a fashion that we would know what to expect if it was true. Assuming that our null hypothesis is correct, then, we would expect that an equal number would report that they preferred each of the powders. In other words, the results expected from our sample would be:

Washing powder	Zip	Whito	Acme	Blanco	Bleacho
No. expected to prefer that powder	200	200	200	200	200

The frequencies that we obtain in our sample we will call the *observed frequencies*, and the frequencies we expect on the basis of our null hypothesis we will call the *expected frequencies*. We shall now devise a significance test based on the 'goodness of fit' of the observed frequencies to the expected frequencies.

Now if you think about this carefully, you will realise that, whatever our null hypothesis, we do not have complete freedom in calculating the expected frequencies. This is because if we are to compare the observed and expected frequencies, then clearly both must total 1000. We are free to assign arbitrary expected values to any four of the washing powders – the fifth one would then be fixed so that the total frequencies would be 1000. We might, for example, assign an expected value of 150 to Whito, 300 to Acme, 200 to Blanco and 50 to Bleacho. If we do this, then the expected value for Zip *must* be 300 to cover all the 1000 housewives in the sample. In other words, we have $v=4$ degrees of freedom in calculating the expected values. Generalising, for problems like this if we have n observed values, then we have $v=n-1$ degrees of freedom in assigning expected values.

The method we shall apply for testing the null hypothesis is to measure the total deviation of the observed from the expected frequencies, i.e. $\Sigma(O-E)$.

Product	Observed	Expected	$(O-E)$
Zip	187	200	-13
Whito	221	200	21
Acme	193	200	-7
Blanco	204	200	4
Bleacho	195	200	-5

As you would expect $\Sigma(O-E)=0$, so we are faced with a similar problem to when we were attempting to measure dispersion. If $\Sigma(O-E)$ always equals zero, then we cannot use it as a measure of testing our null hypothesis. When considering the standard deviation, we got round this problem by squaring the deviations, and we can use the same method in this context; i.e. calculate $\Sigma(O-E)^2$. However, a further adjustment is necessary: we divide the $(O-E)^2$ values by E. Now why do we do this? Well, the reason is not apparent in this example, so let us consider another case.

Observed	Expected	$(O-E)$	$(O-E)^2$
150	200	-50	2500
150	100	50	2500

Clearly the deviation of 50 is twice as significant on an expected value of 100 as it is on an expected value of 200, and to take this into account we can weight the $(O-E)^2$ values by dividing by E. So we have

Observed	Expected	$(O-E)$	$(O-E)^2$	$\dfrac{(O-E)^2}{E}$
150	200	-50	2500	12.5
150	100	50	2500	25

which shows precisely the information required. Now if we calculate the sum of the

$$\frac{(O-E)^2}{E}$$

values, we have a weighted sum of the deviations of the observed and expected values, and we call this statistic χ^2.

$$\chi^2 = \sum \frac{(O-E)^2}{E}$$

Calculating the value of χ^2 for our washing powder example we have

Observed	Expected	$(O-E)$	$(O-E)^2$	$\dfrac{(O-E)^2}{E}$
187	200	-13	169	0.845
221	200	21	441	2.205
193	200	-7	49	0.245
204	200	4	16	0.080
195	200	-5	25	0.125
		0		3.500

If our null hypothesis is true, then our expected value for χ^2 must be zero. But as we are sampling, the actual value of χ^2 will fluctuate from sample to sample. Surely, then, we require the probability that χ^2 is at least as great as 3.5. Now just as with the *t*-distribution, there are many chi-square distributions – one for each degree of freedom. The chi-square distribution with $v=4$ is shown in Fig. 16.1, and we

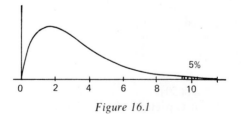

Figure 16.1

see that there is a 5% probability that our value for χ^2 should exceed 9.5. Tables of areas of the χ^2 distribution are reproduced at the back of this book. Referring to these tables, we can adopt the decision rules:
  (a) Accept H_0 and reject H_1 if $\chi^2 < 9.49$
  (b) Accept H_1 and reject H_0 if $9.49 < \chi^2 < 13.28$ (5% level of significance)
  (c) Accept H_1 and reject H_0 if $\chi^2 > 13.28$ (1% level of significance)
As our value of χ^2 is 3.5, we would accept the hypothesis that housewives are unable to distinguish between the washing powders.

Errors Resulting from the Use of χ^2

Before we go any further, it is worth considering the errors that can occur if we use χ^2. A glance at Fig. 16.1 shows that the distribution is continuous, and we have used it to test discrete data. Clearly, then, this is a possible source of error. Now this error is not really serious *unless there is only one degree of freedom*, and when $v = 1$ we compensate for this error by applying *Yate's correction*. All that is involved in this correction is that we subtract $\frac{1}{2}$ from the *absolute* difference between the observed and expected values. (You should notice that Yate's correction is very similar to the correction we make when approximating a binomial distribution with a normal distribution.) Let us examine an example to see how we apply the correction.

In a sample of 1000 people, 452 said they would vote Socialist at the next election. We wish to test the hypothesis that 50% of the electorate vote Socialist. On the basis of this hypothesis, then, we have:

	Observed	Expected
Socialist	452	500
Not Socialist	548	500

In this case, we have only one degree of freedom, so our decision rules are:
  (a) Accept H_0 and reject H_1 if $\chi^2 < 3.84$
  (b) Accept H_1 and reject H_0 if $3.84 < \chi^2 < 6.63$ (5% level of significance)
  (c) Accept H_1 and reject H_0 if $\chi^2 > 6.63$ (1% level of significance)
Also, as $v = 1$ we must apply Yate's correction

Observed	Expected	$(O-E)$	$\lvert O-E \rvert - \frac{1}{2}$	$(\lvert O-E \rvert - \frac{1}{2})^2$	$\dfrac{(\lvert O-E \rvert - \frac{1}{2})^2}{E}$
452	500	-48	47.5	2256.25	4.5125
548	500	48	47.5	2256.25	4.5125
				$\chi^2 =$	9.0250

So we can see that the sample result is significant at the 1% level. We reject the null hypothesis and conclude that less than 50% of the electorate vote Socialist.

There is a second type of error that can arise from using the χ^2 distribution. The calculation of χ^2 assumes that the expected frequencies are not 'too small', meaning that they are not less than 5. Should any expected frequency be less than 5, then it must be combined with an adjacent frequency. Of course, if we do this for an expected frequency then we must also do it for the corresponding observed frequency. As we shall see in the next section, this problem frequently arises when testing goodness of fit to probability distributions.

Testing Goodness of Fit to a Probability Distribution

Do you remember that in the chapter on probability distributions we investigated the pattern of V1 rockets falling on London during World War II? We divided an area of 144 square kilometres into 576 equal squares, and counted the number of bombs per square. We wanted to find if the bombs were falling at random, or were 'clustered' to a greater degree than could be ascribed to chance. If the bombs did fall randomly, then we should be able to predict the frequency distribution of bombs per square by using the Poisson distribution. The observed distribution was:

No. of bombs per square	0	1	2	3	4	5
Frequency	229	211	93	35	7	1

This distribution forms our observed frequencies, and has a mean of 0.93 bombs per square. We now formulate the null hypothesis that the bombing pattern could be predicted by the Poisson distribution with a mean 0.93. (This may not sound like a null hypothesis, but it would if we restated it slightly – there is no difference between the bombing pattern and the Poisson distribution with a mean of 0.93.) On the basis of our null hypothesis, we can calculate the expected frequencies like this:

$$576e^{-0.93}\left[1+0.93+\frac{0.93^2}{2!}+\frac{0.93^3}{3!}+\frac{0.93^4}{4!}+\frac{0.93^5}{5!}\right]$$
$$=576[0.3946+0.3670+0.1706+0.0529+0.0123+0.0023]$$
$$=227.3+211.4+98.3+30.5+7.1+1.3$$

When we dealt with the Poisson distribution previously, we were content to deal with probabilities. Here we are more interested in expected values, and we can obtain these by multiplying the probabilities by 576 – the total frequency. Notice that the sum of the expected frequencies is 575.9 – implying that we expect 0.1 squares to have more than 5 bombs. It would seem sensible, then, to combine this 0.1 into the 5 bombs per square class. We can now calculate a value for χ^2 to see how well the observed data fits the expected data.

Observed	Expected	$(O-E)$	$(O-E)^2$	$\dfrac{(O-E)^2}{E}$
229	227.3	1.7	2.89	0.0127
211	211.4	−0.4	0.16	0.0008
93	98.3	−5.3	28.09	0.2858
35	30.5	4.5	20.25	0.6639
7 }	7.1 }	−0.5	0.25	0.0294
1 }	1.4 }			

$$\chi^2 = 0.9926$$

We must now investigate the number of degrees of freedom in calculating the expected values. The first thing to notice is that after combining the last two classes we have five classes in total. We used up one degree of freedom in making both sets of frequencies have the same total, and we used up another degree of freedom by making both sets of frequencies have the same mean. So we must have had $5-2=3$ degrees of freedom when calculating the expected values. Generalising, for a Poisson distribution with n classes, there will be $v=n-2$ degrees of freedom in calculating the expected frequencies.

Consulting the χ^2 table, with $v=3$ we would reject the null hypothesis at the 5% level if χ^2 exceeds 7.81, and at the 1% level if χ^2 exceeds 11.34. Now, as our value of χ^2 is far less than these values, we must accept the null hypothesis and conclude that the observed frequencies fit the Poisson frequencies excellently. The differences between the observed and expected values could well be accounted for by sampling fluctuations.

Now let us see if the data would fit a binomial distribution. First, we must find the probability that a particular square is bombed. Now we know that in any binomial distribution, the mean is np. In this case the mean is 0.93, and we can take n to be 5. So

$$0.93 = 5p$$
$$p = 0.186$$

and $q = 1 - 0.186 = 0.814$. So for samples of five squares, the probability distribution would be given by $(0.814 + 0.186)^5$

$$= (0.814)^5 + 5(0.814)^4(0.186) + 10(0.814)^3(0.186)^2$$
$$+ 10(0.814)^2(0.186)^3 + 5(0.814)(0.186)^4 + (0.186)^5$$
$$= 0.3574 + 0.4083 + 0.1866 + 0.0426 + 0.0049 + 0.0002$$

Multiplying the probabilities by 576 would give the expected frequencies:

Observed	Expected	$(O-E)$	$(O-E)^2$	$\dfrac{(O-E)^2}{E}$
229	205.9	23.1	533.61	2.59
211	235.2	-24.2	585.64	2.49
93	107.5	-14.5	210.25	1.96
35	24.5	10.5	110.25	4.50
$\left.\begin{array}{c}7\\1\end{array}\right\}$	$\left.\begin{array}{c}2.8\\0.1\end{array}\right\}$	5.1	26.01	8.97
				20.51

The null hypothesis we have used here is that the observed frequencies could be described by the binomial distribution $(0.814+0.186)^5$. To test the goodness of fit, we now need to know the degrees of freedom in calculating the expected values. As with the Poisson distribution, we used up two degrees of freedom – one to make the totals agree and one to make the means agree. Again, we have $5-2=3$ degrees of freedom, and so we can use the decision rules of the last example. Applying these rules, we must reject the null hypothesis at the 1% level. The observed data could not be described by a binomial distribution.

We shall not give an example of testing goodness of fit to a normal distribution, as the method is essentially similar, but it would be as well to investigate the number of degrees of freedom involved in such tests. To fit a normal distribution to observed data, we will use up three degrees of freedom, as the distributions must have the same mean, standard deviation and total. Assuming we have n classes in our expected frequencies, then, to test goodness of fit to a normal distribution would involve $n-3$ degrees of freedom.

Contingency Tables

To illustrate a further application of χ^2 testing, let us now examine a question recently set by the A.C.A.

Using the χ^2 distribution as a test of significance, test the statement that the number of defective items produced by two machines, as shown in the following table, is independent of the machine on which they were made.

	Machine Output		
	Defective Articles	Effective Articles	Total
Machine A	25	375	400
Machine B	42	558	600
	67	993	1000

Use the 0.01 level of significance χ^2 distribution table given below:

Distribution of χ^2

Degrees of Freedom	Probability (0.01 Level of Significance)
1	6.64
2	9.21
3	11.34
4	13.28

We deliberately chose this question because it is such a bad one! Firstly, look at the table: what a strange choice of heading for the columns! They imply that if an article is not defective then it must be effective. But defective and effective are not opposites to each other – surely what the examiner means is that if an article is not defective then it is satisfactory? We would prefer to see 'satisfactory' or 'non-defective' as a heading for the second column. Secondly (and far more seriously) look at the χ^2 table. The heading of the second column gives the impression that the figures in that column are probabilities! Now this really is very naughty – we know that probabilities cannot exceed unity! You know, of course, that these figures are *values* of χ^2, for, after all, χ^2 is just another standard score, and it is comparable with the standard scores Z and t that we inspected in earlier chapters. Taking these two errors into account, we can still attempt the question.

We are asked to test the statement that the number of defective items is independent of the machines on which they were made, and we adopt this as our null hypothesis. Now if the statement is not true, then the number of defectives will depend on the machine on which they were made, and the table will enable us to calculate the degree of dependence. A table constructed in this way (to indicate dependence or association) is called a *contingency table*. 'Contingency' means dependence – many of you, for example, will be familiar with the term 'contingency planning'; i.e. plans that will be put into operation *if* certain things happen.

As usual, let us suppose that our null hypothesis is true. Given this assumption, then we are only interested in the totals in the table, i.e. that out of 1000 articles, 67 were defective, and that out of 1000 articles 400 were produced on machine A. Using only this information, we can now predict the expected number of defectives produced by the two machines. We have –

probability that an item is produced on machine A $= \frac{400}{1000} = \frac{2}{5}$ and the probability that an item is defective is $\frac{67}{1000}$

As we assume from our null hypothesis that these events are independent, we can use the multiplication law to calculate the probability that a defective item is produced on machine A.

i.e. $\frac{2}{5} \times \frac{67}{1000}$

So if 1000 items are produced, the expected number of defectives produced by machine A is

$$\frac{2}{5} \times \frac{67}{1000} \times 1000 = 26.8$$

Now as machine A produces 400 items, then $400 - 26.8 = 373.2$ items can be expected to be non-defective. Likewise, it follows that as we can expect 67 defective items, $67 - 26.8 = 40.2$ of them can be expected to be produced by machine B. Finally, as we can expect B to produce 600 items, we can expect $600 - 40.2 = 559.8$ of the items to be non-defective. The expected table, then, would look like this:

	Machine Output		
	Defective Articles	Non-defective Articles	Total
Machine A	26.8	373.2	400
Machine B	40.2	559.8	600
	67.0	933.0	1000

Notice that after we have calculated just one of the values in the table, the remainder will be fixed by subtraction. So we have $v = 1$ degree of freedom in calculating the expected values for a 2×2 contingency table and we must apply Yate's correction.

Observed	Expected	$(O - E)$	$\lvert O - E \rvert - \frac{1}{2}$	$\dfrac{(\lvert O - E \rvert - \frac{1}{2})^2}{E}$
25	26.8	-1.8	1.3	0.063
375	373.2	1.8	1.3	0.005
42	40.2	1.8	1.3	0.042
558	559.8	-1.8	1.3	0.003
				$\chi^2 = 0.113$

With $v = 1$ we would reject the null hypothesis if $\chi^2 > 6.64$ (1% level). Now as our value is much less than this, there is no reason to reject the null hypothesis – the number of defective items is independent of the machine on which they were produced.

If you are going to use the above technique, then make absolutely sure that the samples are *independent*. We could not use it if the same sample is being tested under different conditions (i.e. 'before and after' investigations). It could not be used in the following case: a sample of 100 housewives were given a standard washing powder to test and report whether the powder was satisfactory or unsatisfactory. The same women were then asked to test a new super powder. The results were –

New Powder

		Satisfactory	Unsatisfactory
Old Powder	Satisfactory	20	10
	Unsatisfactory	50	20

Examining this table, we see that 60 women 'changed their minds', i.e. 50 changed from unsatisfactory to satisfactory, and 10 changed from satisfactory to unsatisfactory. Now suppose we formulate the null hypothesis that the type of powder had no effect on their response (i.e. they could not distinguish between them), then we would expect an equal number to change their minds in either direction. So we would expect 30 to change from unsatisfactory to satisfactory and 30 to change from satisfactory to unsatisfactory. This now enables us to calculate χ^2.

Observed	Expected	$(O-E)$	$\lvert O-E \rvert - \frac{1}{2}$	$\dfrac{(\lvert O-E \rvert - \frac{1}{2})^2}{E}$
50	30	20	19.5	12.675
10	30	-20	19.5	12.675
				25.350

Applying the decision rules for $v = 1$, we must reject the null hypothesis at the 1% level. The difference between the observed and expected values cannot be attributed to chance and we must conclude that association between response and type of powder is established.

If we were to test for association for tables larger than a 2×2, then we could use a very similar analysis. Let us consider a 2×3 table comprising independent samples. Suppose that a random sample of men and women indicated their view on a certain proposal as follows:

	In Favour	Opposed	Undecided	
Women	118	62	25	205
Men	84	78	37	199
	202	140	62	404

At a level of significance of (a) 0.01 and (b) 0.05, test the hypothesis that there is no difference in opinion between men and women in so far as this proposal is concerned.   (C.I.P.F.A.)

We adopt the null hypothesis that there is no association between response and sex. On this basis we may deduce that for a randomly chosen person from this sample;

$$P(\text{woman}) = \tfrac{205}{404}$$
$$P(\text{in favour}) = \tfrac{202}{404}$$
$$P(\text{opposed}) = \tfrac{140}{404}$$

So the expected number of women in favour to the proposal is

$$\tfrac{205}{404} \times \tfrac{202}{404} \times 404 = 102.5$$

and the expected number of women opposed to the proposal is

$$\tfrac{205}{404} \times \tfrac{140}{404} \times 404 = 71$$

We can now obtain the remaining expected values by subtraction i.e.

Expected number of undecided women $= 205 - (102.5 + 71) = 31.5$
Expected number of men in favour $\quad = 202 - 102.5 = 99.5$
Expected number of men opposed $\quad = 140 - 71 = 69$
Expected number of undecided men $\quad = 62 - 31.5 = 30.5$

So the expected table looks like this:

	In Favour	Opposed	Undecided
Women	102.5	71	31.5
Men	99.5	69	30.5

Observed	Expected	$(O-E)$	$\dfrac{(O-E)^2}{E}$
118	102.5	15.5	2.34
62	71	-9	1.14
25	31.5	-6.5	1.34
84	99.5	-15.5	2.41
78	69	9	1.17
37	30.5	6.5	1.38
		$\chi^2 =$	9.78

In this example, we have two degrees of freedom in calculating the expected values. Consulting the table, we see that there is a 5% chance of χ^2 exceeding 5.99 and a 1% chance of χ^2 exceeding 9.21. Hence, we reject the null hypothesis at both the 5% level and the 1% level.

Summary on Degrees of Freedom

We see then, that the χ^2 test is very versatile, and it might be useful here to summarise the number of degrees of freedom.

(a) For goodness of fit tests with n classes, $v = n - 1$.

(b) For goodness of fit tests to a binomial or Poisson distribution with n classes, $v = n - 2$.

(c) For goodness of fit tests to a normal distribution with n classes, $v = n - 3$.

(d) For tests of association for a contingency table with m rows and n columns $v = (n - 1)(m - 1)$.

In conclusion, it should be noted that of all significance tests, χ^2 is probably the most widely used. However, many statisticians are highly critical of χ^2 testing, reasoning that there are other tests available which are far more suitable. We do not consider this book to be aimed at a level sufficient to discuss the criticisms in detail, but we will leave you one point to ponder. None of the null hypotheses we have considered with respect to goodness of fit can be *exactly* true, so if we increase the sample size (and hence the value of χ^2) we would ultimately reach the point when all null hypotheses would be rejected. All that the χ^2 test can tell us, then, is that the sample size is too small to reject the null hypothesis!

EXERCISES TO CHAPTER SIXTEEN

16.1 (a) What does the χ^2 test test?

(b) The number of rejects in six batches of equal size were:

Batch	Number of Rejects
A	270
B	308
C	290
D	312
E	300
F	320

Test the hypothesis that the difference between them is due to chance using a level of significance of 0.05.   I.C.M.A.

16.2 The number of breakdowns that have occurred during the last 100 shifts is as follows:

Number of breakdowns per shift	0	1	2	3	4	5
Frequency:						
Expected number of shifts	14	27	27	18	9	5
Actual number of shifts	10	23	25	22	10	10

Show whether the manager is justified in his claim that the difference between the number of actual and expected breakdowns is due to chance. It has been customary to use a significance level of 0.05.

I.C.M.A.

16.3   A manufacturer of fashion garments for the younger age groups suspects that the market for his product has changed recently. Sales records for previous years showed that 14% of buyers were below 16 years of age, 38% were 16 to 20 years of age, 26% were 21 to 25 years and 22% were over 25. A random sample of 200 recent buyers, however, showed the following results:

Age	Under 16	16–20	21–25	Above 25
Frequency	22	62	60	56

Required:
(1) Compare the results of the sample with those expected from previous records.
(2) What null hypothesis should be tested using these data?
(3) Carry out a chi-squared (χ^2) test of significance.
(4) Express your conclusions in terms meaningful to management.

Section of χ^2 Table

Degrees of freedom	1	2	3	4	5
$\chi^2_{0.05}$	3.84	5.99	7.82	9.49	11.07

A.C.A.

16.4   The quality control department of a certain firm randomly selects 200 components and tests them for surface defects. The results were as follows:

Number of surface defects	0	1	2	3	4	5	6 and over
Number of components	90	62	31	13	3	1	0

Fit a Poisson distribution to this data, and test for goodness of fit.

16.5   Assuming that a component never contains more than five defectives, fit a binomial distribution to the data in 16.4, and test for goodness of fit.

16.6   The following experiment was performed 64 times: a coin was tossed until it came up heads and x, the number of tosses to achieve a head, was recorded. The following data were obtained:

x	Frequency
1	24
2	17
3	16
4	3
Greater than 5	4
Total	64

Are the data consistent with the hypothesis that the coin was fair?

C.I.P.F.A.

16.7   An examination of the purchase department's records for a random sample of 100 orders for a certain commodity reveals the following distribution of lead-times, that is, delays between placing an order and receiving the consignment.

Lead-times	Orders
Under 14 days	28
14 and under 21 days	52
21 days and over	20

If it is assumed that the lead-times are normally distributed with mean 16 days and standard deviation 5 days, what frequencies of orders would be expected for each category of lead-time?

Apply the chi-squared test at a 90% significance level to check whether the observed data contradict the assumptions of normality.

O.N.C.

16.8   (a) An association between two characteristics, which is apparent from some data, is found to be of borderline statistical significance. Explain this conclusion and say what action should be taken in order to reach a clearer decision.

(b) Three types of machine A, B and C, are used by a company to produce items which are very prone to a certain type of imperfection. A random sample of 100 items from each machine showed the number of perfect and imperfect items to be as follows:

	Perfect	Imperfect
A	33	67
Machine B	39	61
C	48	52

Required: Use the chi-squared (χ^2) test to examine at the 0.05 level of significance whether there is any association between machine type and proneness to imperfection.

Section of χ^2 Table

Degrees of freedom	1	2	3	4	5	6
$\chi^2_{0.05}$	3.84	5.99	7.82	9.49	11.07	11.59

A.C.A.

16.9   Suppose that a random sample of men and women indicated their view on a certain proposal as follows:

	In Favour	Opposed	Undecided
Women	118	62	25
Men	84	78	37

At a level of significance of (a) 0.01, (b) 0.05, test the hypothesis that there is no difference in opinion between men and women in so far as this proposal is concerned.   C.I.P.F.A.

16.10   Two factories using materials purchased from the same supplier and closely controlled to an agreed specification produce output for a given period classified into three quality grades as follows:

	Output in Tons			
Quality grade:	A	B	C	Total
Factory:				
X	42	13	33	88
Y	20	8	25	53
Total	62	21	58	141

(a) Do these output figures show a significant difference at the 5% level?

(b) What hypothesis have you tested?   I.C.M.A.

16.11   Suppose that a random sample of men and women indicated their view on a proposal of public importance as follows:

	Opposed	Undecided	In Favour
Men	156	74	170
Women	122	50	236

At levels of significance of (a) 0.01 and (b) 0.05, test the hypothesis that there is no difference between the views of men and women on this issue.   I.C.M.A.

16.12   A certain drug was administered to 100 volunteers with common colds, and 35 reported that the drug brought some relief. The next winter, a new improved drug was given to the same group, and this time 43 reported that the drug brought some relief. Are we justified in assuming that the second drug is more likely to bring relief?

16.13 Pharmaceuticals Ltd. have developed three new respiratory drugs. They submitted the drugs to clinical trials, the results of which are given in the table below. Determine whether or not these figures indicate a real difference in the response of the diseases to the drugs, and explain your conclusion. Use the chi-square (χ^2) distribution as test of significance with the 0.01 level of significance table provided.

Drug	Percentage of Patients Recovered	Percentage of Patients Not Recovered
A	65	35
B	90	10
C	85	15

Distribution of χ^2

Degrees of Freedom	Probability (0.01 level of significance)
1	6.64
2	9.21
3	11.34
4	13.28

A.C.A.

16.14 (a) A marketing information firm has kept records on a random sample of 144 drivers who bought new cars in 1965. Drivers were classified according to age in 1965 and records kept include data on how many other new cars each driver has bought in the last ten years. This information is tabulated below.

Additional New Cars Bought	Age of Driver			Total
	20 and under 30	30 and under 40	40 and over	
0	19	5	12	36
1	23	13	12	48
2	11	18	7	36
More than 2	7	12	5	24
Total	60	48	36	

Determine whether there is any evidence that there is a relationship between propensity to buy new cars and age of drivers in U.K.

(b) How useful might your conclusion be for a car assembly firm which is investigating the problem of advertising directed at specific age groups? I.C.A.

16.15   A market research agency has been commissioned to report on the smoking habits of men and women in a particular area. Two samples were taken, one of 200 men and the other of 200 women. The findings are shown in the following table:

	Smokers	Non-Smokers	Total
Men	110	90	200
Women	104	96	200

You are required to:

(a) test the hypothesis that difference in sex has no effect on the number of smokers in the two samples, and

(b) explain your conclusion in (a).

Use the chi-square (χ^2) distribution as a test of significance, with the 0.05 level of significance table below.

Distribution of χ^2

Degrees of Freedom	Probability (0.05 level of significance)
1	3.84
2	5.99
3	7.82
4	9.49

16.16   The Acca Co. Ltd. tests all components built into its products to ensure that they have attained the standard of quality required. There are three checkers, *A*, *B* and *C*, who undertake this work. The table below shows the numbers of components accepted and rejected by the checkers when they tested three batches of component 1703 recently delivered to the factory. You are required to test the hypothesis that the proportions of components rejected by the three are equal and explain the significance of your conclusion. Use the chi-square (χ^2) distribution as a test of significance, with the 0.05 level of significance table provided.

The Acca Co. Ltd. Components Quality Test

	Checker *A*	Checker *B*	Checker *C*	Total
Accepted	44	56	50	150
Rejected	16	24	10	50

Distribution of χ^2

Degrees of Freedom	Probability (0.05 level of significance)
1	3.84
2	5.99
3	7.82
4	9.49

A.C.A.

16.17 The number of students passed and failed by three examiners in a certain examination were as follows:

	Mr. X	Mr. Y	Mr. Z
Passed	50	47	56
Failed	5	14	8

Test the hypothesis that the proportions of students failed by the three examiners are equal.

Table of Chi-square

Degrees of Freedom	$p = 0.1$	0.05	0.01
1	2.7	3.8	6.6
2	4.6	6.0	9.2
3	6.3	7.8	11.3
4	7.8	9.5	13.3
5	9.2	11.1	15.1
6	10.6	12.6	16.8

C.I.P.F.A.

16.18 The following data is based on a random sample of 1000 businessmen:

	Profit Maximisers	Revenue Maximisers	Total
Studied economics	200	100	300
Did not study economics	200	500	700
Total	400	600	1000

Test by *two* different statistical techniques whether the above information suggests any association between education in economics and the objectives of businessmen.

Table of Chi-square

Degrees of Freedom	$p = 0.1$	0.05	0.01
1	2.7	3.8	6.6
2	4.6	6.0	9.2
3	6.3	7.8	11.3
4	7.8	9.5	13.3
5	9.2	11.1	15.1
6	10.6	12.6	16.8

C.I.P.F.A.

16.19 Samples of students with varying educational backgrounds obtained the following results in their final degree examinations:

	Third Class	Second Class (lower)	Upper Second/ First
Secondary	24	58	18
Comprehensive	36	112	52
Grammar	80	230	90
Public/Direct Grant	60	200	40

Test whether there is any association between pre-university education and the class of degree. C.I.P.F.A.

Chapter Seventeen

Regression and Correlation

One of the most sought-after type of person is the type who can make accurate predictions. A person who can do this is a great asset to any company or government. In this chapter, we are going to attempt to explain the statistical basis of making such predictions. However, you mustn't get the impression that after reading this chapter you will be able to forecast future events perfectly. After all, if we, the authors, could do this we would not be lecturing at Liverpool Polytechnic – instead we would be earning a lucrative living at the expense of the local bookmakers and the football pools firms. Now clearly, if we are going to make predictions, we must have some basis on which they can be made. Firstly, then, we will examine this aspect.

Bivariate Distributions

Some little time ago, there was an argument in a Board of Studies at Liverpool Polytechnic. Some of the lecturers were quite certain that the more regularly a student attended lectures, the greater was his chance of scoring high marks in his examinations. Other lecturers were not so sure – they argued that perhaps the really bright student can work highly successfully on his own, and only needs tutorial time for the lecturer to explain the points that he does not understand. Now the only way to settle arguments like this is to examine the facts, so a random sample of twenty students was chosen and their marks in accountancy and their percentage attendance were examined. The results were as follows:

Examination marks in accountancy	48	49	59	31	59	89	60	55	34	68
Percentage attendance	74	68	90	92	85	95	93	97	70	85
Examination marks in accountancy	58	55	73	56	78	77	42	38	50	26
Percentage attendance	70	82	94	98	88	92	86	67	79	52

Now this sample is rather different from others that we have considered: whereas in other samples each item has a single value, in

this sample each item has two values. We call distributions like this
bivariate distributions.

We cannot of course draw any conclusions at all from this sample
as it stands – it would be much more meaningful to graph the data.
Examining Fig. 17.1, we see that the sample does give some evidence
that the higher the attendance, the greater is the mark that a student
is likely to obtain. Can you see that the general trend of the points
on this diagram is an upward slope from left to right? Certainly, no
candidate with a very low attendance scored a very high mark, but
the odd-man-out in this array is the man with a high attendance

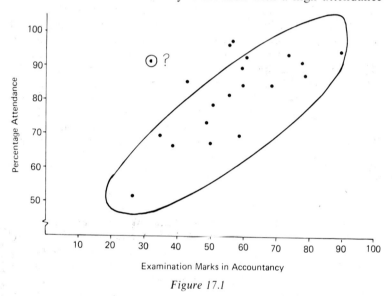

Figure 17.1

(92%) and rather low mark (31). We have marked this candidate with
a question mark. Statisticians call graphs of bivariate distributions
scatter diagrams, and use them to obtain some indication as to
whether there is any *association* between the variables. Having discovered from the scatter diagram that association (or relationship)
appears to exist, we should now attempt to measure the degree of
association between variables. If we can do this, and if the degree
of association is high, then we can use our knowledge of one variable
to predict the other.

Regression and Correlation

Regression analysis attempts to discover the *nature* of the association
between the variables, and does this in the form of an equation. We

can then use this equation to predict one variable given that we have sufficient information about the other variable. The variable we are trying to predict we call the *dependent variable*, and in the scatter diagram it is conventional to plot this using the y (vertical) axis. The variable we use as our basis for prediction we call the *independent variable*, and it is customary to plot this on the x (horizontal) axis. Before we undertake regression analysis, then, it would be useful to decide which is the dependent and which is the independent variable. It seems more reasonable to say that given the percentage attendance we could predict examination marks, rather than to say that given the examination marks we could predict percentage attendance. So here we will make attendance our independent variable (x) and examination mark our dependent variable (y).

Correlation attempts to express the *degree* of the association between the variables. When measuring correlation, it does not matter which variable is dependent and which is independent. Regression analysis implies a 'cause and effect' relationship, i.e. a low attendance causes poor examination performance. But variables can be correlated even though they in no way affect each other – they may be both influenced by a third variable. For example, it has been shown that there is a high degree of correlation between infant mortality and overcrowding – but the point is that both variables are closely affected by level of income.

The Regression Line

Let us see if we can express the nature of the association between the variables in the form of an equation. The way we shall do this is to draw a line that is the *best fit* to the bivariate distribution. Now what form should this line take? Sometimes the line that forms the best fit to the data is a straight line. If this is the case, we say that there is a *linear relationship* between the variables. However, in other cases a curve would be the best fit, and in such cases we say there is a *curvilinear* relationship between the variables. We shall confine ourselves, in this book, to examining linear relationships. Do you remember from your algebra that the equation of the straight line is $y = a + bx$, where a and b are constants? What we must do is find the values of the constants a and b.

Our problem, then, is to decide how to draw the straight line that gives the best fit to a series of points on a scatter diagram. One way we can do this is to place a ruler on the graph paper, juggle about with it until it 'looks right', and draw the line. We could then find where this line cuts the y axis (this would give us the constant a) and then find the gradient of the line (this would give the constant *b*). The trouble with this method is that we can never be sure that the line chosen gives the best fit – we will always have the nagging doubt that if we tried again we might get a better fit. If we use this method then we are relying on a *subjective assessment*, and in quantitative studies this is just not good enough. What we need is an objective assessment of how well the points fit the line. Really, we must decide what we mean by a good fit; and a good fit is one that makes the *total error* in fitting as small as possible. Fig 17.2 shows a typical type of error we might make when fitting a point to the line. For various values of the independent variable (call them x_i) we can observe values of the dependent variable (call them y_i). But when we obtain the line of best fit, then we assume that the value of the dependent

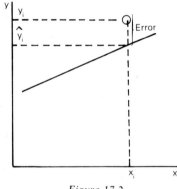

Figure 17.2

variable associated with x_i could well be $\hat{y}_i$. Clearly, the error we have made in this case is $y_i - \hat{y}_i$.

One criterion we could use might be to select the line that makes the sum of these errors as small as possible. At first sight this might appear to be very sensible, but unfortunately it gives very poor results indeed, because positive errors can be made to cancel negative errors. In Fig. 17.3, both the lines satisfy the criterion equally well (the sum of the errors is zero) but whereas the fit in (a) seems quite good, the fit in (b) is clearly very bad.

If we attempted to minimise the total absolute error, then we would prevent positive errors cancelling negative errors. Again, this does not work well in practice as we show in Fig. 17.4 where although (a) gives the better fit, (b) minimises the sum of the absolute errors. In fact, the line drawn in (b) ignores the middle point altogether!

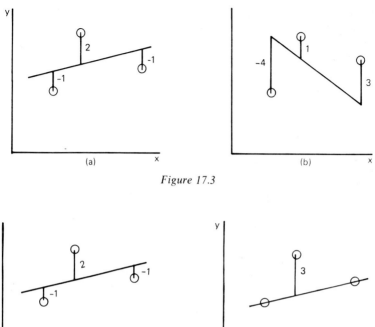

Figure 17.3

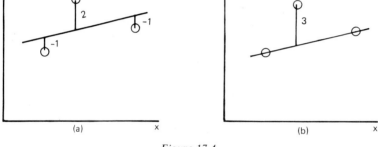

Figure 17.4

It will come as no surprise to you to learn that the statisticians have rejected both criteria as highly unsatisfactory. They consider the line of best fit to be the one which minimises the sum of the squares of the errors – the so-called *'least-squares line'*. The criterion has three advantages: firstly as we are squaring the errors, we remove the chance of negative errors cancelling positive errors; secondly, all the points are taken into account, so this criterion avoids lines like the one in Fig. 17.4(b); thirdly, squaring places stress on large errors, and the minimising criterion will mean that we are attempting to avoid large errors.

The Least-Squares Regression Line

Having decided on the least-squares criterion, we must now investigate the mechanism of fitting the line. Firstly, we note that for the

Statistics

values x_i of the independent variable we can observe the values of the dependent variable y_i, and the value of the dependent variable on the fitted line is

$$\hat{y}_i = a + bx_i$$

So the error we make in fitting is

$$y_i - \hat{y}_i = y_i - a - bx_i$$

The sum of the squares of all the errors is

$$S = \Sigma (y_i - a - bx_i)^2$$

and to satisfy the criterion we must find the values of a and b that minimise S. We can do this by solving the so-called *normal equations*[1]

$$\Sigma y_i = na + b \Sigma x_i$$
$$\Sigma x_i y_i = a \Sigma x_i + b \Sigma x_i^2$$

Look at these equations carefully, and you will notice that we need to know five quantities, Σy_i, Σx_i, $\Sigma x_i y_i$, Σx_i^2 and n (the number of observations). We can now calculate the regression line for the percentage attendance (x) and the examination marks in accountancy (y) noting that there are $n = 20$ observations:

x_i	y_i	x_i^2	$x_i y_i$
74	48	5476	3552
68	49	4624	3332
90	59	8100	5310
92	31	8464	2852
85	59	7225	5015
95	89	9025	8455
93	60	8649	5580
97	55	9409	5335
70	34	4900	2380
85	68	7225	5780
70	58	4900	4060
82	55	6724	4510
94	73	8836	6862
98	56	9604	5488
88	78	7744	6864
92	77	8464	7084
86	42	7396	3612
67	38	4489	2546
79	50	6241	3950
52	26	2704	1352
1657	1105	140199	93919

[1] For a formal derivation of the normal equations see Owen and Jones, *Modern Analytical Techniques*, pp. 301–3.

Substituting these values in the normal equations, we have

$$1105 = 20a + 1657b$$
$$93919 = 1657a + 140199b$$

Probably you do not like solving simultaneous equations – few people do. So it will come as a relief to you to learn that instead of solving the simultaneous equations, general expressions for a and b can be used.

$$a = \frac{1}{n}(\Sigma y_i - b\Sigma x_i)$$

$$b = \frac{\Sigma xy - \dfrac{\Sigma x \Sigma y}{n}}{\Sigma x^2 - \dfrac{(\Sigma x)^2}{n}}$$

Now as the expression for a requires a knowledge of b, it will be necessary to find b first.

$$b = \frac{93919 - \dfrac{1657 \times 1105}{20}}{140199 - \dfrac{(1657)^2}{20}} = 0.812$$

$$a = \frac{1}{20}(1105 - 0.812 \times 1657) = -12.02$$

So we can now state that the equation linking percentage attendance and examination mark in accountancy is

$$y = -12.02 + 0.812x$$

Interpolation and Extrapolation

The regression equation that we have just obtained is called the regression line of y on x. It shows how the values of y depend upon the values of x. Having obtained this regression line, what can we do with it? Well, we could use it for purposes of prediction. Consulting our data, we notice that the candidate who had a 74% attendance obtained an examination mark of 48%. Let us now see if we can predict his examination mark, given his percentage attendance. We have $x = 74$, so

$$y = -12.02 + 0.812 \times 74$$
$$= 48.068$$

– which is an extremely good prediction.

We must warn you to be very careful when making predictions based on a regression equation, and it would be useful to ask just what we mean when we make a prediction for y given the value of x. When we make such predictions, we are stating that y is subject to random fluctuations for each given value of x, and our prediction is the *average value* of y. Diagrammatically, the actual situation looks like this:

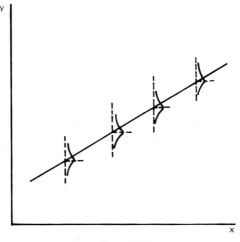

Figure 17.5

It would be useful to explain just why the values of y are subjected to these fluctuations. One reason for this is because of *stochastic errors* – which means that we cannot reproduce experiments exactly. Suppose we considered just one of the students, and gave him a repeated number of examinations in accountancy. We would expect his marks to vary from examination to examination because, firstly, the student will not be equally well prepared for each examination, and secondly, because we cannot guarantee that each examination is equally difficult. In other words, each examination will occur under uniquely different circumstances, and the marks obtained will reflect this. So we can see that stochastic errors are the effect of other variables that we have not accounted for in our analysis. In the example we have been considering, the most important omitted variable is without doubt the differences in ability.

Now you may argue that in many cases stochastic error can be avoided. This is certainly true with respect to experiments involving the natural sciences. Here, we will find that it is possible to hold the variables not under consideration constant (for example, the volume of a gas is affected by both temperature and pressure, but it is quite possible to observe the effect on the volume of a gas if the temperature is varied but the pressure remains constant). However, even under these conditions, fluctuations can still occur through *measurement error*, so even in such cases we must be careful when making predictions. The most care, of course, is needed when dealing with economic data, because this is highly susceptible to both stochastic error and measurement error.

Earlier, we predicted the examination mark for the candidate with a 74% attendance, and compared it with his actual score. Now let us predict the score for a fictitious candidate – one with a 65% attendance. Here we have

$$y = -12.02 + 0.812 \times 65 = 40.76$$

The estimate we have made here is within the range of our observed x values $(52 - 98\%)$, and we give the name *interpolation* to such estimates. But we might wish to make an estimate outside this

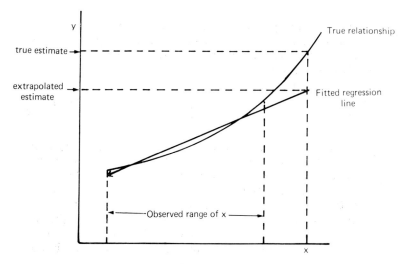

Figure 17.6

range – for example, the estimated mark for a candidate with a 100%
attendance would be

$$y = -12.02 + 0.812 \times 100 = 69.18$$

and we give the name *extrapolation* to such estimates. Now both
types of estimate are liable to stochastic and measurement error, but
an extrapolated estimate is liable to further error. The danger here
is that although a straight line may form a good fit to points within
the range of the x values, it may not be a good fit outside this range.
This is illustrated in Fig. 17.6, and we can see that great caution is
needed when making extrapolated estimates.

Linear Regression and Time Series

In chapter six, we saw how moving averages could be used to analyse
a time series, and we will now show you how a similar analysis can
be performed using linear regression. The table below shows how
the sales of a certain product have varied over four years.

Yr./Qr.	1	2	3	4
1973	40	60	90	70
1974	50	70	110	80
1975	70	80	120	90
1976	80	100	130	100

Now we are assuming here that sales are dependent on time, so we
will call time x and sales y. To convert the time periods into a 'variable', we will number the time periods from 1 to 16, and we now
have a bivariate distribution.

x	1	2	3	4	5	6	7	8	9	10	11	12	13	14	15	16
y	40	60	90	70	50	70	110	80	70	80	120	90	80	100	130	100

In this example, we will show you how you can simplify the calculations involved in the regression equation. We can do this by using
the method we employed when calculating the mean and standard
deviation – taking an arbitrary origin. Before we do this, however,
we wish to restate what we said earlier – that it is much preferable
to buy a pocket calculator and use the method already explained.
For those of you who cannot obtain a calculator (or are preparing
for examinations that do not allow their use) let us take an arbitrary
origin of 8 for x and 70 for y.

$(x_i - 8) = x'$	$(y_i - 70) = y'$	$(x')^2$	$x'y'$
-7	-30	49	210
-6	-10	36	60
-5	20	25	-100
-4	0	16	0
-3	-20	9	60
-2	0	4	0
-1	40	1	-40
0	10	0	0
1	0	1	0
2	10	4	20
3	50	9	150
4	20	16	80
5	10	25	50
6	30	36	180
7	60	49	420
8	30	64	240
8	220	344	1330
$= \Sigma x'$	$\Sigma y'$	$\Sigma (x')^2$	$\Sigma x'y'$

What effect do you think taking an origin will make on our formula for a and b? In taking an origin we have shifted each point (horizontally for x and vertically for y) by an identical distance. Students who have studied modern mathematics will realise that we have performed a *translation* on all the points. Now the important thing is that the array of the points remains the same: the line of best fit to the original points will have an identical gradient to the line of best fit to the translated points. So you can see that the constant b is unaffected by taking an origin. However, although the *slope* of the line is the same for both arrays, the *position* of the line is clearly different, so the value of the intercept a will not be the same in each case. To obtain a, we must work in original units. If you find this argument difficult to follow, examine Fig. 17.7, which should clarify matters.

We can, then, calculate b directly.

$$b = \frac{\Sigma x'y' - \dfrac{\Sigma x' \Sigma y'}{n}}{\Sigma (x')^2 - \dfrac{(\Sigma x')^2}{n}}$$

$$= \frac{1330 - \dfrac{8 \times 220}{16}}{344 - \dfrac{(8)^2}{16}}$$

$$= 3.59$$

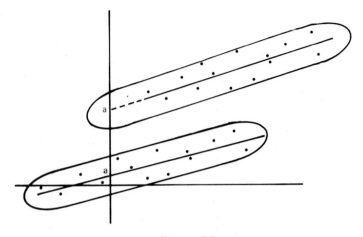

Figure 17.7

The formula for calculating a is

$$a = \frac{1}{n}(\Sigma\, y - b\,\Sigma\, x)$$

but we need the true values of x and y. For the x values, we took an origin of 8 after 16 observations, so the true value for x is

$$8 \times 16 + 8 = 136$$

and the true value for y is

$$70 \times 16 + 220 = 1340$$

$$\text{so}\quad a = \frac{1}{16}(1340 - 3.59 \times 136)$$

$$= 53.235$$

The equation of the trend line is

$$y = 53.235 + 3.59x$$

To obtain trend values, we would insert $x = 1, 2, 3, \ldots, 16$ in this equation. We could then use the method of chapter six to analyse the deviations from trend and seasonal variation.

Explained and Unexplained Variations

At the beginning of the chapter, we stated that regression analysis is used to state the relationship between two variables in the form of an equation, and we could then use the equation to predict a value for the dependent variable given knowledge of the independent variable. However, before doing this we should satisfy ourselves as to the strength of the relationship, because the stronger is the relationship, the more confident we can be about our predictions. So we need to be able to measure the *degree* of relationship between variables, and we do this by calculating the *coefficient of correlation*. Now the coefficient of correlation does not require us to label one variable dependent and the other independent: it merely measures the proportion in one variable (it doesn't matter which) that can be *explained* by knowledge of the other variable.

Let us now examine the concept of 'explained variation' more closely. Consider the following bivariate distribution, where x is the independent, and y the dependent variable:

x	y
1	1
2	2
3	6
4	7
5	10
6	16
7	21
$\Sigma x = 28$	$\Sigma y = 63$

Now suppose you were asked to predict y *without any knowledge of the corresponding values of x*. Under such circumstances, the best prediction that you could make would be to calculate the value of the arithmetic mean, i.e.

$$\bar{y} = \frac{\Sigma y}{n} = \frac{63}{7} = 9$$

(we saw in chapter twelve that this was the best estimate we could make) In Fig. 17.8, the horizontal line $\bar{y} = 9$ represents our estimate and the variation of the points about this estimate is shown by the dotted lines. Notice the sum of the deviations is zero – as we would expect. We can use this diagram to calculate the variance of y.

$$S^2 = \frac{\Sigma (y - \bar{y})^2}{n}$$

$$= \frac{(-8)^2 + (-7)^2 + (-3)^2 + (-2)^2 + 1^2 + 7^2 + 12^2}{7}$$

$$= 45.71$$

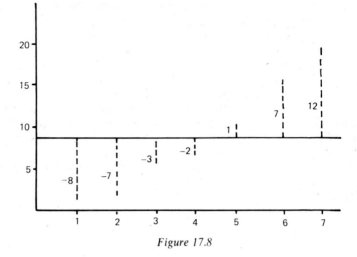

Figure 17.8

If we were asked to predict values for y given the corresponding values of x, then we could greatly improve our estimate using regression analysis.

x	y	x^2	xy
1	1	1	1
2	2	4	4
3	6	9	18
4	7	16	28
5	10	25	50
6	16	36	96
7	21	49	147
$\Sigma x = 28$	$\Sigma y = 63$	$\Sigma y^2 = 140$	$\Sigma xy = 344$

$$b = \frac{\Sigma xy - \dfrac{\Sigma x \Sigma y}{n}}{\Sigma x^2 - \dfrac{(\Sigma x)^2}{n}}$$

$$= \frac{344 - \dfrac{28 \times 63}{7}}{140 - \dfrac{(28)^2}{7}}$$

$$= 3.29$$

$$a = \frac{1}{n}\left[\Sigma\, y - b\,\Sigma\, x\right]$$

$$= \frac{1}{7}(63 - 3.29 \times 28)$$

$$= -4.16$$

So the least-squares line of best fit is

$$y = -4.16 + 3.29x$$

We can now draw this regression line on to the scatter diagram. This regression line represents our new estimate of y (which we call $\hat{y}$),

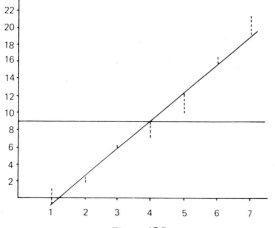

Figure 17.9

and the dotted lines show the deviations of y from our new prediction. Notice that the variation of y about our new prediction is much less than previously – so we would expect the variance to be much less. We shall now verify this.

x	y	$\hat{y} = -4.16 + 3.29x$	$(y - \hat{y})$	$(y - \hat{y})^2$
1	1	−0.87	1.87	3.50
2	2	2.42	−0.42	0.18
3	6	5.71	0.29	0.08
4	7	9.00	−2.00	4.00
5	10	12.29	−2.29	5.24
6	16	15.58	0.42	0.18
7	21	18.87	2.13	4.54
			0	17.72

$$S^2 = \frac{17.72}{7} = 2.53$$

So our knowledge of x has reduced the total variance from 45.71 to 2.53 – this knowledge has helped us to 'explain' a considerable part of the total variance. Look at it this way: if we have no knowledge of x, then the best prediction we can make of the value of y is 9. However, if we are given that x is (say) 6, then using the regression equation we can predict y to be $\hat{y} = 15.58$. Now when $x = 6$, we observed y to be 16, so

$$\text{Total variation} \quad = y - \bar{y} = 16 - 9 = 7$$
$$\text{Explained variation} \quad = \hat{y} - \bar{y} = 15.58 - 9 = 6.58$$
So $\quad \text{Unexplained variation} = y - \hat{y} = 16 - 15.58 = 0.42$

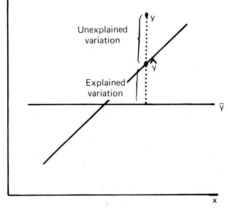

Figure 17.10

We see, then, that in this example much of the variation in y can be explained by variations in x. Now if the unexplained variation is very small, we can conclude that there is a high degree of correlation between x and y. If all the variation in y could be explained by variations in x, then we would have *perfect correlation* and all of the points would lie on the regression line. In statistical analysis it is highly unlikely that perfect correlation would be found.

Measuring Correlation

From the last section, you can see that the unexplained variation can be used as a measure of correlation, i.e. the degree of the relationship between the two variables. Let us now see if we can develop a formal measure of correlation. Firstly, we must define some symbols.

Let $S^2 y$ be the 'total variance' of y, that is, the variance of y calculated without knowledge of the corresponding values of x. Also, let $S^2\hat{y}$ be the variance that remains unexplained after taking account of the associated values of x.

From the previous example, then, $S^2y = 45.71$, and $S^2\hat{y} = 2.53$. It follows from the above definition that the variance that has been 'explained' by regression analysis must be the difference between the 'total' and 'unexplained' variance, i.e.

$$S^2y - S^2\hat{y}$$

We can measure correlation, then, by calculating the proportion of the explained variation to the total variation, i.e.

$$\frac{S^2y - S^2\hat{y}}{S^2y}$$
$$= 1 - \frac{S^2\hat{y}}{S^2y}$$

What sort of results can we expect from this measure? Well, let us suppose that we have perfect correlation – then all variations in y can be explained by variations in x, and so $S^2\hat{y}$, the unexplained variance, would be zero. This means that our measure of correlation would be exactly equal to one. Now suppose that we have no correlation – the variance we obtain for y would be the same whether or not we used regression analysis. In other words, total variation is equal to unexplained variation $(S^2y = S^2\hat{y})$, so our measure of correlation would have a value of zero. So we see that our measure of correlation must lie between zero and one, and the closer the measure is to one, then the stronger is the degree of association.

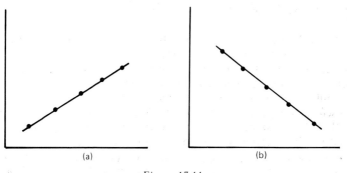

Figure 17.11

Now this measure has one great drawback. Fig. 17.11 gives two cases of perfect correlation, though we can see that they are of quite different types. In case (a) we notice that y increases as x increases, and we call this a *positive correlation*. In case (b), however, y decreases as x increases and we call this a *negative correlation*. It would seem sensible, then, not merely to measure correlation, but also to state whether it is positive or negative. We can do this by defining the *correlation coefficient* (r) as

$$r = \pm \sqrt{1 - \frac{S^2\hat{y}}{S^2 y}}$$

and from what we learned earlier it follows that

$$-1 \leqslant r \leqslant 1$$

So if correlation is positive we take the positive root, and if it is negative we take the negative root.

Although this is a perfectly workable definition of correlation, it is not really in a convenient form. There are two reasons for this. Firstly, calculating $S^2\hat{y}$ as we did previously is rather awkward, so we require a formula that will make the calculations easier. The second problem involves selecting the appropriate root – is it positive or is it negative? As the formula stands now, the only way we can decide on the appropriate root is to examine the bivariate distribution and decide whether correlation is positive or negative. If you have a large number of values to deal with, then making this decision may not be easy. Now both objections are overcome to a large extent if we use the formula

$$r = \frac{\text{covariance}(xy)}{\sqrt{\sigma_x^2 \sigma_y^2}} \qquad \text{(see footnote 1)}$$

where $\text{covariance}(xy) = \frac{1}{n}\left[\Sigma xy - \frac{\Sigma x \Sigma y}{n}\right]$

You will often meet this statistic under the name *Pearson's Correlation Coefficient* or sometimes the Product Moment Correlation Coefficient. Notice the similarity of this formula and the formula we quoted earlier for calculating b. In fact, $\frac{1}{n}$ times the numerator of the b formula is the covariance, and $\frac{1}{n}$ times the denominator is σ_x^2. This is a useful feature, as it enables us to develop regression and correlation together. As an example, we shall now calculate the correlation coefficient for the example we considered in the last section.

[1] For a formal derivation of this formula, see Owen and Jones, *Modern Analytical Techniques*, pp. 328–30. Sometimes you will see the formula in the form

$$r = \frac{\Sigma(y - \bar{y})(x - \bar{x})}{\sigma_x^2 \sigma_y^2}$$

x	y	x^2	y^2	xy
1	1	1	1	1
2	2	4	4	4
3	6	9	36	18
4	7	16	49	28
5	10	25	100	50
6	16	36	256	96
7	21	49	441	147
$\Sigma x = 28$	$\Sigma y = 63$	$\Sigma x^2 = 140$	$\Sigma y^2 = 887$	$\Sigma xy = 344$

$$\text{covariance}(xy) = \frac{1}{n}\left[\Sigma xy - \frac{\Sigma x \Sigma y}{n}\right]$$

$$= \frac{1}{7}\left[344 - \frac{28 \times 63}{7}\right]$$

$$= 13.14$$

$$\sigma^2(x) = \frac{1}{n}\left[\Sigma x^2 - \frac{(\Sigma x)^2}{n}\right]$$

$$= \frac{1}{7}\left[140 - \frac{(28)^2}{7}\right]$$

$$= 4$$

$$\sigma^2(y) = \frac{1}{n}\left[\Sigma y^2 - \frac{(\Sigma y)^2}{n}\right]$$

$$= \frac{1}{7}\left[887 - \frac{(63)^2}{7}\right]$$

$$= 45.71$$

$$r = \frac{\text{cov}(xy)}{\sqrt{\sigma_x^2 \sigma_y^2}}$$

$$= 0.97$$

We will now show that this formula yields the same value as our original definition.

$$r = \pm\sqrt{1 - \frac{S^2\hat{y}}{S^2y}}$$

Earlier, we calculated $S^2\hat{y}$ to be 2.53, so we have

$$r = +\sqrt{1 - \frac{2.53}{45.71}} \quad \text{(as we can see that correlation is positive)}$$

$$= \sqrt{0.945}$$

$$= 0.97$$

The Interpretation of r

One very disturbing feature of some statistics textbooks is that although they explain how to calculate r in a logical and efficient manner, they completely ignore any interpretation you should give to your results. Now we think this is quite ridiculous – what is the

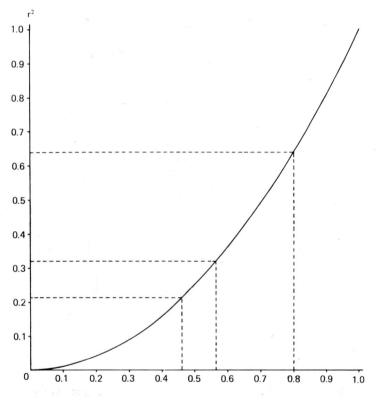

The relationship between the correlation coefficient and the coefficient of determination

Figure 17.12

point of calculating a statistic if you cannot interpret it? In the last section, we saw that $r = +0.97$ for the data we were considering – and clearly, strong positive correlation must exist between the variables. But what does $r = 0.97$ mean? Again, suppose we have two bivariate distributions, the first with $r = 0.8$, and the second with $r = 0.4$. Clearly, correlation is stronger in the first case than the second, but would we be justified in saying it was twice as strong?

In fact, it is much more meaningful to consider the square of the correlation coefficient. Do you remember that r^2 measures the proportion of total variation that can be explained by variations in x? If $r = 0.97$, then $r^2 = 0.94$ – and we can conclude that 94% of the variation in y can be explained by variations in x, leaving only 6% to be explained by other factors. So it would be reasonable to conclude that there is a high degree of correlation between the variables. The statistic r^2 is often called the *coefficient of determination*, and we can use it to answer the second problem – is a correlation coefficient of 0.8 twice as strong as a correlation coefficient of 0.4? If $r = 0.8$, r^2 is 0.64 – 64% of variation in y can be explained by variations in x. If $r = 0.4$, $r^2 = 0.16$ – 16% of variations in y can be explained by variations in x. So we conclude that a correlation coefficient of 0.8 is $\frac{0.64}{0.16} = 4$ times stronger than a correlation coefficient of 0.4. In Fig. 17.12 we have plotted the coefficient of correlation against the coefficient of determination. Reading from this graph, we see that a correlation coefficient of 0.8 is twice as strong as a coefficient of 0.565, and three times as strong as a coefficient of 0.462.

Having decided on how correlation should be interpreted, we would now like to issue a few words of warning. If analysis suggests that correlation exists, we are *not* justified in concluding that this indicates that cause and effect is established. We must not fall into the trap of concluding that cause and effect exists when it is nonsense to do so. Sometimes a high correlation is obviously nonsensical – for example there is a high positive correlation between the annual issue of TV licences and the annual admissions into mental institutions. It would be ludicrous to suggest that cause and effect exists here. The only logical conclusion one can draw is that, quite by chance, both statistics were increasing at the same rate. In this case it is obvious that cause and effect is not proved by a high correlation coefficient – but sometimes things are not quite so clear-cut. The high correlation between infant mortality and degree of overcrowding does seem to reasonably suggest that high overcrowding does cause high infant mortality, but in actual fact both are probably indicative of income levels. If, then, we can never use correlation as proof of cause and effect, you may wonder whether correlation is worthy of study. Well, we think it is. Correlation can give added weight to a relationship that theory suggests should exist, for example, we could use it to verify the economic theory that consumption depends upon income. Again, correlation can sometimes suggest that causal relationships might exist in areas that were not previously suspected – a technique often used in medical research. Here, correlation can often point to promising avenues of investigation.

Finally, we would like to point out that a low correlation coef-

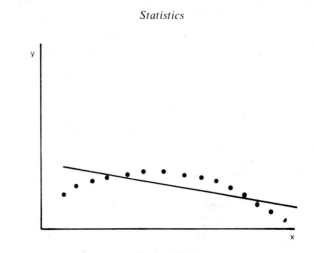

Figure 17.13

ficient does not necessarily mean a low degree of association. After all, the correlation coefficient measures the strength of a linear relationship, but the relationship might be curvilinear. The relationship between the variables in Fig. 17.13 is obviously very strong, though correlation analysis would not indicate this.

Significance Test of the Correlation Coefficient

Let us now return to the problem we considered at the beginning of this chapter, whether the student's attendance record affected his performance in examinations. We know that the correlation coefficient can help us answer this question, and we have already calculated

$$\Sigma x = 1657, \quad \Sigma y = 1105, \quad \Sigma x^2 = 140199, \quad \Sigma xy = 93919, \quad n = 20$$

and you can verify for yourself that $\Sigma y^2 = 66205$.

$$\mathrm{cov}(xy) = \frac{1}{20}\left[93919 - \frac{1657 \times 1105}{20}\right]$$

$$= 118.49$$

$$\sigma^2(x) = \frac{1}{20}\left[140199 - \frac{(1657)^2}{20}\right]$$

$$= 145.83$$

$$\sigma^2(y) = \frac{1}{20}\left[66205 - \frac{(1105)^2}{20}\right]$$

$$= 257.69$$

$$r = \frac{118.49}{\sqrt{145.83 \times 257.69}}$$
$$= 0.61$$
$$r^2 = 0.37$$

So we can conclude that 37% of the variation in examination marks can be explained by variation in attendance, the remaining 63% being explained by such factors as differences in aptitude, whether or not individual students were 'on form' on the day of the examination, etc.

The problem we must now face is this: are we justified on this evidence in concluding that there is some correlation between attendance and examination performance? After all, the data we have examined is a sample, and we know that conclusions based on samples can be wide of the truth! The obvious way of facing this problem is to undertake a significance test on our sample correlation coefficient. We will assume that the sample has been drawn from a population of all examination candidates with a correlation coefficient P. Moreover, we will assume that the population is uncorrelated, so we have

$$H_0: P = 0$$

Now we wish to test whether or not our sample correlation coefficient r supports our null hypothesis, so the alternative hypothesis is

$$H_1: r \neq P \text{ or } r \neq 0$$

On the (usual) assumption that H_0 is true, we now want to know the sampling distribution of the correlation coefficient. In fact, r has a t-distribution with $(n-2)$ degrees of freedom, so consulting the t tables for a two-sided test with $20-2 = 18$ degrees of freedom, we can obtain our decision rules.

(a) Accept H_0 and reject H_1 if $t < 2.101$
(b) Reject H_0 and accept H_1 if $2.101 < t < 2.878$ (5% level of significance)
(c) Reject H_0 and accept H_1 if $t > 2.878$ (1% level of significance)

To calculate the t-score for our correlation coefficient, we apply the formula

$$t = \sqrt{\frac{r^2(n-2)}{(1-r^2)}}$$

In effect, then, we are testing the significance of the coefficient of determination. The t-score for our correlation coefficient is

$$t = \sqrt{\frac{(0.61)^2(20-2)}{1-(0.61)^2}}$$
$$= 3.27$$

So, applying our decision rules, we would accept H_1, concluding that the sample correlation coefficient is significant at the 5% and at the 1% level.

Now suppose we perform a significance test on a sample correlation coefficient, and on the basis of the test we conclude that correlation exists. We must still remember that this does not prove a cause and effect relationship. Also this test has a further restriction as it assumes that the sample was drawn from a normal population.

Rank Correlation

Earlier, we stated that if large values of y are associated with large values of x, and if small values of y are associated with small values of x, the variables are positively correlated. Now if we *rank* the variables (i.e. order them as 1st, 2nd, 3rd, etc.) we can obtain a good idea as to whether or not the variables show any correlation. The following data refers to ordinary industrial shares in a certain year:

Month	Price Index	Dividend Yield
Jan.	142	4.5
Feb.	140	4.6
March	138	4.7
April	150	4.4
May	168	3.9
June	169	4.0
July	180	3.7
Aug.	182	3.5
Sept.	188	3.4
Oct.	183	3.6
Nov.	179	3.7
Dec.	190	3.3

If we write the price index in ascending order, we can easily assign ranks to the series,

Price index	138	140	142	150	168	169	179	180	182	183	188	190
Rank	1	2	3	4	5	6	7	8	9	10	11	12

Dividend yield	3.3	3.4	3.5	3.6	3.7	3.7	3.9	4.0	4.4	4.5	4.6	4.7
Rank	1	2	3	4	$5\frac{1}{2}$	$5\frac{1}{2}$	7	8	9	10	11	12

A dividend yield of 3.7 occurs twice. Instead of making 3.7 as 'equal 5th' we assign a rank of $5\frac{1}{2}$ to this score. Let us now rewrite our data in chronological order, this time using the ranks

Month	Rank (Price Index)	Rank (Dividend Yield)	D	D^2
Jan.	3	10	-7	49
Feb.	2	11	-9	81
March	1	12	-11	121
April	4	9	-5	25
May	5	7	-2	4
June	6	8	-2	4
July	8	$5\frac{1}{2}$	$2\frac{1}{2}$	6.25
Aug.	9	3	6	36
Sept.	11	2	9	81
Oct.	10	4	6	36
Nov.	7	$5\frac{1}{2}$	$1\frac{1}{2}$	2.25
Dec.	12	1	11	121
			0	566.5
			$=\Sigma D$	$=\Sigma D^2$

Notice that in March, the price index was at its lowest and the dividend yield was at its highest level. Likewise, in December price was at its lowest and dividend was at its highest. There would appear to be a negative correlation here. In fact, we could calculate the correlation coefficient using ranks rather than actual figures, and this would give us quite a good approximation to the value of the correlation coefficient. Moreover, if we use ranks, the calculations are much easier as the formula for the correlation coefficient simplifies to:

$$P = 1 - \frac{6\Sigma D^2}{n(n^2 - 1)} \quad {}^{1}$$

where D is the rank difference. This is known as *Spearman's Rank Correlation Coefficient*. In this case, then, we have

$$P = 1 - \frac{6 \times 566.5}{12(12^2 - 1)}$$
$$= -0.98$$

So we see here that there is a high degree of negative correlation. You should now calculate the true value of the correlation coefficient, and compare it with the rank correlation coefficient that we have derived.

Finally, notice that $\Sigma D = 0$ (think about this for a minute and you will realise that this must be so), and this acts as a useful check on our calculations.

[1] For formal derivation see *Modern Analytical Techniques*, pp. 338–40.

EXERCISES TO CHAPTER 17

17.1 (a) What is meant when two series of recorded figures such as expenditure on advertising and volume of sales are said to be linearly correlated?

(b) If, in such a case, a regression line can be established what practical use does it have?

(c) With the aid of scatter diagrams distinguish between positive and negative correlation.   O.N.C.

17.2 Describe the construction of a scatter diagram and a line of best fit. Illustrate by means of scatter diagrams the following three types of relationship between two variables:

(a) strong positive relationship;
(b) weak negative relationship;
(c) absence of relationship.   A.C.A.

17.3   *Advertising and Related Sales of Two Companies*

Company X		Company Y	
Sales (£000)	Advertising (£000)	Sales (£000)	Advertising (£000)
190	9.0	439	51.4
100	14.5	632	58.8
279	18.3	856	82.2
241	11.4	896	86.8
176	20.8	626	73.6
314	23.1	717	78.8
223	29.6	749	67.4
120	25.1	605	64.1
156	34.6	468	66.4
73	38.2	513	58.9
104	18.7	803	74.6
71	30.9	484	54.5
184	38.6	726	71.9
101	42.6	771	81.0
253	36.9	664	72.1

(a) What is meant by (i) *positive correlation,* (ii) *zero correlation?*
(b) Describe briefly the limitations of scatter diagrams.
(c) Draw *one* scatter diagram on which both firms' results are illustrated.
(d) Interpret the results of the diagram.   O.N.C.

17.4 (a) Calculate the coefficient of correlation for the following data:

Domestic Manufacturing Ltd. Payroll and Value of Product × Output

Month	Total Payroll (£000)	Total Value of Product × Output (£000)
Jan.	5	8
Feb.	6	9
March	7	9
April	9	11
May	8	13

(b) What is the purpose of finding the correlation coefficient in respect of the above data, and what does the value of the coefficient indicate?   A.C.A.

17.5 *Television Receiving Licences Current 1972. Monochrome and Colour*

	Monochrome (millions)	Colour (millions)
Jan.	15.2	1.4
Feb.	15.1	1.5
March	15.0	1.6
April	14.9	1.7
May	14.9	1.9
June	14.8	2.0
July	14.8	2.1
Aug.	14.7	2.2
Sept.	14.7	2.3
Oct.	14.5	2.5
Nov.	14.4	2.6
Dec.	14.2	2.8

Sources: Post Office; Department of Trade and Industry.

(a) Prepare a scatter diagram based on the data given above, mark in the mean point and briefly comment on what is revealed.
(b) Explain the difference between the product moment coefficient of correlation and the rank correlation coefficient, mentioning any advantages either might have over the other.
(c) What is the association between correlation and regression?
                                                                O.N.C.

17.6 Explain what is meant by the term 'product moment correlation coefficient'.

Age (in years)	18	20	21	27	23	34	24	42	38	44
Length of training required (in days)	8	5	6	8	7	11	8	10	6	8

The length of training required by operatives to be able to carry out a routine task is shown in the above table along with the age of the trainees. By calculating the product moment correlation coefficient determine whether the length of training required correlates with age.   O.N.C.

17.7 (a) Explain what is meant by 'product moment correlation coefficients' and 'rank correlation coefficients' and give examples where each one has advantages over the other.

(b)

x	24	26	21	23	22	19	18	17	15	16
y	35	33	31	29	25	24	23	21	20	19

Calculate the product moment correlation coefficient between the variables x and y.   O.N.C.

17.8 (a) Measurements on two variables are found to yield a correlation coefficient of 0.35. Give two reasons why it cannot necessarily be inferred that the two variables are causally related.

(b) The following table gives the mean daily temperature and the amount of electricity consumed on 8 consecutive Mondays during a year.

Temperature (°F)	37	32	35	40	40	44	42	48
Electricity consumption (megawatt hours)	3.7	3.8	3.7	3.6	3.7	3.4	3.4	3.3

Required: Code the data about the assumed means of 40 and 3.5 so that $x =$ temperature -40; $y =$ electricity consumption -3.5, and use the formula below, or some alternative you prefer, to calculate the coefficient of correlation between temperature and electricity consumption. Comment on your result.

$$r = \left(\Sigma xy - \frac{\Sigma x \Sigma y}{n} \right) \bigg/ \sqrt{\left(\Sigma x^2 - \frac{(\Sigma x)^2}{n} \right)\left(\Sigma y^2 - \frac{(\Sigma y)^2}{n} \right)}$$

A.C.A.

17.9 The following data taken from a manufacturing company's budget relates to volume of sales and the corresponding expenses. Obtain the product moment correlation coefficient and comment, in the light of your result, on the relationship between volume of sales and the total expenses.

Volume of sales (thousands of units)	5	6	7	8	9	10
Total expenses (£000)	74	77	82	86	92	95

O.N.C.

17.10 It is often suggested that low unemployment and a low rate of wage inflation cannot coexist. Examine the evidence below (1957–66) and discuss whether it supports the above contention, producing where necessary relevant statistical measures.

Year	Unemployment %	Change in Wages %
1957	1.6	5.0
1958	2.2	3.2
1959	2.3	2.7
1960	1.7	2.1
1961	1.6	4.1
1962	2.1	2.7
1963	2.6	2.9
1964	1.7	4.6
1965.	1.5	3.5
1966	1.6	4.4

Does the recent experience (1967–70) agree with your discussion above?

1967	2.5	4.0
1968	2.5	7.7
1969	2.5	5.7
1970	2.7	9.5

Source: Key Statistics 1900–70, L.C.E.S.

C.I.P.F.A.

17.11

$$r = \frac{\Sigma (x - \bar{x})(y - \bar{y})}{n\sigma_x \sigma_y}$$

Describe with examples what this coefficient measures and state the maximum and minimum values that 'r' can take.

An applicant for a certain post has to take five intelligence tests; he obtains the following results

Intelligence Test (x)	Score Obtained (y)
1	+2
2	+2
3	−3
4	+1
5	+3

By using the above formula or a formula of your own choice calculate the value of the product moment correlation coefficient 'r'. Comment on the view that his score increases as he progresses from one test to the next.

O.N.C.

17.12   (a) Explain the value of a scatter diagram in investigating the association between two sets of figures. Illustrate the scatter diagrams associated with different values of the correlation coefficient.

(b) The following table records annual rainfall and sunshine in a British coastal resort:

	1955	1956	1957	1958	1959	1960	1961	1962	1963	1964	1965
Rainfall (in)	15.1	15.8	14.9	16.6	12.6	17.4	16.1	13.7	15.5	17.8	13.2
Sunshine (hr)	1692	1634	1835	1741	1876	1561	1921	1942	1822	1542	1874

Calculate the rank correlation coefficient between rainfall and sunshine.   O.N.C.

17.13   (i) Ten students enter for two papers in the final examination of a professional body. The marks obtained by each student are:

	Paper 1	Paper 2
Total marks awarded for paper	100	10
Marks obtained by student A	58	7
B	56	5
C	54	8
D	65	10
E	58	5
F	60	7
G	59	6
H	51	2
I	53	4
J	56	6

Calculate the product moment correlation coefficient r between the two sets of marks and give a clear explanation of the meaning of your result.

(ii) Without doing any further calculations show the effect, if any, on r, of increasing all the marks by 15%.   O.N.C.

17.14

1971	Finished Output— (thousand tons)	Expenditure on Electricity (£)
Jan.	20	106
Feb.	22	138
March	25	158
April	26	172
May	21	120
June	23	142
July	28	184
Aug.	20	102
Sept.	25	164
Oct.	29	192

Express the relationship between the finished output and the expenditure on electricity during the period January to October 1971 in the form of the product moment coefficient of correlation and comment on the meaning of the figure obtained. O.N.C.

17.15 (a) Explain what are meant by the terms 'correlation coefficients' and 'scatter diagrams' and comment on their use.

(b) Two instructors assess the apprentices in a course they are running and give them the following placings

Apprentice	A	B	C	D	E	F	G	H	I	J	K	L
1st Instructor	1	2=	2=	4	5	6=	6=	8	9	10	11=	11=
2nd Instructor	1=	3	5	1=	4	6	10	7	8	11	9	12

Calculate the correlation between the two sets of placings.

Using the correlation you have just calculated comment on the agreement between the two instructors. O.N.C.

17.16 The personnel department of a large company is investigating the possibility of assessing the suitability of applicants by using psychological tests instead of normal interview procedures. A comparative test of seven applicants was carried out using both methods. The results were as follows:

Applicant	Ranking by Interview Procedure	Ranking by Psychological Tests
A	4	5
B	1	2
C	7	7
D	6	4
E	2	1
F	3	3
G	5	6

You are required to:
  (a) calculate the rank coefficient of correlation;
  (b) interpret the result established. C.I.P.F.A.

17.17

Month	Broadcast Receiving Licences Current at end of Period Monochrome Television (thousands)	Cinema Admissions Weekly Averages (millions)
1973		
April	13,667	2.89
May	13,549	2.74
June	13,427	2.10
July	13,341	2.86
Aug.	13,197	3.47
Sept.	13,025	3.15
Oct.	12,779	2.70
Nov.	12,514	2.42
Dec.	12,286	2.06
1974		
Jan.	12,051	3.21
Feb.	11,923	2.95
March	11,766	2.89

Sources: Post Office; Department of Trade and Industry.

(a) Using a ranking method, calculate the appropriate statistic to give some assessment of the relationship which exists between TV licences issued and attendance at cinemas. Comment on your results.

(b) Distinguish between negative correlation and perfect positive correlation with the help of scatter diagrams. What is *spurious* correlation? O.N.C.

17.18 (i) Describe, with examples, what is meant by a scatter diagram.

(ii) Describe, with examples, what the coefficient of rank correlation measures. Give the range of values that this coefficient can take.

Two personnel managers each interview eight applicants for a vacant post. After the interviews each manager awards each applicant a mark, as given below.

	Candidate							
	A	B	C	D	E	F	G	H
Manager X	12	17	14	7	10	12	6	3
Manager Y	16	15	18	5	13	10	7	4

Convert the marks into ranks and then calculate and interpret the coefficient of rank correlation. O.N.C.

17.19 (a) Explain what is meant by scatter diagram and coefficient of rank correlation.

(b) Two personnel managers each interview the same five candidates for a vacant post. After the interviews the managers rank the candidates according to suitability for the post.

		Candidate			
	A	B	C	D	E
Manager X	2	1	5	3	4
Manager Y	3	5	4	1	2

Obtain and interpret a coefficient of rank correlation for the two sets of rankings. O.N.C.

17.20 (a) Explain the connection between correlation and regression and briefly indicate how the latter may be measured.

(b) The table given below shows the ranking obtained by ten typists who were first given speed tests and then subjected to speed checks as they worked in normal conditions. Using the rank coefficient of correlation determine whether the speed tests are a reliable guide to the speed likely to be attained by a typist working in normal conditions.

Typist	Ranking	
	In Tests	In Normal Conditions
A	1	3
B	2	4
C	3	6
D	4	1
E	5	2
F	6	8
G	7	9
H	8	10
I	9	7
J	10	5

(c) State which method of measuring correlation would give a more accurate result for (b) than the rank coefficient. What information would you have needed to have been able to use this more accurate method? O.N.C.

17.21 A group of redundant employees accepted for a re-training scheme are given an aptitude test, and six months after completion of their training period they are ranked according to the quality of their output. The following are the rankings:

Employee	Aptitude Test	Work Quality
A	2	1
B	3	2
C	1	3

Employee	Aptitude Test	Work Quality
D	6	4
E	7	5
F	4	6
G	8	7
H	5	8
I	12	9
J	11	10
K	9	11
L	10	12

You are required to use an appropriate statistical technique to determine whether the aptitude test is a reliable predictor of a worker's ability to perform quality work. A.I.A.

17.22 The table below shows the rate of growth of national income over the period 1950–64 and the level of gross investment as a percentage of national income from 1950 to 1962 in a number of countries.

Country	Gross Investment (%)	National Income Growth Rate (%)
Belgium	19.2	3.4
Denmark	18.8	3.6
France	19.5	4.9
Germany	25.9	7.1
Italy	21.8	5.6
Netherlands	26.0	4.9
Norway	28 1	3.8
United Kingdom	16.4	2.6
United States of America	18.4	3.5

Source: O.E.C.D. Statistics.

(a) Plot the data on a graph.
(b) Rank each country by:

  (i) level of investment and
  (ii) rate of growth.

  Calculate Spearman's coefficient of rank correlation.
(c) Interpret your answer in (b).
(d) If you were the Chancellor of the Exchequer in Norway, what comments would you have to make on your country's growth rate related to the level of investment? O.N.C.

17.23 (a) Explain the meaning of the term 'regression line' and describe one method of obtaining such a line.
(b) A record of maintenance cost is kept on each of several nearly

identical automatic machines. These data are to be compared with such machines' age to determine whether there is any association; and if there is, how strong the association is. Use the following data to decide, by finding a correlation coefficient, the answer to these points.

Maintenance Costs (£)	Age (yrs)
120	6
50	2
180	7
60	5
110	3
20	1
90	6

O.N.C.

17.24 A company has found that the number of private cars with current licences can be used as a basis for estimating its production requirements. The relevant figures for the past nine years taken from the Annual Abstract of Statistics are as follows:

	In thousands
1964	8,247
1965	8,917
1966	9,513
1967	10,303
1968	10,816
1969	11,228
1970	11,515
1971	12,059
1972	12,717

Using the method of least squares, you are required to:
 (a) estimate the number of private cars with current licences in 1974;
 (b) provide an estimate for 1974 but assuming that because of other factors, e.g. labour unrest, only 60% of the normal annual increase will be realised in 1974.

Answers should be submitted in millions correct to one decimal place of a million.

I.C.M.A.

17.25 The rate of growth of national income per head of population and the percentage of national income taken by the government in taxation in a number of countries is shown in the table:

Country	Taxation as Percentage of National Income (1966–7)	Growth Rate per Head (%) 1963–8
	x	y
United Kingdom	35.5	1.8
France	39.4	4.2
West Germany	37.5	3.5
Netherlands	40.0	4.3
Norway	41.0	3.0
Sweden	46.3	3.2
Switzerland	25.4	2.2
U.S.A.	28.3	2.8

Source: O.E.C.D. Statistics.

Plot the points on a scatter diagram and, using the 3-point method, draw the *line of regression* of y on x. Comment on your result.

Explain briefly how you would calculate the *line of regression* of x on y. O.N.C.

17.26

General Knowledge Test of 100 Questions Given to 20 Students of Different Ages

Student	Age Years	Months	Number of Questions Answered Correctly
A	16	8	39
B	16	2	40
C	17	9	45
D	17	1	47
E	18	6	46
F	18	7	67
G	19	10	45
H	20	4	53
I	19	8	49
J	20	7	46
K	20	10	54
L	20	8	52
M	22	0	57
N	22	2	53
O	21	11	61
P	21	5	56
Q	19	11	48
R	21	8	56
S	18	11	52
T	21	10	64

(a) What is meant by a regression line?
(b) Draw a scatter diagram to illustrate the above results.

(c) Sketch in a line of best fit.

(d) Estimate, using this line of best fit, the number of questions likely to be answered (correctly) by a 17-year-old student.

O.N.C.

17.27 (a) Write a short note on regression lines.

(b) Explain the difference between 'the regression line of y on x' and 'the regression line of x on y'.

(c) Calculate the product moment correlation between the following sets of figures:

Intelligence Test Scores	Income at Age 23 (in £100's)
121	16
84	6
105	19
93	18
126	18
109	17
97	22
112	13
116	14
86	9
97	20
103	21

O.N.C.

17.28 The following table gives the annual turnover and annual expenditure on advertising of fifteen mail order firms.

Annual Turnover (£100,000) (Y)	Annual Expenditure on Advertising (£1000) (X)
4.5	22
5.1	28
5.3	31
5.4	31
5.9	35
6.0	43
6.5	43
6.6	48
6.6	43
6.8	49
6.9	56
7.0	52
7.0	57
7.5	58
8.7	61

Plot these figures on a scatter diagram and calculate a regression line by use of the three-point method. Draw this regression line on

the scatter diagram. Describe how this line can be used to estimate
the likely turnover for a given expenditure on advertising. Comment
on the accuracy of such an estimate. O.N.C.

17.29　Sales of groggets for each of the past five years have been
as follows:

Year ended 31 May 1972	12,500
Year ended 31 May 1973	15,480
Year ended 31 May 1974	18,640
Year ended 31 May 1975	21,480
Year ended 31 May 1976	24,400

The seasonal pattern of sales is represented by the quarterly indices
70, 90, 160, 80. You are required to use the least-squares method
to determine the trend line of the company's sales, project the trend
line into the following year and calculate the expected sales for each
quarter of that year. A.I.A.

17.30　(a) From the following information draw a scatter diagram
and by the method of least squares draw the regression line of best
fit.

Volume of sales (in thousands of units)	5	6	7	8	9	10
Total expenses (£000)	74	77	82	86	92	95

(b) What will be the expected total expenses when the volume of
sales is 7500 units?

(c) If the selling price per unit is £11, at what volume of sales will
the total income from sales equal the total expenses? I.C.M.A.

17.31　The following data has been collected over eight periods:

Period	Units of Output	Total Cost (£)
1	10,000	32,000
2	20,000	39,000
3	40,000	58,000
4	25,000	44,000
5	30,000	52,000
6	40,000	61,000
7	50,000	70,000
8	45,000	64,000

Draw a scatter diagram and by the method of least squares draw
a straight line which best fits the data.

Give the equation of the line and estimate the cost likely to be
incurred at the output levels of 26,000 units and 48,750 units.

I.C.M.A.

17.32 A machine will run at different speeds but the higher the speed the sooner a certain part has to be replaced. Trial observation gives the following data:

Speed (revolutions per minute)	Life of Drill-head (hours)
18	162
20	154
20	171
21	165
23	128
26	138
26	140
28	129
31	125
32	106
32	97
40	95
41	103
42	109
43	69

Plot the figures on a scatter diagram. Determine the equation to the regression line. Plot the line on the scatter diagram and estimate the life of the drill-head if the machine operates at 30 revolutions per minute. I.C.M.A.

17.33 *Personal Saving 1967–70*

Quarter/Year	1967 (£ millions)	1968 (£ millions)	1969 (£ millions)	1970 (£ millions)
I	673	684	918	923
II	569	582	555	662
III	570	533	549	658
IV	391	412	477	647

Source: Economic Trends.

Fit a straight line trend to the above data, and find the seasonal components. Compare the actual figures for 1970 with those predicted using this trend and seasonal components approach. Consider the possible reasons for the divergences, paying particular attention to the quarter with the largest divergence.

C.I.P.F.A.

17.34
*Annual Percentage Change in Manufacturing in a Number of Countries,
1950–60*

Country	Annual Percentage Change	
	Total Output	Output per Man-hour
Germany	10.0	5.6
Italy	8.9	6.7
Austria	6.8	5.3
France	6.5	5.9
Netherlands	6.1	4.6
Belgium	3.8	3.5
U.S.A.	3.7	3.2
Canada	3.5	3.0
U.K.	3.4	2.6
Denmark	3.3	2.3
Sweden	3.3	3.2
Ireland	2.8	2.1

Source: C. T. Saunders: *Journal of the Royal
Statistical Society, A.*, 1963.

Calculate the regression equation for total output on output per
man-hour. Estimate the percentage change in total output corresponding to a 4% change in output per man-hour. How would you
estimate the percentage change in output per man-hour corresponding to a 4% change in total output?   C.I.P.F.A.

17.35

Region	Average Weekly Household Income (shillings)	Average Weekly Expenditure on Household Goods (shillings)
North	370	23
East and West Riding	400	22
North Midlands	402	23
East	407	24
London and South-east	455	28
South	451	20
South-west	399	21
Wales	381	19
Midlands	471	27
North-west	407	23
Scotland	390	21

Source: Regional Statistics 1965.

From the data given above, estimate by least squares the expected
expenditure on household goods in a region which had an average
household income of 500 shillings in 1965.   C.I.P.F.A.

17.36 The advertising expenditure and product sales of a company for eight consecutive months are as follows:

Month	1	2	3	4	5	6	7	8
Advertising expenditure (£000)	26	52	18	47	51	36	18	26
Sales (hundreds)	102	142	135	115	156	171	127	110

The company has developed a relationship predicting the sales in each month from the amount of advertising expenditure in that and the previous month as:

$$s_i = 85 + 0.6a_i + 0.9a_{i-1}$$

where s_i are the predicted sales in month i, in hundreds, and a_i is the advertising expenditure in month i, in thousands of pounds.

Required:
(1) Calculate the estimated sales in months 2 to 8 using the formula and comment on the results.
(2) What is:
    (i) the maximum discrepancy in any month between actual sales and expected sales?
    (ii) the maximum percentage discrepancy, when the discrepancy is expressed as a percentage of actual sales?
(3) What would be the effect on sales if advertising expenditure were reduced by £5000 per month? A.C.A.

Chapter Eighteen

Further Applications of Sampling

We hope that by now you will appreciate the paramount importance of sampling to statistics. In fact, most statisticians would argue that the need for statistics arises out of the necessity for sampling. You will remember that sampling was necessary because of the great difficulties or high cost of examining the entire population – and so great are the difficulties in many cases that we could discover nothing about the population without resorting to sampling. In this book, we have tried to warn you of some of the pitfalls of drawing conclusions based on sample evidence, and given some hints on how to avoid them. We have applied sampling theory to three main areas: significance testing, estimation and correlation; but it would be wrong to leave you with the impression that we have covered all the applications – far from it! In this chapter, we propose to examine briefly three further applications of sampling.

Assessing the Value of Stock

As any accountant knows, the determination of the value of stock at the end of the financial year is a major undertaking, even for a relatively small firm. It is both expensive and time-consuming; often the firm has to close down for a day, or staff have to be paid to work until late at night or on Sunday. It is natural, then, that efforts have been made to apply sampling principles to the problem of stock taking.

Let us assume initially that a firm carries some 5000 different commodities in stock, and that at the end of the financial year the total stock value is required by the auditors to prepare the annual accounts. The manager decides to assess this value by taking a 10% sample. Each item of stock may be given a number ranging from 0000 to 4999, and a table of random numbers used to select the individual items to be checked. If the group of numbers chosen from the random number table was 5000 or greater it was ignored. The process was repeated until 500 different commodities had been selected.

For each commodity the holding in the store was physically

checked and the commodity value determined (i.e. holding × unit cost). Then having obtained the total value of the 500 commodities (or 10% of the stock) it is simple to estimate the total stock value by multiplying by 10.

Does it surprise you to learn that a stock total obtained in such a way can be wildly inaccurate? The point is that commodities held in stock vary widely in value. It is possible that our firm holds many items with a valuation of a few pence only, some items with a value of a few pounds, and a few items with a value of several hundred pounds. In such a case simple random sampling will greatly understate the true value of stock, and only very rarely overstate it. It can be used, of course, if the value of items in stock covers only a limited range. It could have been used by F. W. Woolworth and Co. when many years ago they proudly boasted that they sold 'nothing over sixpence'. Even more dramatic is the situation with Harpers Penny Bazaar in the United States who sold everything at a price of a penny. Can you see that the total stock value could be determined by a sample of one commodity only, provided that the number of commodities is known?

These examples imply that if, in some way, we can reduce the price range of the commodities we are examining, we can reduce the size of the sample and increase our accuracy. Hence the normal procedure is to stratify the commodities by value, taking samples from each stratum and obtaining the total estimate by combining the separate stratum estimates.

In this stratification it is not necessary for the sample chosen to be the same relative size within each stratum. A small percentage error in the value of low-priced goods will not critically affect the total stock value, but the same percentage error in the value of goods costing several hundred pounds can materially affect the stock valuation, and hence the gross stock figure. So, in designing such a sample, it is usual to take a very small percentage of cheap goods, the percentage rising as the value of the commodity rises. Let us examine an example to see how these ideas might work out in practice.

A warehouse holds 9280 different commodities, and the breakdown of the commodity values is as in table 18.1.

We wish to value the stock by drawing a stratified sample, and our criterion for stratification will be the estimated value within each stratum. We can obtain these values if we multiply the mid-point of each stratum by its frequency, but we will be unable to do this for the last stratum as it is open-ended. For this reason, we will sample all the items in the group '5000 and over'. In any case, the value of items in this stratum is so very much greater than other items, that a 100% sample of this group makes good sense.

Table 18.1

Price (pence)	No. of Commodities
1– 10	2694
11– 20	1452
21– 50	864
51– 100	772
101– 300	702
301– 500	640
501–1000	599
1001–2000	675
2001–5000	750
5000 and over	132
	9280

Mid-point (1)	Frequency (2)	(1) × (2)
5.5	2694	14817
15.5	1452	22506
35.5	864	30672
75.5	772	58286
200.5	702	140751
400.5	640	256320
750.5	599	449550
1500.5	675	1012838
3500.5	750	2625375
	9148	4611115

Suppose it is decided to sample 10% of the commodities (= 928). Now we have already decided that all of the items in the last stratum will be examined, so this leaves $928 - 132 = 796$ to be chosen from the other strata. Let us first examine the stratum 2001–5000. The estimated value of this stratum is 2625375p, which is

$$\frac{2625375}{4611115} = 0.569$$

of the total estimated value. Now we want to examine a sample from this stratum proportional to its relative value, so we must examine

$$0.569 \times 796 = 453 \text{ items}$$

Likewise for the stratum 1001–2000 we must examine

$$\frac{1012838}{4611115} \times 796 = 175 \text{ items}$$

Repeating this procedure for all the strata, we can derive the following table:

Price (pence)	No. of Commodities	Sample Size	% Size
1– 10	2694	3	0.1
11– 20	1452	4	0.3
21– 50	864	5	0.6
51– 100	772	10	1.3
101– 300	702	24	3.4
301– 500	640	44	6.9
501–1000	599	78	13.0
1001–2000	675	175	25.9
2001–5000	750	453	60.4
5000 and over	132	132	100.0
	9280	928	

As you can see, as we approach the really high-priced strata, the percentage of items sampled increases dramatically – but so does the accuracy.

It is often argued that stocktaking in this way leads to error, but two things must be borne in mind. A complete stock check will not eliminate error entirely. There will be errors arising in counting; in extending total values; in adding; and the pressures of doing things in a hurry may, in fact, lead to many errors that would not be made in a sample survey when more time is available to take a careful check.

Secondly, the desire for greater accuracy costs time and money. Generally, the rate of increase in accuracy tends to diminish while the rate of increase in cost tends to rise. The careful manager must always ask himself whether the increase in accuracy justifies the heavy additional cost involved.

Quality Control

If you conducted a 'popularity poll' of all the jobs in a factory, it is an odds on bet that the inspector would be low down the list. The factory operatives dislike the inspector because they see him as the person who rejects part of their output, and so reduces bonus earnings. Management all too often (although incorrectly) see the inspector as a necessary evil – a cost that they would dearly like to dispense with! Some managers even call inspectors 'unproductive labour'. Fortunately, rational people recognise that inspectors perform a most important function. After all, quality *does* matter. Mass production has meant that goods are available to us as consumers at prices we can, on the whole, manage to afford. Unfortunately, mass production can also mean that a proportion of the goods produced will inevitably be of inferior quality. We have all had experience of annoying faults developing in the goods we buy. The inspector can, and should, be the guardian of quality.

Now we do not wish to give you the impression that inspectors should solely be seen as fulfilling an important social function – they also serve the firm well (despite the cynical attitude of some sectors of management). Quality also matters to the firm – for the firm that produces shoddy goods will eventually find its sales falling, and will find an unacceptable part of its output returned as rejects.. The efficient inspector is a positive asset to the firm.

Having recognised the need for inspection, we must now decide on the form that the inspection will take. Some firms inspect finished goods in special inspection shops. The fault with this method is that as faults are found after the goods have been made, it is possible that the firm has produced large batches of defective items that have not been discovered until it is too late to do much about it. The purpose of inspection is not merely to identify defective items, but also to stop further defectives occurring. Inspection should occur as near to the point of production as possible, and inspection should be frequent. A fairly common, and commendable, system of inspection is the 'patrolling inspector'. The 'patrolling inspector' visits each machine as frequently as possible and inspects items produced by that machine, so if lapses from quality are occurring the trouble can be rectified before too many defectives have been produced. Also, the inspector who works to a sensible system will keep good records of how each machine is performing. This often enables him to spot the lapses from accepted standards before they occur.

In very few cases would there be 100% inspection – not only would this be costly, but in many cases the machines can produce faster than the inspectors can inspect! Quality control, then, in the main depends upon sampling theory. The actual inspection system used will depend on the nature of the possible faults that can occur. Industry abounds with examples of goods and components that must be within certain measurable dimensions (or tolerance limits) and we will examine a quality control system for such goods. We shall consider the case of a manufacturer producing metal rods, which must have diameters within the tolerance limits 1 cm to 1.01 cm, i.e. 1.005 ± 0.005. When we dealt with the standard deviation we found it convenient to take an arbitrary origin, and remove the decimal point by taking a different unit of measurement. We shall resort to this method again. Taking 1 cm as an origin, and one ten thousandth of a cm as unit, the tolerance limit becomes 50 ± 50. How can we set up a suitable quality control system for this manufacturer?

Step One

Before we can set up any quality control system, we must have some idea of the mean and standard deviation of the diameters of the rods produced by the machinery. Suppose we measure a large number of rods, and obtain the following information

Mean diameter $= 52$
Standard deviation of diameters $= 13.76$

Step Two

We now check that the machinery is capable of meeting the tolerances, because if it cannot, then there is little point in continuing. To do this, we will assume (quite reasonably) that the diameters of rods are normally distributed. If you consult the table at the end of this book you will learn that 99.8% of items in any normal distribution can be expected to lie within the range

$$\bar{x} \pm 3.09\sigma$$

In this case, then, we can expect (with 99.8% probability) that the diameters will lie within the range

$$\pm 3.09 \times 13.76 = \pm 43$$

Now to meet the tolerances, the diameters must be within the limits ± 50, so we can conclude that the machinery is capable of meeting the tolerances.

Step Three

We must now decide on just how the inspection will take place. Of course, there is nothing to stop the inspector randomly selecting a rod, measuring its diameter, and making some judgement as to the performance of the machinery. However, we have learnt enough about sampling to realise that it is most unwise to draw conclusions based on a sample of one item. It is far safer to draw a sample of a number of rods, and form judgements on the basis of the mean diameter. We will assume that the inspector will base his conclusions on the mean diameters of samples of five rods.

Step Four

When we examined sampling theory, we saw that if samples of n items were drawn from a population with a mean $\bar{x}$ and a standard deviation σ, then 95% of the means of such samples would lie within the range.

$$\bar{x} \pm \frac{1.96\sigma}{\sqrt{n}}$$

Now strictly speaking, this will not apply to the system we are considering as the sample size we have chosen can hardly be considered large. However, it is the normal practice in quality control to assume that the Central Limit Theorem does apply to small samples. The justification for this is that many samples will be drawn, and these many small samples can be considered as equivalent to a large sample. In the case of the rods, then, 95% of sample means will be within the range

$$52 \pm \frac{1.96 \times 13.76}{\sqrt{5}}$$

$$= 40 \text{ to } 64$$

In other words, we can expect 19 out of 20 sample means to be within the range 40 to 64. We call this range the *warning limits* for sample means.

In a similar fashion, we can deduce that 99.8% of sample means will lie in the range

$$\bar{x} \pm \frac{3.09\sigma}{\sqrt{n}}$$

or in the case of our example

$$52 \pm \frac{3.09 \times 13.76}{\sqrt{5}}$$

i.e.   33 to 71

So we can expect 499 out of 500 sample means to fall within the range 33 to 71 and we call these limits the *action limits*.

We now have a basis for controlling the quality of output. As long as only one sample mean in 20 lies outside the warning limits, and one sample mean in 500 lies outside the action limits, we are producing a uniform quality and the process is said to be under control. We will consider later what action should be taken if these limits are violated.

Step Five

In step two, we verified that the machinery was capable of meeting the tolerances. However, it is also necessary to ensure that the control system is capable of detecting any lapses from the tolerance limits. We might get this situation if the machine setting (i.e. the mean) was rather high. Suppose that the mean was 60. Now we already know that individual items have a range of ± 43, so if the mean was 60 then the individual diameters could be as high as 103, and the upper tolerance limit would be exceeded.

If we look carefully at Fig. 18.1, the first thing we notice is that

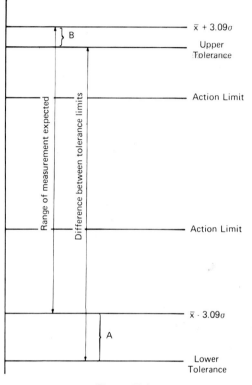

Figure 18.1

the upper tolerance limit minus the lower tolerance limit exceeds the range of measurement expected $(A > B)$. According to the test conducted in step two, we can conclude that the machinery is capable of meeting the tolerances. However, the upper tolerance limit is below the upper range for individual items, so it is possible that the upper tolerance limit will be exceeded (i.e. individual lengths can penetrate into area B). If we were now to use the action limits as our quality control system, i.e. check that the means of samples do not fall outside these limits, then the samples could indicate that the production was under control and *lapses from the upper tolerance limit would go undetected.*

Can you see that if the tolerances are outside one of the limits $\bar{x} \pm 3.09\sigma$, then no undetected lapses from tolerances will occur? More formally, we can state that the tolerance limits must be at least

$$3.09\sigma - \frac{3.09\sigma}{\sqrt{n}}$$

outside the action limits if no undetected lapses from tolerance are to occur. Putting it another way, the upper action limit must be at least this amount below the upper tolerance limit, and the lower action limit at least this amount above the lower tolerance. This is called the *allowable width of the control lines* (A.W.C.L.). Writing T_U for the upper tolerance limit and T_L for the lower tolerance limit, we have

$$\text{A.W.C.L.} = T_L + \left[3.09\sigma - \frac{3.09\sigma}{\sqrt{n}} \right] \text{ to } T_U - \left[3.09\sigma - \frac{3.09\sigma}{\sqrt{n}} \right]$$

Substituting, we have

$$0 + \left[3.09 \times 13.76 - \frac{3.09 \times 13.76}{\sqrt{5}} \right]$$

to

$$100 - \left[3.09 \times 13.76 - \frac{3.09 \times 13.76}{\sqrt{5}} \right]$$

i.e.   24 to 76

As the action limits (33 to 71) lie well within this range, we conclude that no undetected lapses from tolerance will occur.

Step Six

We can now set up the *control chart for sample means*. In Fig. 18.2 the action and warning limits have been inserted. We have assumed that the inspection system is under way; that twenty samples of five items have been drawn; and their means plotted on the control chart. All of the samples are well within the action limits. Notice that two sample means fall outside the warning limits – but we would only expect one to do so. Is this significant? Probably not – it is quite likely that all of the means of the next twenty samples will be within the warning limits.

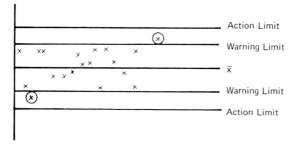

Figure 18.2

Suppose we use the means chart as our basis for controlling quality. We draw samples of five items every (say) 15 minutes, and plot the means on the chart. Our results may look like this:

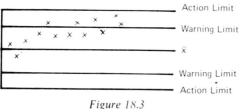

Figure 18.3

Carefully compare the last two diagrams. In the first case, the sample means are clustered fairly evenly about the mean. In the second case, the means are clustering about the upper warning limit. What does this second case signify? It would appear that the mean diameter has increased – the setting of the machinery has drifted upwards. Would we be justified in halting production and lowering the setting of the machine? Now breaks in production are expensive, and we must be sure that drifting has occurred before a resetting is justified. Common sense tells us that in the first diagram there is insufficient evidence of a drift.

Suppose we now reset the machine and continue to draw samples. The first sample drawn has a mean less than the lower action limit. What shall we do? We expect only one sample in 500 to be outside these limits – yet the first sample drawn is outside the lower action limit. It is possible that the first sample drawn is that one sample in 500 – the rogue sample is just as likely to be the first as any other. However, exceeding the action limits by definition demands that we take some action. The appropriate action is to draw more samples immediately – we certainly would not be justified in waiting 15 minutes to draw the next sample. If their means are clustered about

$\bar{x}$, then it seems likely that we have indeed met the odd 1 in 500 case. However, if the means are clustered about the lower warning limit, then trouble is indicated.

Acceptance Sampling for Accountants

A further example of the application of sampling techniques to save time and money is found in the field of audit work, where the accountant may be faced with the problem of checking thousands of invoices and entries into cash books, ledgers, and sales and purchase journals. If a complete check is to be made it may take weeks of painstaking work in order to discover the very small proportion of bookkeeping entries that have been incorrectly made. The question must arise whether the increased accuracy resulting from a 100% check really justifies the additional cost of the audit.

In recent years, statistical sampling techniques have been devised to assist the accountant faced with the large quantities of checking necessary to undertake a full audit in a large firm. One of the most useful of these techniques is known as *acceptance sampling*. In this we try to achieve a balance between two extremes. On the one hand we have a full audit which is often unnecessary and very expensive for the client; on the other hand we could take a sample so small that important errors are not discovered. This latter situation, of course, may cost the client far more than he can ever hope to save in reduced audit fees.

The principles of such sampling are relatively straightforward. We first of all determine the level of errors we are prepared to accept – an *acceptable error level*. This gives us a standard by which we can judge our sample. If the level of error disclosed by our sample does not exceed this level then all is well. But if it is greater, something has gone wrong and further checks – possibly even a full audit – may be necessary. We are, in fact, setting up a normal null hypothesis and establishing decision rules.

If $P_0 = $ the acceptable level of error

and $P_1 = $ the level of error disclosed by our sample

then our null hypothesis becomes

$$H_0 = P_0 > P_1$$

Now obviously, one of the most important problems here is to determine what is an acceptable level of error and at what level of confidence we will accept the sample. Thus we have initially to obtain some information about the relative qualities of the entries, and in particular what is the level of error we are likely to find. Firstly, let us consider the question of how we are going to measure error. Many writers state, and even more imply, that we are concerned with the percentage of invoices which are incorrect. In our opinion, this measure is irrelevant. The accountant is concerned with money as a measuring rod, and what is surely more important is the percentage error in monetary totals of the entries. After all, due to some mistake in the method of calculation of amounts to be charged, we may find that 20% of invoices totalling £1.50 or more are incorrect by up to 5 pence. The maximum percentage error in the amounts charged to customers would be

$$\frac{5}{150} \times \frac{20}{100} \times 100 = 0.67\%$$

a very small percentage error. However, if 20% of invoices totalling £10 had an error of £1, this would give a 2% error. Merely to take the percentage of invoices that are incorrect hides such important differences in error in monetary terms. In this section, then, we will take as our measure of error, the percentage error in monetary totals.

It may be, of course, that all the information we need is available from past experience. For example, we may know that the average error found on invoices is 2% with a standard deviation of 0.75%. We would expect to find on this year's audit that 95% of samples we take would have an average error not greater than $2\% + 1.645 \times 0.75 = 3.23\%$ and we would accept the sample at the 95% confidence level if this were so. Think carefully about what this implies. All that we are saying is that we are 95% confident that the level of error is no greater than it was last year. We are *not* saying that our acceptable error level is satisfactory. It may be that, in your opinion, a level of error of 2% is intolerable, and that steps should be taken to improve the quality of bookkeeping records. If, however, you are prepared to accept 2% as a tolerable level of error, we have a yardstick by which we can judge our sample results. One thing you must never do is *guess* an acceptable level of error. Accounting systems and the nature of business transactions differ. What might be acceptable for a highly complex organisation with a vast range of prices, surcharges and discounts, would probably be quite intolerable for a more compact firm with an internal audit section.

Unless, however, we have used sampling techniques before, we are unlikely to have all the information we want, and it will be necessary to undertake an initial large sample survey to determine the quality of the records with which we are concerned. Let us suppose that we take a random sample of 1000 invoices, and note the percentage errors that we find in this sample. Our results could be classified as

% Errors	No. of Invoices	d	fd	fd^2
0–1	10	−3	−30	90
1–2	70	−2	−140	280
2–3	240	−1	−240	240
3–4	360	0		
4–5	250	1	250	250
5–6	60	2	120	240
6–7	10	3	30	90
	1000		−10	1190

$$\bar{x} = 3.5\% - \frac{10}{1000} = 3.49\%$$

$$\sigma = \sqrt{\frac{1190}{1000} - (0.01)^2} = 1.09\%$$

We can set up 95% confidence limits as

$$3.49 + 1.65 \times \frac{1.09}{\sqrt{1000}}$$

$$= 3.49 + 0.057 = 3.547\%$$

If we wanted 98% confidence limits we could accept our sample provided that the error rate was not greater than

$$3.49 + 2.06 \times \frac{1.09}{\sqrt{1000}} = 3.56\%$$

These rates of error we may call the *acceptable error rate*. Provided that the percentage error does not exceed this rate, the accountant can accept this sample as indicating a satisfactory level of accuracy in the population of invoices.

Can you see why we have undertaken a 'one-sided test'? It does not matter if we obtain a sample with an error rate of less than 3.49%. This is acceptable. It is an increase in the error rate that the auditor is worried about.

You will realise too that in spite of the calculations to three places of decimals, there is still room for the accountant to exercise his own judgement. 'Acceptable' and 'satisfactory' are relative terms – relative in this case to the 3.49% error we found in our initial sample. But is this in itself acceptable? Ought we perhaps to make suggestions to ensure that errors of even this magnitude are reduced, and our calculations based on a lower average error rate?

We now have to determine the size of the sample, and although normally sample size is independent of the size of the population, in acceptance sampling we first need to know the size of the population of invoices. Our best size sample has already been worked out for us in a series of tables such as *Sampling Tables for Estimating Error Rates* by Brown and Vance, which are based on a formula linking population size, the expected proportion of errors in the population and the level of confidence at which it will be decided to accept the sample.

It may, of course, be desirable to stratify the population into invoices of differing values such as, for example, under £5, £5 to £20, and over £20. Naturally the acceptable error level would be smaller for larger invoices since the probability of a loss is greater. Then, too, you must remember that our calculations have only set up a criterion on the basis of which to accept or reject a sample. It may well be that the auditor considers that an average rate of error of 3.49% is intolerable and leads him to suggest alterations in the accounting system. Given, however, that it is acceptable, what do we do if the error rate shown by the sample exceeds 3.56%? The answer is a matter of judgement. You may decide to take a second sample to confirm the result. After all there is still a fair chance of a Type II error. If the error rate persists, there is little alternative to undertaking a complete audit. Fortunately, experience shows that if you find the average rate of error to be acceptable, it is not often that conditions change so radically that the onerous task of undertaking a full audit is necessary.

We could not leave this chapter without referring to other widespread uses of statistics in business. Graphs and diagrams, averages and index numbers abound in every firm. But today statistics has allied itself to mathematics to open up a whole new field of decision-taking techniques.[1]

EXERCISES TO CHAPTER 18
18.1   The following table shows the numbers of employees in each of five small factories of a company, together with their employee reference numbers:

Factory	No. of Employees	Employee Ref. Nos.
A	128	001–128
B	96	201–296
C	32	301–332
D	64	401–464
E	80	501–580

[1] For some of these techniques see *Modern Analytical Techniques*, by F. Owen and R. Jones.

It is necessary to obtain quickly an estimate of the proportion of all employees prepared to work overtime during a certain week. Assuming sufficient time is available for you to telephone only 25 employees and that you are required to carry out a stratified random sampling scheme with the factories as strata.

(a) how many employees from each factory will you include in your sample?

(b) using the random number table below, write down the reference numbers of the employees selected in your sample;

(c) write a brief memorandum to your superior indicating the conclusions you have drawn from your survey results. (Assume that employees whose reference numbers are divisible by 5 are prepared to work overtime and the remainder are not.)

Random number table:

3265	7402	5126	4357	6929	5108	2905	6463	7285	0923
1344	5125	2785	0629	1437	0852	1957	3408	2675	1804
1938	7840	6917	8235						

O.N.C.

18.2   A machine is programmed to produce ball-bearings having a mean diameter of 17.50 millimetres and a standard deviation of 0.06 millimetres. In order to determine that the machine maintains proper standards a sample of 9 ball-bearings is taken every hour and the mean diameter is calculated from the sample.

(a) Calculate a 95% confidence limit related to the above standards.

(b) Using the limits calculated in (a) draw a control chart plotting the following sample means:

(c) Comment on the results in relation to the limits you have calculated.

| Sample reference | 1 | 2 | 3 | 4 | 5 | 6 | 7 | 8 | 9 |
| Mean in mm | 17.47 | 17.50 | 17.49 | 17.52 | 17.54 | 17.57 | 17.51 | 17.52 | 17.50 |

I.C.M.A.

18.3   A chemical plant shows the following hourly production over a period of ten hours:

| Hour | 1 | 2 | 3 | 4 | 5 | 6 | 7 | 8 | 9 | 10 |
| Production | 140 | 131 | 142 | 121 | 134 | 145 | 131 | 148 | 132 | 136 |

The manager of the plant states that this mean production rate is what is expected of him and asks you to calculate from this data the upper and lower control limits that he can use on a control chart that he proposes to set up. These limits are to be adequate to cover

a risk level of 1 in 20 in order to warn him (or the plant operator) of possible changes in the process.
  Calculate:

  (a) the mean, variance and standard deviation of these ten production figures;
  (b) the upper and lower control limits for the chart; and
  (c) illustrate the chart and show on it the control limits with some specimens of hourly recordings.   I.C.M.A.

18.4 Experience has shown that under normal conditions a process produces items of mean diameter 3.00 inches with a standard deviation of 0.01 inches.
  Required: Find the standard error of the mean of samples of 4 items and state the limits within which sample means will lie for:

  (i) 95% of samples;
  (ii) virtually all samples.

Draw up a control chart for the means of samples of 4 items showing inner and outer limits. Plot the means given in the following table on your chart and comment on the picture revealed.

Means of Samples of Size 4 Taken at 10-Minute Intervals

Time	3.00	3.10	3.20	3.30	3.40
Mean diameter	3.003	3.004	2.995	3.001	2.992
Time	3.50	4.00	4.10	4.20	4.30
Mean diameter	2.996	3.001	3.003	3.006	3.011
Time	4.40	4.50	5.00	5.10	5.20
Mean diameter	3.005	2.995	2.997	2.993	2.990
Time	5.30	5.40	5.50	6.00	6.10
Mean diameter	2.991	2.992	2.990	2.986	2.984

I.C.M.A.

18.5 (a) In a large sample taken of production 42 items were rejected out of a total of 1000. It was decided that control samples of 200 would be taken at a given frequency. Calculate the expected mean and the 95% and 99% levels for the control chart.
  (b) The chart, based on figures calculated in answer to (a) above, was brought into use and after a period during which 15 control samples were taken the following rejects were recorded:

Sample Reference	Number of Rejects
1	8
2	11
3	9
4	6
5	12

Sample Reference	Number of Rejects
6	8
7	13
8	11
9	14
10	15
11	18
12	10
13	8
14	12
15	7

Draw the chart showing the upper action and warning limits and plot on it the above results.

What appears to have happened to cause the sudden change between samples reference 11 and 12?   I.C.M.A.

Chapter Nineteen

Statistical Sources[1]

In our modern society, we are inundated by masses of statistics, collected and published by government departments, trade associations, trade unions, private firms and a multitude of private research bodies. Never before have we had such a wealth of information about the society in which we live, and it would take many volumes even to outline the scope of statistical information available today. How then can anyone hope to find, amongst this mass of data, precisely the information they are seeking?

It will perhaps help if we can draw an arbitrary line, placing on one side information produced by private firms, trade unions and trade associations – the private sector – and on the other side data provided by the public sector – government departments, local authorities, banks and so on. Broadly, we can say that the private sector data is concerned with one firm, one body of workers, etc. It tends to be limited in scope, and to some extent interests only a relatively few people. We doubt very much that you would find in government records the cost of a first-class passage from Boston to Liverpool in 1890 – but it is in the records of the Cunard shipping company. It is what we might call *micro* statistical information. Equally it is likely that only some body such as the Building Trades Federation could tell you what proportion of bricks used in housebuilding are rustic or facing brick. To the trade this information might critically affect production plans. Now if the information you want is of this variety, write to the appropriate trade association, firm or union. If they have no data they will pass you on to someone who has. Unless you are undertaking research, however, it is not often you will be called on to hunt for such data.

When you look at the data published by the public sector you will find it of a very different kind. Firstly, it tends to relate to the country as a whole rather than to one small sector of it. We are now

[1] Students are urged to obtain a copy of the Stationery Office publication *Government Statistics – a brief guide to Sources*, published by and issued free by Press and Information Services, Central Statistical Office, Great George Street, London SW1P 3AQ.

concerned with the number of houses built in the country or in a particular city rather than with the type of bricks used. Thus the information is general rather than specific; *macro* rather than micro statistical information. Secondly it is of importance to a very wide range of people – administrators, historians, economists, sociologists, industrialists, planners – to a very wide cross-section of the community.

The Annual Abstract of Statistics

In the United Kingdom possibly the best source of this latter type of data is the Annual Abstract of Statistics published by the Central Statistical Office. It collates and summarises information relating to the United Kingdom produced by government departments (such as the Department of Education and Science) and obtained from national surveys (such as the census of distribution or the census of population). As you might expect it tends to give information for the United Kingdom as a whole rather than individual towns or industries. If we need more detail we may have to refer to far more comprehensive reports issued by the appropriate government departments. Population statistics, for example, comprise 29 tables in the Annual Abstract, but the Office of Population Census alone publishes comprehensive and detailed reports on each individual county, together with a Preliminary Report, and a general report. Additionally, the Registrar General's Annual Review and Quarterly Reviews supplement the Census reports.

The Annual Abstract is precisely what its name implies – an abstract, but it is a good starting point for any investigation. Not only does its fifteen sections cover such diverse topics as weather, output, finance, education and transport, but in most cases information is given on a comparative basis for at least ten years so that any marked trend can be spotted easily. For more recent years most data is given monthly. Additionally, the Central Statistical Office publish the Monthly Digest of Statistics, bringing the information in selected fields up to date month by month.

Population and Vital Statistics

Not every statistician will agree with us but we tend to think that of all the data produced by the government, that relating to population is the most useful. General knowledge of the population and its age–sex distribution is of course necessary for efficient administration, but think of what else is needed. We need age distribution to plan schools for the next generation, to assess the effect of changes in (say) family allowances, or to plan a policy for pensions; we need a knowledge of the causes of death to allocate funds for medical research; information on housing is the first step in planning a housing policy; questions on educational qualifications help the formulation of an educational policy – and so on. Information on all these topics, and many more, can be found in the reports on the Census of Population and the Annual Reports of the Registrar General. There is little doubt that the Census of Population is one of the most useful sources of data, and certainly, along with its necessary accompaniment – the compulsory registration of births, deaths and marriages – it is the most useful single source of information relating to vital statistics.

The census consists of a complete enumeration of the persons in a country on a given night together with questions on age, sex, marital status, occupation and the industry in which they work. In addition the modern census collects information on social conditions such as the housing of the population or the educational standards reached. In the United Kingdom the first census was taken in 1801 and apart from 1941, one has been taken every 10 years since that date. The government now have, in fact, the powers to take a census every five years if they so wish, and one such was taken in 1966.

Obviously, every census must ask certain questions which are never changed – such as name, sex, age, etc., but the opportunity is usually taken to ask additional questions to throw light on social problems that rear their head from time to time. In 1921, for example, questions were asked relating to widows and orphans in view of the manpower losses between 1914 and 1918; in 1961 a 10% sample was asked to answer additional questions relating to educational attainment; and in 1966 questions were asked relating to the mobility of the population, on car ownership and garage space, and on the journey to work.

While such statistics are essential, in many developing countries a complete census is not possible, probably because of the distances involved, the lack of administrative machinery for collection and analysis of data, possibly because of the literacy rate, or the knowledge that the population would not willingly give the information required. In such cases, a limited census or even a sample survey may well be the only way to obtain the information about the population and its living conditions.

It would be foolish to pretend, however, that even in the United Kingdom the census information is completely accurate. There are sources of error at every stage. The distribution and collection of forms is in the hands of part-time enumerators who are each responsible for an area. We can never be absolutely sure that every house has received a form or that every form is returned. It is not likely, of course, but is at least possible that an enumerator may not know where a house is, and may not bother to find out, particularly if the weather is very bad, as it was on census day 1951. A much more probable source of error, however, lies in completing the questionnaire. Some people may misunderstand the question, others may only be able to guess the answer; others will believe that the answer they give is correct when, in fact, it is not. Educational standards in the U.K. vary tremendously and the quality of the completed questionnaires is bound to vary – some mistakes will inevitably occur. Admittedly some mistakes will be picked up by the enumerator on the doorstep; others will be spotted during the process of tabulation. But some will remain. How can any enumerator know that John Smith is not in fact married to the woman living in his house if he claims that he is married?

The census office itself is a fruitful source of error – such as errors arising in transferring information from the forms to punched cards or magnetic tape. That errors do exist has been shown by special post-census sample surveys designed to check accuracy, and by such techniques as comparing the death certificates of people who die shortly after the census with information given in their completed questionnaires. Yet errors are relatively few and the census office is able to claim a remarkably high degree of accuracy for most of the data obtained from the census.

Information of this nature is supplemented annually by the reports of the Registrar General in respect of births, deaths, marriages, divorces, etc., while figures for immigration and emigration can be brought up to date from Home Office statistics. In the U.K. such figures are highly reliable since there are legal pressures to ensure that registration takes place. It is not possible to bury a corpse without a death certificate, or to obtain a passport without a birth certificate, doctors and hospitals notify the Registrar of all births to ensure that parents ultimately register their children. Not all countries, however, have these same pressures and in some countries the births of female children are regularly not notified, while in others deaths are not registered. Sometimes of course the discrepancy becomes obvious when the rate of male and female births (which stays remarkably stable) begins to change, or when the death rate differs markedly from a neighbouring country with very similar social conditions. Nor must we think that the information required is confined to the mere fact of the birth or marriage. The Population (Statistics) Acts require that informants also give such information as the age of parents, their occupation, the duration of the marriage and so on. So much information is available, in fact, that the analysis of the data has given rise to a whole new branch of statistics – demography, the analysis of vital statistics.

Economic Statistics

Since the time of the Domesday Book in the eleventh century governments have been interested in data on how the economy is progressing. In the very early days it was, of course, merely a question of listing manpower for military purposes and personal wealth for taxation purposes. It is interesting to remember that in many underdeveloped parts of the world people are still averse to giving information for fear that it might be used to assess them for taxes. By the sixteenth century interest had developed in statistics of overseas trade since the philosophy of Mercantilism demanded a balance of payments surplus as a criterion of success. But the twentieth century is, after all, the century of economic planning, and for successful planning a mass of wide-ranging information is needed. Today government departments produce statistical data on almost every aspect of economic life, on prices and incomes, on employment and productivity, on production and distribution, on trade and finance. Once again you will find information on all these in the Annual Abstract, but let us take one or two of the major fields and look behind the statistical tables.

(a) Price Indexes

It is commonplace that whenever a body of workers ask for an increase in wages, one of the points that they make strongly is that the increase is designed to compensate for the rise in the level of prices, and they usually quote in evidence changes in the Index of Retail Prices. In Britain this index, introduced in 1947 to replace the old Cost of Living Index, is probably the best method of measuring changes in the standard of living that we have. Constructed monthly and published in the Department of Employment Gazette it is used not only as a measure of inflationary trends, but also as the foundation of incomes policy.

If you think back to chapter five you will recall that there are three main elements in the construction of a price index – the selection of commodities to be included, the determination of weights for each commodity or group of commodities, and obtaining the appropriate prices at the relevant point of time.

The present index originated in 1953 with the Household Expenditure Survey conducted by the then Ministry of Labour. This was an effort to discover the precise pattern of household expenditure in the

United Kingdom. A sample of 20,000 households was selected and each person over 16 in the sample was asked to keep a detailed record of what he spent over a three-week period. The survey produced a 65% response, some 13,000 forms being returned. In the event it was found that low-income families, and particularly those living mainly on state pensions, had an expenditure pattern so different from the majority of households that they could not be regarded as typical and so were ignored. Thus the usable sample was cut down to 11,600 household budgets. It was felt that this sample reflected the spending habits of over 90% of the public and was sufficiently accurate to form the basis of a new index of retail prices. The weights to be used were determined by the percentage of income spent on individual commodities, and the survey also indicated the commodities that should be included in the index. Thus with a total weight of 1000, the weight for food was 350 and alcoholic drink 71, indicating that the average consumer spent 35% of his income on food and 7.1% of his income on alcoholic drink. On this basis a new index was introduced based on 17th January 1956 = 100. This index remained in existence for six years only, until January 1962.

Now as you know, if an index is to be really useful, the base should not be changed too frequently. Why, then, was this index dropped after only six years? It was soon realised that as wages and prices rose in the post-war world, people's consumption patterns changed fairly rapidly. Three cases in particular are outstanding: we were spending a far higher proportion of our income on such things as houses and motor-vehicles, but we were spending a much lower proportion on food. Hence it was decided that the weights used in the construction of the index should be changed year by year. This annual revision was based on a smaller Family Expenditure Survey covering a sample of 5000 households each year. These surveys are continuous throughout the year and each member of the household is required to keep a detailed account of his spending for a fortnight. It is not, of course, possible to use a single year's survey as a basis for revising the weights. Some items such as cars, carpets and washing machines are bought only infrequently, and this is likely to cause a large sampling error. So the weights are determined by the average of the previous three years' expenditure patterns disclosed by the survey. A study of the way the weights have changed over the years tells us a great deal about the way our expenditure patterns have changed.

Group	Weights used in construction of I.R.P.						
	1914	1952	1956	1962	1966	1970	1974
Food	60	399	350	319	298	255	253
Alcoholic drink		78	71	64	67	66	70
Tobacco		90	80	79	77	64	43
Housing	16	72	87	102	113	119	124
Fuel and light	8	66	55	62	64	61	52
Durable household goods		62	66	64	57	60	64
Clothing and footwear	12	98	106	98	91	86	91
Transport and vehicles			68	92	116	126	135
Services		91	58	56	56	55	54
Meals consumed away from home						43	51
Miscellaneous		44	59	64	61	65	63
Others	4						
	100	1000	1000	1000	1000	1000	1000

You can see how over the years the percentage of income spent on food has fallen from 60% in 1914 to 25% in 1974. Since few people were starving in the U.K. in 1974 this is indicative of the rising standard of living. We can see also, signs of the revolution in power. Coal, the major fuel in 1914, absorbed 8% of income, whereas by 1974 coal and electricity absorb only 5.2%. The percentage of income spent on tobacco has also fallen rapidly, but most important of all in indicating the quality of life is the fact that if we take the four basic necessities of life – food, clothing, housing and fuel and light, we find that in 1914 90% of income was spent on these; by 1974 we spent only 52%. A study of these weights reveals a great deal about society.

Having solved the problem of obtaining a satisfactory weighting, and having made sure that the commodities covered by the index are those actually bought by the man in the street, we are still left with the crucial problem of what prices to use. Everyone knows that even in a small town or village, prices vary widely from shop to shop. Hypermarkets and supermarkets sell goods at prices which smaller shops cannot possibly hope to match. Prices differ according to the brand of the commodity we buy and, of course, prices differ from area to area, reflecting partly the degree of competition in the area and partly the costs of distribution. Every motorist knows that even in his own area there may be as much as 6p difference in the price of a gallon of petrol. If he travels long distances he will also see that as he moves away from the vicinity of the oil refineries, the *general* level of prices tends to rise. The result is that while some people are paying x pence for a gallon of petrol, others may have to pay as much as ten pence more. Which of these prices are we to use when we are constructing a retail price index? The Department of Employment uses an interesting technique to try to ensure that the prices they use are representative.

On the Tuesday nearest to the 15th of the month prices are collected by visiting several shops selling the same type of good, care being taken that the types of shop visited are those that handle the bulk of household spending. This is done in several areas of different types ranging from London and the cities to small townships with a population under 5000. Thus, both different types of retail outlets and different geographical areas are represented.

Price relatives are now calculated for each item in each town. Let us take bread as an example. The price relatives for a particular city where five shops have been visited are 182.3, 181.9, 183.1, 182.5 and 182.4. These price relatives are combined with those for other cities to give a simple unweighted average. Thus we have a price relative for cities. The same analysis is now carried out for other population groups, and the resultant price relatives averaged to give a price relative for bread for the country as a whole. In the same way we get price relatives for every commodity covered by the index.

So far, weighting has not mattered, but now we begin to combine the items to obtain an index for each of the major classes, and the question of weights becomes important. Although we know that in 1974 the class 'food' was given a weighting of 253, in order to obtain the index of food prices, this total weight has to be broken down into its constituent parts. We might, for example, apply weights of 29 to milk and cheese products, 31 to bread and cereals and so on. Once this has been done it is a simple matter to obtain an index for food, and having done the same for all other groups, to obtain an overall index of retail prices.

Can you see now why so many individuals cannot believe what the Retail Price Index tells us? As individuals we buy only a selection, and often only a small selection of the items included in the index. The items we buy may have gone up in price more than others that we do not buy, and it seems to us that the index understates the price rises. Or we may buy from a grocer whose prices have been steady when others are charging more. The index will then seem to overstate the rise in prices. Like many statistical measures, the Index of Retail Prices is a good and useful measure when applied to large numbers. It is not so useful when applied to the individual.

(b) *Manpower, Production and Distribution*

If you ask any economist for his 'short list' of aims for economic policy it is almost certain that among the items listed would be 'to promote economic growth'. At the risk of annoying our economist friends we will interpret this to mean simply that we are trying to increase the volume of output. Equally surely we would guess that another aim would be 'to eliminate unemployment', and a third to 'raise the standard of living'. So long as such things as these are accepted as aims of economic policy, it is little wonder that modern governments devote a great deal of time to the collection of statistics of manpower, production and distribution.

Manpower

It might seem strange, but in spite of the twentieth century being the age of manpower planning, it was not until 1945 that we had any reliable detailed information from the Ministry of Labour[1] about the size and distribution of the working population. Before 1939 there was highly reliable data relating to unemployment, but so far as the working population was concerned, all we had were estimates based on the Census of Population, the Census of Production and the Ministry of Labour's annual estimate. The war changed all that. It is impossible for a country to wage total war without detailed knowledge of the manpower available, and of industry's need for manpower. So the U.K. emerged from the war in 1945 with more information about manpower than ever before – but as you will appreciate it is not possible to rely on pre-war and post-war comparisons.

Just as the wartime planning necessitated the collection of manpower statistics, so post-war planning demanded, not only knowledge of the size of the working population, but also its age and sex structure, its occupational skills, etc. Collection of such statistics was facilitated in 1948 by the passing of the National Insurance Act and the introduction of the Standard Industrial Classifications. The former required every gainfully employed person to register and in theory we should have obtained a complete census of all those in employment. Unfortunately, there are some omissions resulting from the failure of some individuals to register – particularly married women and the self-employed. The Standard Industrial Classification was designed to provide a standard pattern of classification by industry which could be used by all industrial statistics and so facilitate comparison. Unfortunately from this point of view, there were major revisions in the classification in 1958 and 1968, and there have been many minor changes since. The effect of the major changes was to reclassify some industries as distributive and service industries which had previously been classed as manufacturing. You can see the effect this had in the following table, which classifies manpower according to two different Standard Industrial Classifications.

[1] Now the Department of Employment and Productivity.

Changes in the Composition of Employment (000's)
June 30th 1959

	[S.I.C.] 1948	[S.I.C.] 1958
Males		
Manufacturing	6,271	5,738
Distribution	1,578	1,689
Other	7,459	7,881
Females		
Manufacturing	2,898	2,739
Distribution	1,422	1,520
Other	3,569	3,630
Total	23,197	23,197

Source: Treasury Bulletin for Industry 1962.

The more recent changes have not been as drastic as this. They have involved largely the subdivision of industry into two or more component parts, as with the extracting in 1974 of 'Handtools and Implements' from the more general industry 'Cutlery Spoons Forks etc.'.

	Thousand Employees		
	1972	1973	1974
Hand Tools and Implements	—	—	21
Cutlery Spoons Forks etc.	35	35	15

Unless you are very careful you can be left with the impression that there has been an upheaval in certain industries at the time the classification was changed. However minor such changes may seem, however desirable they may be, they have one unfortunate effect – many of the series are not comparable over more than a few years.

One of the simplest ways of collecting data relating to employed persons was to use the quarterly exchange of insurance cards, since those who do hand in full insurance cards at the end of a quarter form a random sample of the working population. In fact, for many years, the annual figures published were based on cards handed in during the second quarter, supplemented by returns from employers having five or more workers. This gave a sample estimated to cover 75% of the working population. Now that the United Kingdom has abolished insurance cards, it seems that a major source, apart from the employers' annual return, will be found in the records of the Department of Health and Social Security or the Inland Revenue.

We would not wish to leave you with the impression that manpower statistics are concerned only with totals. Statistics are also produced relating to unemployment, unemployment rates, temporary lay-offs, days lost through strike action, average salaries and wages in the different industrial groups, holiday entitlement, etc. Moreover, most of the data is brought up to date monthly in the Department of Employment Gazette, and quarterly in the publications on Incomes, Prices, Employment and Production. Information today is far removed from the guesses and estimates of the 1930's.

Production

Without doubt one of the most important sources for data on industrial production is the Census of Production, the results of which are published by the Business Statistics Office. The full census is a massive document, but you will find a first-class summary of the relevant information in the Annual Abstract of Statistics. Although the expression 'census' is used, we must not imagine that it covers every firm in the United Kingdom. Firstly, there is a rather narrow definition of production. The census covers extractive, manufacturing and building industries. So important sectors of the economy such as agriculture and fisheries, distribution and the service industries are excluded. Secondly, even within this limited field, not every firm is included. The small firm is only required to give the nature of the trade and the size of its labour force. However, in some industries where a significant proportion of total output is produced by small firms, the full census requires such firms to make a simplified return.

In spite of its limited scope, the Census of Production provides us with a great deal of information. It shows us the way in which national industrial output is divided between different industries, and the study of this data over time brings out the trend and relative importance of individual industries. Central planning would be difficult without data like this, especially in respect of the distribution of labour and the allocation of capital resources. It is particularly important for the information it gives relating to changes in stocks of raw materials and finished goods, to capital expenditure on plant and machinery, and to building work undertaken. Without information such as this, national income statistics would be much less reliable, and the Index of Industrial Production subject to major errors.

Naturally, much of the information contained in the census report can be obtained elsewhere. The Department of Energy publishes much information on the coal industry and all forms of fuel production; The British Steel Corporation produces data on steel production; the building industry is covered by reports from the Department of the Environment. If you are interested in the details of a

Censuses of production: summary table

Standard Industrial Classification 1968 order numbers	Gross output (production) [1][2]	Net output	Stocks and work in progress [3]		Capital expenditure *less* disposals [4]	Wages and salaries	Average number of persons employed [5]	Net output per person employed
			At end of year	Change during year				
	£ million						Thousands	£
All census industries II–XXI								
1948	12,961	5,377	..	..		3,164	10,149	530
1951	18,733	6,838	..	..	768	3,960	10,669	641
	21,897	8,435	..	..	984	4,951	10,894	774
1954	20,709	8,180	..	..	990	4,748	10,450	783
1958	26,980	10,438	..	..	1,402	6,145	10,570	988
	34,467	14,423	6,189	+176	1,884	7,799	10,705	1,347
1963	34,456	14,406	6,276	+169	1,886	7,793	10,684	1,348
1968[7]	48,216	20,284	9,085	+594	2,662	10,316	10,263	1,976
1970[7]	51,414	20,972	10,543	+981	3,080	10,710	8,797	2,384
1971[7]	54,747	22,528	10,899	+493	3,146	11,483	8,579	2,626
1972[7]	57,755	25,047	11,688	+781	2,939	12,470	8,236	3,041
1973	..	..	..	..	..	..	..	:
Manufacturing industries III–XIX								
1948	10,754	4,077	2,148	+293	289	2,260	7,308	558
1951	15,909	5,271	3,243	+654	489	2,863	7,829	673
	18,259	6,438	3,536	+204	561	3,584	8,014	803
1954	17,170	6,234	3,503	+211	568	3,427	7,672	813
1958	22,039	7,848	4,621	+14	861	4,454	7,781	1,000
	27,819	10,851	5,714	+176	1,025	5,712	7,960	1,363
1963	27,772	10,820	5,798	+169	1,026	5,704	7,952	1,361
1968	38,697	15,289	8,501	+622	1,525	7,768	7,826	1,954
1970	47,368	18,502	10,183	+984	2,164	9,738	8,030	2,304
1971	50,348	19,865	10,517	+490	2,703	10,438	7,834	2,536

Estimates for all firms

Year								
1948	2,632	525	287	+32	41	207	718	766
1951	3,227	608	416	+76	64	254	773	814
1954	3,819	742	448	+27	71	311	789	963
1958	3,235	645	429	+30	62	260	657	982
1963	4,285	917	586	+15	91	367	726	1,263
	5,195	1,269	725	+43	137	491	756	1,670
1968	5,347	1,292	749	+44	139	499	766	1,636
1970	7,568	1,841	1,018	+60	199	713	793	2,323
1971	9,158	2,348	1,239	+102	238	869	789	2,976
1972	9,769	2,597	1,286	+90	259	985	795	3,269
1973	10,345	2,903	1,339	+82	279	1,072	778	3,734
	11,885	3,507	:	:	377	1,229	786	4,462

IV, V

Chemicals and allied industries

Year								
1948	762	269	143	+16	38	122	351	768
1951	1,283	372	250	+80	103	163	387	981
1954	1,687	529	264	+37	97	206	401	1,319
1958	1,663	538	263	+38	113	211	409	1,316
1963	2,319	736	379	+1	198	291	444	1,656
	2,957	1,058	446	−3	138	374	443	2,388
1968	2,900	1,068	447	−4	143	392	468	2,282
1970	4,353	1,516	676	+68	311	527	449	3,375
1971	5,158	1,933	852	+71	467	664	462	4,184
1972	5,731	2,086	964	−114	501	718	448	4,642
1973	6,170	2,265	1,021	+51	395	771	432	5,247
	7,673	2,693	:	:	294	877	487	6,162

PRODUCTION

Index of industrial production[1]

Average 1970 = 100

	Order numbers and Minimum List Headings [2]	1970 Weights	1965	1966	1967	1968	1969	1970	1971	1972	1973	1974
Total all industries	II–XXI	1000	89.1	90.6	91.7	97.1	99.7	100.0	100.5	102.6	110.2	106.4
Mining and quarrying	II	37	122.3	115.3	114.5	111.4	104.9	100.0	99.7	84.0	93.6	83.6
Coal mining	101	30	140.3	129.8	126.8	117.1	107.7	100.0	98.4	84.0	84.2	70.0
Other mining and quarrying	102–109	7	74.1	76.7	81.6	88.0	93.4	100.0	105.0	115.6	132.7	139.7
Manufacturing industries: total	III–XIX	745	87.6	89.2	89.8	95.7	99.4	100.0	99.7	102.3	110.9	108.0
Food, drink and tobacco	III	84	88.6	91.3	93.0	95.6	98.6	100.0	100.7	105.0	109.3	110.0
Food	211–229	52	92.0	94.5	95.6	97.4	99.6	100.0	100.1	104.2	106.4	104.7
Drink and tobacco	231–240	32	82.9	86.0	88.5	92.7	96.8	100.0	101.7	106.4	114.0	118.7
Chemicals, coal and petroleum products	IV–V	65	74.6	78.9	82.7	89.3	94.7	100.0	102.3	107.5	120.3	125.5
Coal and petroleum products	IV	7	75.0	79.7	76.4	84.0	92.1	100.0	103.4	102.6	110.0	106.1
Chemicals and allied industries	V	58	74.6	78.8	83.4	89.9	95.0	100.0	102.2	108.1	121.6	128.0
Metal manufacture	VI	57	103.5	97.7	92.0	97.9	100.3	100.0	91.2	91.0	99.4	91.5
Ferrous	311–313	43	104.3	97.9	91.4	96.8	100.4	100.0	89.8	89.4	97.3	87.7
Non-ferrous	321–323	14	100.9	96.7	94.0	101.2	100.0	100.0	95.4	96.7	106.1	103.5
Engineering and allied industries	VII–XII	319	87.4	89.5	90.0	94.6	99.8	100.0	99.4	100.0	108.0	105.9
Total engineering	VII–IX	182	79.0	84.7	87.5	91.2	96.7	100.0	101.1	100.5	111.6	110.2
Mechanical engineering	VII	100	82.7	87.8	88.3	92.0	97.0	100.0	100.1	95.0	103.5	104.0
Instrument engineering	VIII	15	72.3	75.0	76.9	86.0	92.4	100.0	100.8	93.1	102.1	105.0
Electrical engineering	IX	67	75.5	82.4	83.2	91.2	97.1	100.0	102.6	110.3	125.9	120.6
Shipbuilding	X	16	90.2	92.1	93.0	95.0	94.8	100.0	96.6	91.8	95.1	95.6
Vehicles	XI	73	97.3	96.3	94.5	100.5	105.9	100.0	99.3	103.7	105.0	98.5
Motor vehicles	381	45	89.7	88.5	83.8	93.5	99.1	100.0	100.5	102.2	104.6	95.3
Other vehicles	380, 382–385	28	120.6	114.6	113.8	112.0	116.9	110.0	97.4	106.0	105.7	103.8

Industry	SIC [2]	Weight [1]										
Textiles	XIII	49	86.1	83.9	84.1	97.1	100.2	100.0	100.7	103.0	108.6	100.4
Leather, leather goods and fur	XIV	3	109.3	107.7	96.7	104.4	103.0	100.0	103.0	104.5	101.0	96.3
Clothing and footwear	XV	24	100.8	100.9	97.8	101.8	100.4	100.0	105.4	107.8	114.4	110.8
Bricks, pottery, glass, cement, etc.	XVI	27	94.8	94.1	97.7	102.2	103.7	100.0	107.7	114.2	126.5	117.8
Bricks, cement, etc.	461, 464–469	17	97.2	95.1	100.8	103.9	102.7	100.0	106.3	113.6	124.8	109.4
Pottery and glass	462, 463	10	90.6	92.3	92.0	99.7	105.2	100.0	109.8	115.1	129.1	130.8
Timber, furniture, etc.	XVII	22	97.9	95.9	98.8	106.5	99.7	100.0	103.0	113.5	132.6	112.4
Paper, printing and publishing	XVIII	64	90.4	92.8	92.5	96.2	99.3	100.0	97.3	102.6	112.1	109.4
Other manufacturing industries	XIX	31	78.6	81.9	85.2	95.7	99.5	100.0	99.7	104.2	116.5	113.8
Construction	XX	146	95.1	96.7	100.4	103.4	102.0	100.0	102.9	104.5	107.2	98.1
Gas, electricity and water	XXI	72	79.9	83.0	86.0	91.6	96.2	100.0	103.9	111.2	117.8	118.6
Market sector analysis: [3]												
All industries other than construction	II–XIX, XXI (part)	850	88.1	89.5	90.2	98.0	99.3	100.0	100.1	102.3	110.8	107.9
Consumer goods industries		249				95.5	98.3	100.0	102.6	109.9	119.0	116.7
Cars, etc.		16				106.8	100.9	100.0	108.3	118.5	110.8	97.1
Other durables		45				92.6	96.9	100.0	106.6	121.8	141.0	134.9
Clothing and footwear, etc.		36				99.1	100.3	100.0	103.8	105.9	111.2	108.6
Food, drink and tobacco		75				96.0	98.5	100.0	100.7	105.1	109.3	110.6
Other		77				92.7	97.2	100.0	100.4	107.7	120.8	120.0
Investment goods industries		239				94.0	99.5	100.0	98.6	96.3	104.1	102.4
Electrical		57				93.3	97.3	100.0	99.7	98.1	109.1	105.4
Transport		73				98.5	104.3	100.0	96.6	97.6	101.8	98.6
Other		109				91.4	97.0	100.0	99.4	94.5	102.9	103.4
Intermediate goods industries		362				97.7	100.0	100.0	99.2	101.0	109.6	105.4
Fuels		99				97.6	98.7	100.0	103.0	102.0	109.9	106.2
Materials		263				97.8	100.5	100.0	97.3	100.6	109.5	105.1

[1] The weights shown are those used in the compilation of the index from 1968 onwards. Figures for earlier years were recalculated on the 1970 base using the basic methods described in the May 1972 issue of *Economic Trends*. For further notes on the general method of constructing the index see *The Index of Industrial Production and other Output Measures, Studies in Official Statistics* No. 17 (H.M.S.O.), November 1970. [2] The Order Numbers and Minimum List Headings are those of the *Standard Industrial Classification, 1968*. [3] A description of this analysis was published in the November 1973 issue of *Economic Trends*. Figures are not available before 1968.

Source: Central Statistical Office.

Coal: supply and consumption

Million tons

	1964	1965	1966	1967	1968	1969	1970	1971	1972	1973	1974
Supply											
Production of deep-mined coal	186.8	180.2	167.6	165.0	157.2	144.2	134.5	134.3	107.8	118.1	98.4
Production of opencast coal	6.8	7.3	7.0	7.1	6.9	6.3	7.8	10.5	9.8	10.0	9.1
Total	193.6	187.5	174.6	172.1	164.1	150.5	142.3	144.8	117.6	128.1	107.5
Recovered slurry, fines, etc.	1.3	1.1	1.5	2.7	3.1	2.7	2.5	2.3	2.3	1.8	1.0
Imports	—	—	—	—	—	—	0.1	4.2	4.9	1.6	3.5
Total	194.9	188.6	176.1	174.8	167.2	153.2	144.9	151.3	124.8	131.5	112.0
Change in colliery stocks	+0.5	+0.4	-3.4	+8.2	+0.8	-8.5	-10.1	+1.7	+0.6	+0.1	-3.6
Change in stocks at opencast sites	+0.3	+0.7	+0.4	+0.9	—	-1.0	-1.3	+1.4	+0.1	-0.2	-1.2
Total supply	194.1	187.5	179.1	165.7	166.4	162.7	156.3	148.2	124.1	131.6	116.8
Home consumption											
Electricity supply industry	68.0	70.0	68.6	67.2	73.2	75.9	76.0	71.7	65.6	76.6	66.0
Gas supply industry	20.5	18.2	16.9	14.6	10.7	6.9	4.2	1.8	0.6	0.5	0.1
Coke ovens	25.9	26.3	24.8	23.6	24.9	25.3	24.9	23.2	20.1	21.5	18.1
Low temperature carbonisation plants	1.4	1.5	1.7	2.0	2.2	2.4	2.6	2.7	3.0	2.2	2.6
Manufactured fuel plants	1.3	1.0	1.0	1.2	1.3	1.4	1.5	1.7	1.5	1.4	1.1
Railways	3.8	2.8	1.7	0.8	0.2	0.2	0.1	0.1	0.1	0.1	0.1
Collieries	3.7	3.4	3.1	2.9	2.4	2.0	1.9	1.6	1.4	1.4	1.2
Industry[1]:											
Iron and steel	2.1	1.8	1.3	0.9	0.8	0.9	0.8	0.6	0.3	0.4	0.4
Other industries	25.9	25.5	23.9	22.0	21.8	20.5	18.5	15.0	11.2	11.5	10.5
Agriculture	0.?	0.?	0.?	0.?	0.?	0.?	0.?	0.1	0.1	0.1	0.1

Anthracite and dry steam coal	1.6	1.8	1.8	1.7	1.9	1.9	2.0	1.6	1.7	1.7	1.5
Miners' coal	4.3	4.2	3.8	3.6	3.2	2.9	2.7	2.5	2.2	2.2	2.1
Public services	3.4	3.5	3.4	3.2	3.0	3.1	2.9	2.4	2.1	2.0	1.9
Miscellaneous	1.8	1.8	1.4	0.9	0.5	0.6	0.8	0.7	0.6	0.4	0.4
Total home consumption	187.2	184.6	174.7	163.8	164.5	161.1	154.4	138.7	120.9	131.3	115.9
Overseas shipments and bunkers	6.0	3.7	2.8	1.9	2.7	3.5	3.2	2.6	1.8	2.7	1.6
Total consumption and shipments	193.2	188.3	177.5	165.7	167.2	164.6	157.6	141.3	122.7	134.0	117.5
Change in distributed stocks [3]	+0.8	−0.7	+1.9	+0.2	−0.6	−1.7	−1.0	+6.5	+1.0	−1.5	−1.2
Balance [4]	+0.1	−0.1	−0.3	−0.2	−0.2	−0.2	−0.3	+0.4	+0.4	−0.9	+0.5
Stocks at end of year [5]											
Distributed [3]	17.3	16.6	18.4	18.6	17.1	15.4	14.4	20.9	21.9	16.8	15.6
At collieries	18.2	18.6	15.3	23.4	23.8	15.3	5.3	7.0	7.5	7.6	4.0
At opencast sites	2.2	2.9	3.3	4.3	4.2	3.2	1.8	3.2	3.4	3.1	1.9
Total stocks	37.7	18.1	37.0	46.3	45.1	33.9	21.5	31.1	32.8	27.5	21.5

TIME SERIES. Figures relate to periods of 52 weeks.

[1] From October 1973 the figures relate to colliery disposals to industry. [2] From April 1973 the figures relate to colliery disposals for the domestic market. [3] Great Britain. Stock change end-1973 excludes industrial and domestic stocks. For an analysis of these stocks see Table 183. [4] This is the balance between supply and consumption, shipments and changes in known distributed stocks. [5] Figures shown for stocks at end of year for 1967 and 1972 relate to position at 23 December. Stock change in 1968 is calculated on stocks at 30 December 1967.

Source: Department of Energy.

particular industry, say the tonnage of herrings landed at Hull, you would turn to the very comprehensive reports of the government departments, extracts from which appear in the Annual Abstract of Statistics. But the only place all this information is brought together is in the report on the Census of Production. Without this we would find it very difficult to estimate the total value of industrial production in the country.

In the United Kingdom, the first Census of Production was undertaken in 1907, and between the wars four more were taken. From 1948 it was intended to take a full census every year, but in fact the cost both to the state and to industry was heavy, and in the event a full census has been taken only every five years, while in the intervening years we have undertaken a sample survey, or a limited survey in which fewer questions are asked.

The census suffers from the normal defects of any effort to provide comprehensive and accurate information. It is expensive and it takes a considerable time to analyse and publish, and can only be undertaken at long intervals. To provide up-to-date information between censuses, the Department of Trade and Industry publish quarterly a series of sample statistics relating to different aspects of industry such as changes in stocks, capital expenditure and industrial buildings. The Department also sells statistical surveys of individual industries. To illustrate the type of information available in this field we append an extract from the Census of Production summary table, the Index of Industrial Production and a table from the wide range of information on coal published by the Department of Energy.

Distribution
Although Napoleon called England a nation of shopkeepers, it was not until 1951 that any official enquiry attempted to determine how many retail establishments there are in the United Kingdom, what kind of shops (multiples, independents) they were, what they sold or what was their turnover. The effort to obtain such information well illustrates the problems we face when we are attempting to take a census in a completely new field. Before any information could be obtained the government had to build up a sampling frame. This was done from May to October 1950, enumerators all over the country listing names and addresses of traders who fell within the scope of the census, 'as far as could be judged from the outside of the premises'. They were not allowed to enter the shop and talk to the owner or his employees, but were asked to distinguish between shops, stalls, depots and other kinds of premises. So thorough was this initial enumeration that the shops omitted must be negligible.

Having established a sampling frame the next step was to draft the questionnaire. This was the first time such a census had been undertaken, and a careful examination of objectives was necessary. It was decided that the census should provide information about

(a) the number and size of retail and wholesale outlets;
(b) the value of services provided by the distributive sector;
(c) the relative efficiency of distribution in different areas, i.e. the number of shops per head of the population.

Although the first census was a complete survey obtaining a 91% response rate to the questionnaire, a committee on the Census of Distribution and Production (the Vernon Smith Committee) recommended in 1954 that sample surveys be undertaken between the dates of the full census. It was decided to take a 12% census and a most interesting thing about it was the way it was selected.

Firstly, every distributive outlet with a turnover in excess of £100,000 was to be included. This covered all the multiple stores, department stores and the majority of the co-operative societies. But once again there was no up-to-date sampling frame for the smaller independent retailers, so as in 1950 an enumeration had to be made in the relevant sample areas. These areas were chosen as follows:

(1) Certain areas existed in which it was believed that important changes had taken place since 1950, e.g. the new towns and central London. In these areas a complete enumeration of distributive outlets was undertaken and a 20% sample selected.
(2) In Greater London a sample of electoral wards stratified by size and distinguishing between mainly residential and mainly commercial was selected, and every shop in the selected wards was included in the survey.
(3) In the large towns (over 100,000 population) a sample of streets stratified by the number of shops there had been in 1950 was taken.
(4) Other towns were sampled by taking a cross-section of local authority areas stratified by population, by sales in 1950, and by population changes since 1950.
(5) In rural districts a regional sample stratified by population density or population changes was selected.

The survey was undertaken by post with a very energetic follow-up. In the end the response rates were a remarkable 96% for larger traders, 89% for independent traders, and even 75% for street traders, hawkers, etc. It was estimated that the error was no more than 0.5% of the overall totals.

The 1961 Census of Distribution covered wholesale establishments which had been omitted from the sample survey, and to minimise cost only a 5% sample of establishments were given the full questionnaire. The remainder were asked only for details of employment and turnover together with some descriptive information. Thus we now obtain at five-year intervals details of the number, type and size of retail and wholesale firms, their turnover, stocks, capital expenditure, and hire purchase debt.

You may cast some doubt on the value of a census that takes nearly three years to publish its findings, and it is worth asking the reason for the delay. The first reason is the sheer magnitude of the operation – almost half a million retailers are involved, and it is no exaggeration to say that the returns take well over a year to come in. Even if a high proportion of firms are willing to co-operate the follow-up takes a considerable period of time. Time is absorbed too by a vast volume of correspondence from retailers asking questions about the completion of the forms.

Secondly, in the editing of the forms, many errors and omissions are found, and the correction of these errors involves both greater correspondence and delay. Finally, the analysis and printing of results, although computers are now used, is a tedious process.

Nevertheless, the importance of the analysis cannot be overestimated. Not only would National Income Statistics be unreliable without reasonably accurate figures of the contribution of the distributive trades to the Gross Domestic Product, but also the information is vital for the planning of, say, city shopping centres, or for the provision of shopping facilities in new towns. Moreover, the census returns form a new starting point for monthly and quarterly estimates which are vital in day-to-day planning.

National Income Statistics

All of the data that we have discussed in the last few paragraphs is still sectional data, no matter how widely the net is spread. It is concerned with only one aspect of the economy. What we must now do is turn our attention to the performance of the economy as a whole. This is seen only when we bring together the various parts of the economy in the statistics of National Income. We find these statistics in the book *National Income and Expenditure* published by Her Majesty's Stationery Office. This is not the place to go into details of what the expression 'National Income' means. However, we should note that all production is intended to satisfy consumer wants, and the more that is produced the greater can our consumption be. Thus what the National Income Statistics are measuring is basically the way our standard of living is changing.

Now any economist will tell you that National Income can be

measured in three ways – by aggregating expenditure, by aggregating income, or by aggregating output. In theory, whichever method we use should give the same totals, but in practice there is always a difference which appears in the tables as 'residual error'. This has at times been as much as £700 million. Obviously we have not reached perfection!

To the extent that the data we have is accurate, overall planning is facilitated, but we must admit that despite a quarter of a century's experience in producing these figures, and despite many improvements that have taken place, several of the more important aggregates are little more than approximations. It is for this reason that each successive edition of *National Income and Expenditure* (called the 'Blue Book') amends the figures for the previous years.

There are differences in opinion as to what should be included in National Income calculations, and this makes international comparisons very difficult. For example in the peasant economies of the underdeveloped countries food grown by the farmers and eaten themselves is a very important part of the National Income and can be justifiably included. But in the United Kingdom such consumption is not included in the total of National Income. In fact, in this country we include only such goods and services as are exchanged for money; and this cuts out a host of services which contribute to our welfare. If your wife or mother washes your shirt it does not affect the National Income statistics, but if you send it to a laundry the National Income is affected. Thus any change in social habits whereby people begin to pay for things they previously did for themselves will raise the National Income – even though the goods and services available have not increased.

One further point to be borne in mind is that the National Income is necessarily measured in money terms – and the value of money changes. Thus we may find that the National Income has risen by 10% since last year, but if inflation is at the rate of 15%, can we really say we are better off?

In spite of these criticisms, however, the annual Blue Book on National Income and Expenditure contains a mass of information vital to the planners in society and to the students of society.

Beginning with the National Income measured by the expenditure method, the Blue Book reconciles this figure with the National Income measured by the income of the various factors of production (wages, profits, interest and rent). This is far more than an academic exercise. The first table indicates the changing pattern of people's consumption. Here we can see, for example, the changing expenditure on health, defence or education, the switch of expenditure to the service industries and the rise of the consumer durable industry.

The second part of the table indicates the distribution of income in society; the proportion of income earned by the performance of work as compared with the proportion received from rents. Here we can trace the increasing share of the National Income going to the 'working class'. The third reconciliation indicates the Gross National Product by industry. Thus we can assess the contribution of each industrial group to the National Income. Other tables in the Blue Book take many of these points and in turn analyse them in much more detail.

This type of data is obtained from three main sources – the statistics assembled by the Inland Revenue, the Census of Production and Distribution, and the accounts of central and local government. But these are supplemented by a wide range of other sources. Unfortunately the coverage is far from complete, and in many cases the accuracy is impaired by the fact that the data used has been compiled for purposes other than National Income estimates.

The data we have discussed in this chapter is very important, but please remember that it is only a fraction of the data published each year. Much of this is a result of the day-to-day work of the government departments, some is an offspring of special surveys, and a great deal more is the result of the work of the statistical departments of banks, insurance companies, finance houses and the like.

Overlooking and co-ordinating the work of the government departments is the Central Statistical Office producing the Annual Abstract of Statistics, possibly the most important of all sources. You will never digest all the information in this, so where do you start to study for a possible question on sources? Our own advice is firstly to study past examination papers. Some have an occasional question and for this it is probably sufficient to take three or four major surveys and hope for the best. Others have a section on statistical presentation where you can be asked questions on tabulation and report writing as well as sources. Never go into the examination not knowing what to expect.

Well, that concludes this book. If you have absorbed this course you should be well prepared for your examination. Remember that examiners are fair and set questions within the range of work we have covered. It only remains to wish every one of you entering for a statistics examination now and in the future all the success your efforts deserve. For those of you not studying for an examination, we hope that you have found this book both pleasant and thought-provoking.

EXERCISES TO CHAPTER 19

19.1   Outline the procedures which are employed when a Census of Population is undertaken in the United Kingdom, or in a country of your choice.   I.C.S.A.

19.2   Which statistics, published in the United Kingdom, are available relating to population? Mention the main publications in which they are to be found and write a summary of the details given in each.   O.N.C.

19.3   Write an account of the contents of the Population and Vital Statistics section of the Monthly Digest of Statistics.   O.N.C.

19.4   Describe where and in what form figures concerning population of the U.K. can be found. Say what use could be made of this information by an organisation of your own choice, e.g. an insurance company, a chain of supermarkets, a local authority or any other with which you are familiar.   O.N.C.

19.5   Describe the principal official sources of data relating to (a) population and (b) employment.   O.N.C.

19.6   (a) Explain the purpose and use of a Census of Distribution and describe briefly the information collected in the Census of Distribution (Great Britain) 1971.
   (b) Describe the statistical information you would expect to find in the publication *Economic Trends*.   A.C.A.

19.7   Describe the statistical information which is obtained from the Census of Production.   O.N.C.

19.8   Write an essay on the construction and use of *two* official index numbers published by the government.   O.N.C.

19.9   Explain how and by whom the General Index of Retail Prices is prepared, where it is published and what purpose it serves.
                                                                          O.N.C.

19.10   Either
   (a) Outline the structure of The Family Expenditure Survey and explain its purpose. How reliable are its findings? Indicate some of the changes in the 1973 survey which affects the comparison with earlier years.
Or

(b) Describe The General Household Survey, commenting briefly on some of its findings. How useful is the survey to government? O.N.C.

19.11 (a) Describe the construction of the Official Retail Prices Index used in the United Kingdom, and (b) explain how it could be used by:
  (i) businessmen,
  (ii) consumers, and
  (iii) trade unions. A.C.A.

19.12 What methods are available to indicate the general change in retail price levels in a community? Support your answer by referring to the construction of statistical indicators in the United Kingdom or a country of your choice. I.C.S.A.

19.13 Describe the Department of Employment Index of Retail Prices. (Your answer should show knowledge of the purpose of the index, the groups of items included, the method of collecting prices, the method of determining weights and the calculation of the index number itself.) Discuss the importance of such an index. O.N.C.

19.14 Discuss the statistical material available on National Income and Expenditure in the United Kingdom. O.N.C.

19.15 What are the main contents of the monthly employment statistics prepared by the Department of Employment and Productivity? O.N.C.

19.16 As a trade union official, you have been given the task of submitting a well-documented wage claim on behalf of your members.
  (a) What kind of problems would you expect to encounter in making your case?
  (b) What sources of economic statistics would you consult?
  (c) What kind of information would you seek from those sources to justify your claim? O.N.C.

19.17 (a) Write a summary of the contents of either the Department of Employment Gazette or the Monthly Digest.
  (b) Name two tables that regularly appear in the publication you have selected in (a) and briefly summarise the details given in them. O.N.C.

19.18 Describe TWO of the main summary sources of statistics published regularly by government departments.   O.N.C.

19.19 (a) Give details of the official statistical publications that should be found in a statistics department of a large business.

(b) Describe in detail the construction and use of one of the main indicators found in one of these publications.   O.N.C.

19.20 Write briefly on four of the following sources of economic statistics. You should comment on the breadth and detail of the information in the publications you choose.

(a) Economic Trends;
(b) Annual Abstract of Statistics;
(c) The Family Expenditure Survey;
(d) The Monthly Digest of Statistics;
(e) National Income and Expenditure (the *Blue* Book);
(f) The Department of Employment Gazette.   O.N.C.

19.21 Describe the statistical information provided in THREE of the following official publications:

(i) Annual Abstract of Statistics;
(ii) Business Monitors;
(iii) Department of Employment Gazette;
(iv) Family Expenditure Survey Report.   A.C.A.

19.22 (a) If your employer wished to gain information on the following, suggest which publications would provide this:

(i) Wage rates and average earnings.
(ii) Retail and wholesale prices.
(iii) Industrial production.
(iv) Regional and national unemployment.
(v) Value and volume of monthly and annual imports and exports of goods.

(b) Give examples of the purpose for which he may wish to use this information.   O.N.C.

19.23 Describe the construction and use of two of the following Economic and Business Indicators:

(i) General Index of Retail Prices.
(ii) Index of Industrial Production.
(iii) Index Numbers of Wholesale Prices.
(iv) Unemployment and Employment Statistics.
(v) National Income Statistics.   O.N.C.

19.24   (a) What information is available in the Monthly Digest of Statistics concerning any *three* of the following:

(i) Population and vital statistics.
(ii) External trade.
(iii) Prices.
(iv) Social services?

(b) Explain briefly the purpose and the derivation of the Index of Industrial Production.   O.N.C.

19.25   (a) State *two* main official publications which give statistics for the United Kingdom relative to each of the following:

(i) Index of retail prices.
(ii) Short time worked.
(iii) Sales of vehicles.
(iv) Imports.
(v) Personal incomes.
(vi) Temperatures, rainfall and sunshine.

(b) State *two* main monthly publications for which the compilers are:

(i) Central Statistical Office;
(ii) Department of Employment.

Describe briefly the contents of any *one* of these publications.
                                                                      O.N.C.

19.26   State with reasons FOUR important economic indicators which are used in charting the economy.   O.N.C.

ANSWERS

Chapter 1

1.12 Taking classes as 650–659, 660–669, etc., the frequencies are
2, 5, 6, 14, 26, 18, 13, 10, 3, 3 = 100

1.14 Suggested classes: 0–19, 20–39, etc.
Frequencies are: 0, 5, 13, 7, 9, 27, 19, 19, 10, 7, 4 = 120

1.17 Suggested classes: 15–24, 25–34, etc.
Frequencies are: 20, 10, 10, 7, 7, 4, 1, 1 = 60

Chapter 2

2.9 Suggested classes: 110–119, 120–129, etc.
Frequencies are: 1, 3, 7, 14, 8, 5, 2 = 40

2.11 Suggested classes: 10, but under 15; 15, but under 20 ... 40
and over (thou. million)
Frequencies are: 3, 4, 4, 3, 3, 2, 3 = 22

Chapter 3

3.2 (b) 18.588 ± 0.056, i.e. $\pm 0.3013\%$
(c) 341 ± 9, i.e. $\pm 2.64\%$

3.4 Receipts $= £4,900,000 \pm 87,500$
Cost $= £4,350,000 \pm 55,000$
So profit $= £550,000 \pm 142,500$

3.6 (a) Deposits $= 10,969 \pm 40.7$ (million \$)
(b) Cash $= 1360 \pm 10.7$ (million \$)

3.8 (a) (i) $5720 \pm 0.96\%$, (ii) $5480 \pm 1.004\%$
(b) (i) 0.865, (ii) 395

3.10 (b) (i) $\pm 43,000$ tons
(ii) Assuming series discrete, max. error $= +85,914$ tons,
but if continuous, max. error is 86,000 tons
(c) (i) 135.92 ± 2.77 tons
(ii) $29,250 \,\text{lb} \pm 11.43\%$

3.12 (a) $£176,000 \pm £32,802.5$
(b) $\pm 18.64\%$

3.14 (i) EFTA, £1276.6m, EEC £1753.9m
(ii) EFTA, £1270m, EEC £1750m
(iii) 0.52%

3.16   (b) (i) Output $= 2000 \pm 65.5$
                 Unit profit $= £1 \pm 0.1$
                 Weekly profit $= £2000 \pm 272.05$
            (ii) 50 ± 6.5

Chapter 4

4.2   211

4.4   Median $= 2.72$, mean $= 2.48$

4.6   Assume final group is '£30 and under £40'
       If assumed mean is 17.5, and if $c = 5$,
       $$\Sigma f = 376, \ \Sigma fd = -224.5 \rbrace \text{hundreds}$$
       $$\bar{x} = £1451.50$$

4.8   Assuming employment starts at 18, and retirement age is 65,
       $\bar{x} = 43.16$ years

4.10   Assume final group is 70–79
       If assumed mean is 25, and if $c = 10$, $\Sigma f = 756$, $\Sigma fd = 452$.
       $\bar{x} = 30.98$ years

4.12   Frequencies are: 7, 16, 12, 11, 10, 4, $\Sigma f = 60$
       If assumed mean is 549.5, and if $c = 20$, then $\Sigma fd = 13$.
       $\bar{x} = 553.83$ miles

4.14   Factory A: 27.23 years, Factory B, 37.09 years

4.16 $£24 - £36$: 5,085,000
       $£32 - £48$: 4,860,000
       $£24 - £48$: 8,235,000

4.18   Median $= 84$p
       Mode $= 76.9$p
       Taking an assumed mean of 75, and $c = 10$, $\Sigma f = 395$, $\Sigma fd = 453$. $\bar{x} = 86.47$p

4.20   Frequencies are: 3, 13, 23, 25, 22, 9, 4, 1, $\Sigma f = 100$
       Mode $= 17$ years $8\frac{1}{2}$ months

4.22   Taking an assumed mean of 6.5, $\Sigma fd = 212$. $\bar{x} = 7.26$ hours
       Median $= 7.41$ hours

4.24   Taking an assumed mean of 250, and $c = 100$, $\Sigma f = 460$, $\Sigma fd = -6$. $\bar{x} = £248.7$
       Total value of orders $= £114,402$
       Mode $= £200$

4.26   Mean $= £1162.95$
       Mode $= £859.14$
       Median $= £1002.47$

4.28   54,583,214

Chapter 5

5.6   Simple index $= 200$, weighted index $= 194.4$

5.8

Materials:	100	98.8	99.0	97.8	98.6	98.2
	98.8	101.4	101.5	103.1	106.5	112.6
Output:	100	99.6	99.8	99.3	99.7	100.3
	100.9	102.9	103.3	104.1	104.8	105.6
Food:	100	100.7	101.3	100.4	101.5	103.2
	103.2	105.1	105.2	105.4	106.3	107.9

5.10 $x = 121$, Index $= 166.9$

5.12   Index for A $= 163$, for B $= 205$

5.14 $\Sigma p_0 q_0 = 1913$, $\Sigma p_1 q_0 = 1923$
Price index $= 100.5$ $(1974 = 100)$ and 106.9 $(1973 = 100)$

5.16 $\Sigma p_0 q_0 = 23{,}005$, $\Sigma p_1 q_0 = 24{,}676$, $\Sigma p_2 q_0 = 27{,}326$
$\Sigma p_0 q_1 = 21{,}830$, $\Sigma p_1 q_1 = 23{,}558$, $\Sigma p_0 q_2 = 22{,}740$, $\Sigma p_2 q_2 = 26{,}960$
Laspeyre Index: Period $1 = 107.3$, Period $2 = 118.8$
Paasche Index: Period $1 = 107.9$, Period $2 = 118.6$

5.18 $\Sigma p_0 q_0 = 1929$, $\Sigma p_1 q_0 = 2545.1$, $\Sigma p_2 q_0 = 4102.5$, $\Sigma p_0 q_1 = 3642.5$
$\Sigma p_1 q_1 = 4597.5$, $\Sigma p_0 q_2 = 8742.5$, $\Sigma p_2 q_2 = 13791$
Laspeyre Index: $1950 = 131.9$, $1960 = 212.7$
Paasche Index: $1950 = 126.2$, $1960 = 157.7$

5.20 $\Sigma p_0 q_n = 63.8$, $\Sigma p_n q_n = 88$. Paasche index $= 137.9$

5.22 $\Sigma p_0 q_0 = 833$, $\Sigma p_0 q_1 = 805$, $\Sigma p_0 q_2 = 797$, $\Sigma p_0 q_3 = 865$
Index of Production, $1967 = 96.6$, $1968 = 95.7$, $1969 = 103.8$

5.24 $\Sigma wi = 122{,}927.5$
(b) Index of Production $= 122.9$
(c) 125.6
(d) 81.4

5.26   Dividing q_0, q_n and p_0 by 100,000, $\Sigma p_0 q_0 = 131.4601$, $\Sigma p_0 q_n = 106.7955$
Volume index $= 81.2$

5.28 $\Sigma wq_1 = 11{,}909$, $\Sigma wq_2 = 12{,}766$, $\Sigma wq_3 = 14{,}160$
Index of Production, $1964 = 119.1$, $1965 = 127.7$, $1966 = 141.6$

Chapter 6

6.4   Trend: 125, 126, $126\frac{1}{3}$, $127\frac{2}{3}$, 127, $127\frac{2}{3}$, 129, 130, $129\frac{2}{3}$, $129\frac{1}{3}$, $129\frac{2}{3}$, 131, 132
Shift variation: $+1.5$, -12, $+10.5$

6.6   Trend: 62.5, 63.875, 63.75, 63.5, 64.375, 66.25, 67.875, 69.625, 71.25, 70.875, 70.625, 70.125

6.8   Trend: 42.6, 40.2, 39.4, 38.6, 38.0, 38.4, 37.6

6.10   Trend: 67, 67, 67.25, 67.625, 67.5, 67.375, 67.125, 67, 67.375, 67.625, 67.875

6.12   Trend: 30.125, 30.5, 31.25, 32.75, 34.125, 34.875, 36.125, 36.75
        Seasonal Variation: -12, -1, $+33$, -20

6.14   Trend: 100.5, 100.1125, 100.05, 100.5875, 101.4875, 103.8, 106.2625, 108.15
        Seasonal Variation: $+1.3$, $+1.6$, -6.0, $+3.1$

6.16   Seasonal Variation: $+24$, $+25$, -54.5, $+5.5$
        De-seasonalised series: 456, 495, 520.5, 520.5, 517, 516, 494.5, 504.5, 514, 519, 547.5, 525.5

6.18   Trend (men): 10.07, 10.32, 10.62, 10.87, 11.07, 11.33, 11.70, 12.09, 12.43, 12.70, 13.02, 13.52, 13.56, 13.48
        Trend (women): 6.45, 6.59, 6.85, 7.06, 7.04, 7.07, 7.20, 7.31, 7.52, 7.85, 8.35, 8.71, 8.74, 9.02

6.20   Trend: 180.125, 183.75, 205.125, 238, 251.625, 261.875, 259.25, 252.25, 254.125, 249, 245.625, 245.625
        Seasonal Variation: -34, -16, 0, $+50$

6.22   Seasonal Variation: $+1.375$, $+2.375$, -4.125, $+0.375$
        De-seasonalised Series: 12.6, 12.6, 13.6, 13.1, 13.6, 14.6, 14.6, 16.1, 16.6, 16.6, 17.6, 17.1

6.24   Trend: 245.25, 253.375, 303.25, 346.0, 353.0, 371.0, 406.0

6.26   Trend: 173.25, 180.5, 193, 194.5, 188.375, 190.75, 201.5, 212.875, 218.25, 219.25, 225.125, 231.25
        Seasonal Variation: -144.5, -30, $+288.5$, -114

6.28   Trend: 41.9125, 43.1375, 44.0, 44.9125, 45.7, 46.325, 47.0125, 47.5, 48.1, 49.325
        Seasonal Variation: -0.1, $+0.6$, -3.3, $+2.8$

Chapter 7

7.2   (a) 67, (b) 48, (c) 48, (d) 36, (e) 63, (f) 27, (g) 14.08

7.4   Median = £79.5, 45 earn less than £88, 15 earn between £63 and £75, quartile deviation = £23, 11 earn more than £96

7.5   Median is £2271, quartile deviation is £3770

7.8   Week 1: median = 22.5 cwt, S.Q.R. = 9.625 cwt
        Week 2: median = 25 cwt, S.Q.R. = 7.625 cwt

7.10 Taking an origin of £89.95, and $c = £20$, then $\Sigma f = 30$, $\Sigma fd = 2$, $\Sigma fd^2 = 62$. $\bar{x} = £91.28$, $\sigma = £28.72$

7.12 Taking an assumed mean of 137.45, and $c = 25$, then $\Sigma f = 50$, $\Sigma fd = -2$, $\Sigma fd^2 = 92$. $\bar{x} = 136.45\text{p}$, $\sigma = 33.9\text{p}$

7.14 Taking an origin of £1250, and $c = £50$, $\sigma = £1065$

7.16 Taking upper limit of 110, origin 65, $c = 10$, $\Sigma f = 635$, $\Sigma fd = -145$, $\Sigma fd^2 = 1193$. $\bar{x} = 62.72$ thousand, $\sigma = 13.52$ thousand
Reasonable rule might be to keep constituencies with range $\bar{x} \pm \sigma$

7.18 $\Sigma x = 2600$, $\Sigma x^2 = 681{,}710$, $\bar{x} = 260$, $\sigma = 23.9$, c.v. $= 9.19\%$

7.20 Taking average age over 75 as 77.5 (males), 80 (females)
Males: $\bar{x} = 32.42$ years, $\sigma = 21.6$ years, c.v. $= 66.6\%$
Females: $\bar{x} = 35.77$ years, $\sigma = 23.14$ years, c.v. $= 64.7\%$

7.22 Taking lower limit as 11, and upper limit as 80, origin 45.5 and $c = 10$, $\Sigma f = 77$, $\Sigma fd = 2$, $\Sigma fd^2 = 140$, $\bar{x} = 45.76$, $\sigma = 13.48$, c.v. $= 29.46\%$

7.24 Origin of 1300, $c = 200$, then $\Sigma f = 600$, $\Sigma fd = -300$, $\Sigma fd^2 = 2440$. $\bar{x} = £1200$, $\sigma = £390.73$, $\hat{x} = £112.22$, coefficient of skewness $= 0.674$

7.28 Taking origin of 54.5, $c = 10$, $\bar{x} = 54.2$, $\sigma = 12.41$
Maximum value for $\sigma = 11.5$

7.30 (c) (i) 11, (ii) 409, (iii) 79

7.32 (b) (i) 1587, (ii) 95.44%

7.34 (1) 9.6%, (2) 11.52%

Chapter 8

8.2 $\frac{4}{11}$

8.4 (b) (i) 0.6591, (ii) 0.2866
(c) (i) 0.08, (ii) 0.52, (iii) 0.2

8.6 (b) (i) $\frac{1}{3}$, (ii) $\frac{1}{36}$, (iii) $\frac{91}{216}$, (iv) (a) $\frac{7}{15}$, (b) $\frac{1}{15}$

8.8 (a) $\frac{1}{12}$, (b) $\frac{1}{2}$, (c) $\frac{1}{4}$, (d) $\frac{1}{2}$

8.10 (a) 0.03, (b) 0.33

8.12 (a) 0.8938, (b) 0.1025

8.14 (i) 0.79, (ii) 0.044

8.16 (b) 69.2%, (c) $\frac{1}{2}$, (d) (i) 0.128, (ii) 0.684

8.18 (i) 0.8819, (ii) 0.9181, (iii) 341

8.20 (i) $\frac{4}{9}$, (ii) $\frac{1}{9}$, (iii) $\frac{5}{9}$

8.22 0.005

8.24 (i) 0.4, (ii) $\frac{12}{25}$

Chapter 9

9.2 (a) 0.8208, (b) 0.052

9.4 (a) (i) 0.0894, (ii) 0.0338
(b) (i) 0.0902, (ii) 0.0404

9.6 (a) 0.1336
(b) (i) 0.0746, (ii) 0.0758

9.8 0.3526

9.10 0.0144

9.12 0.0778

9.13 0.01659

9.16 (i) 0.0475, (ii) 0.99242

9.18 (a) 0.77453, (b) 0.06681, (c) 0.13591, (d) 0.15866

9.20 $\sigma = 0.02$ mm. Cost of rejects: old machine, £124.20; new machine, £19.40

9.22 (i) 0.0885, (ii) 0.00554, (iii) 0.09404, (iv) 0.90596

9.24 Old machine: $\bar{x}$ 8.1165 oz, cost £241,398
New machine: $\bar{x}$ 8.0466 oz, cost £240,559.20

Chapter 13

13.2 (b) (i) £207.68 to £228.32, (ii) £223.49

13.4 Sample mean outside 95% limits but inside 99% limits

13.6 Origin of £70, $c = £20$, then $\Sigma f = 300$, $\Sigma fd = 91$, $\Sigma fd^2 = 641$.
$\bar{x} = £76.07$, $\sigma = £28.60$, float £78.78

13.8 Origin of £225, $c = 50$, $\Sigma f = 100$, $\Sigma fd = -35$, $\Sigma fd^2 = 607$. $\bar{x} = £207.5$, $\sigma = £121.94$
95% limits £207.5 ± £23.90, 99% limits £207.5 ± £31.46

13.10 4.56% (remember a negative gap means the rod will not fit in the slot)

13.12 0.48 ± 0.031

13.14 30 ± 8.98%, $n = 8070$

13.16 (ii) 39.5%, (iii) 39.5 ± 6.776%, 39.5 ± 8.919%, (iv) 2295, (v) 7320

13.18 (a) £405,445 to £434,555, (b) 424

13.20 60

13.22 81.59% confident, $n = 660$

Chapter 15

15.2 (a) greater than 30, (b) less than 9 but greater than 31

15.4 Reject outside range 4.99804 to 5.00196 cm
Reject if greater than 5.001645 cm

15.6 $H_0: m_1 - m_2 = 3$ inches. $H_1: m_1 - m_2 \ne 3$ inches
$Z = 2.773$
Reject H_0 at 1% level

15.8 $Z = 2.5$, significant at 1% level

15.10 In this question, we cannot use a significance test as the frequencies refer to the population, and not a sample. However, we could use the methods of chapter three to calculate the maximum mean income for 1972 (£679.70) and minimum for 1973 (£670.89). So we cannot conclude with certainty that mean income has increased

15.12 $n_a = 300$, $m_a = 37.03$, $\sigma_a = 4.94$
$n_b = 200$, $m_b = 35.54$, $\sigma_b = 5.41$
$Z = 3.12$
Significant at 1% level

15.14 Using similar method to 15.10, minimum mean for private sector = 200,214, maximum mean for L.A.'s = 158,586. Average for private sector is greater

15.16 $\bar{x} = 63.56$, $\hat{\sigma} = 3.745$, $v = 8$, $t = 2.85$
Significant at 5% but not at 1% level

15.18 $\hat{\sigma} = 2.12$, $v = 8$
95% limits: 15 ± 1.631, 99% limits: 15 ± 2.372

15.20 Taking differences, $m = 7.6$, $\hat{\sigma} = 7.945$, $v = 9$, $t = 3.014$
Significant at 1% level

15.22 s.e. = 0.01882, $Z = 2.125$
Significant at 5% but not at 1% level

15.24 s.e. = 0.0648, $Z = 1.543$
Not significant

15.26 s.e. = 0.0131, $Z = 2.595$
Significant at 1% level

15.28 s.e. = 0.03017, $Z = 3.31$
Significant at 1% level

Chapter 16

16.2 $\chi^2 = 7.884$, $v = 5$, not significant

16.4 $\bar{x} = 0.9$. Expected values: 81.3, 73.2, 32.9, 9.9
$v = 2$, $\chi^2 = 4.292$, not significant

16.6   Expected values: 32, 16, 8, 8
      $v = 3$, $\chi^2 = 10.188$
      Significant at 5% but not at 1% level

16.8 $v = 2$, $\chi^2 = 4.751$, no association

16.10 $v = 2$, $\chi^2 = 1.502$, no association

16.12   Insufficient information given – need to know the number who 'changed their minds'

16.14 $v = 6$, $\chi^2 = 14.741$, association established at 5% level

16.16 $v = 2$, $\chi^2 = 3.379$, no difference in proportion

16.18 $v = 1$, $\chi^2 = 125.4$, most highly significant
      Using difference between proportions, $Z = 11.2$

Chapter 17

17.4 $\Sigma x = 35$, $\Sigma y = 50$, $\Sigma x^2 = 225$, $\Sigma y^2 = 516$, $\Sigma xy = 360$, $r = 0.79$

17.8   Taking $x = (x - 40)\,y = (y - 3.5)$
     $\Sigma x = -2$, $\Sigma y = 0.6$, $\Sigma x^2 = 182$, $\Sigma y^2 = 0.28$, $\Sigma xy = -6.2$, $r = 0.93$

17.10 $\Sigma x = 18.9$, $\Sigma y = 35.2$, $\Sigma x^2 = 37.01$, $\Sigma y^2 = 132.22$, $\Sigma xy = 64.7$, $r = -0.56$
     Including additional years
     $\Sigma x = 29.1$, $\Sigma y = 62.1$, $\Sigma x^2 = 63.05$, $\Sigma y^2 = 330.25$, $\Sigma xy = 133.85$, $r = 0.609$

17.12 $\Sigma d^2 = 374$, $p = -0.7$

17.14 $\Sigma x = 39$, $\Sigma y = 478$, $\Sigma x^2 = 245$, $\Sigma y^2 = 31812$, $\Sigma xy = 2764$, $r = 0.986$

17.16 $\Sigma d^2 = 8$, $p = 0.857$

17.18 $\Sigma d^2 = 12.5$, $p = 0.85$

17.20 $\Sigma d^2 = 76$, $p = 0.5394$

17.22 $\Sigma d^2 = 34.5$, $p = 0.7125$

17.24 $\Sigma x = 45$, $\Sigma y = 95,315$, $\Sigma x^2 = 285$, $\Sigma xy = 508,810$.
     $y = 7904.3 + 537.25x$
     (a) 13.8 (mil), (b) 13.6 (mil)

17.30 $\Sigma x = 45$, $\Sigma y = 506$, $\Sigma x^2 = 355$, $\Sigma y^2 = 3872$. $y = 4.4x + 51.33$
     (b) 84.33, (c) 7.78

17.32 $x = x - 20$, $y = y - 100$
     $\Sigma x = 143$, $\Sigma y = 391$, $\Sigma x^2 = 2413$, $\Sigma xy = 484$. $y = 217 - 3.09x$.
     When $x = 30$, $y = 124.3$

17.34 $\Sigma x = 48$, $\Sigma y = 62.1$, $\Sigma x^2 = 218.5$, $\Sigma xy = 286.59$.
     $y = 1.44x - 0.59$. When $x = 4$, $y = 5.17\%$

17.36   (1) Sales: 139.6, 142.6, 129.4, 157.9, 152.5, 128.2, 116.8 (hundreds)
(2) 1850, 10.82%
(3) decline of 75,000

Chapter 18

18.2   95% limits are 17.4608 to 17.5392
18.4   95% limits are 2.9902 to 3.0098
Limits for virtually all are 2.985 to 3.015 (i.e. $\bar{x} \pm 3\sigma$)

COMMON LOGARITHMS $\quad \log_{10} x$

x	0	1	2	3	4	5	6	7	8	9	Δ_m +	1	2	3	4	5	6	7	8	9
															ADD					
10	·0000	0043	0086	0128	0170	0212					42	4	8	13	17	21	25	29	34	38
						0212	0253	0294	0334	0374	40	4	8	12	16	20	24	28	32	36
11	·0414	0453	0492	0531	0569	0607					39	4	8	12	16	19	23	27	31	35
						0607	0645	0682	0719	0755	37	4	7	11	15	19	22	26	30	33
12	·0792	0828	0864	0899	0934	0969					35	4	7	11	14	18	21	25	28	32
						0969	1004	1038	1072	1106	34	3	7	10	14	17	20	24	27	31
13	·1139	1173	1206	1239	1271	1303					33	3	7	10	13	16	20	23	26	30
						1303	1335	1367	1399	1430	32	3	6	10	13	16	19	22	26	29
14	·1461	1492	1523	1553	1584	1614	1644	1673	1703	1732	30	3	6	9	12	15	18	21	24	27
15	·1761	1790	1818	1847	1875	1903	1931	1959	1987	2014	28	3	6	8	11	14	17	20	22	25
16	·2041	2068	2095	2122	2148	2175	2201	2227	2253	2279	26	3	5	8	10	13	16	18	21	23
17	·2304	2330	2355	2380	2405	2430	2455	2480	2504	2529	25	2	5	7	10	12	15	17	20	22
18	·2553	2577	2601	2625	2648	2672	2695	2718	2742	2765	24	2	5	7	10	12	14	17	19	22
19	·2788	2810	2833	2856	2878	2900	2923	2945	2967	2989	22	2	4	7	9	11	13	15	18	20
20	·3010	3032	3054	3075	3096	3118	3139	3160	3181	3201	21	2	4	6	8	11	13	15	17	19
21	·3222	3243	3263	3284	3304	3324	3345	3365	3385	3404	20	2	4	6	8	10	12	14	16	18
22	·3424	3444	3464	3483	3502	3522	3541	3560	3579	3598	19	2	4	6	8	10	11	13	15	17
23	·3617	3636	3655	3674	3692	3711	3729	3747	3766	3784	18	2	4	5	7	9	11	13	14	16
24	·3802	3820	3838	3856	3874	3892	3909	3927	3945	3962	18	2	4	5	7	9	11	13	14	16
25	·3979	3997	4014	4031	4048	4065	4082	4099	4116	4133	17	2	3	5	7	9	10	12	14	15
26	·4150	4166	4183	4200	4216	4232	4249	4265	4281	4298	16	2	3	5	6	8	10	11	13	14
27	·4314	4330	4346	4362	4378	4393	4409	4425	4440	4456	16	2	3	5	6	8	10	11	13	14
28	·4472	4487	4502	4518	4533	4548	4564	4579	4594	4609	15	2	3	5	6	8	9	11	12	14
29	·4624	4639	4654	4669	4683	4698	4713	4728	4742	4757	15	1	3	4	6	7	9	10	12	13
30	·4771	4786	4800	4814	4829	4843	4857	4871	4886	4900	14	1	3	4	6	7	8	10	11	13
31	·4914	4928	4942	4955	4969	4983	4997	5011	5024	5038	14	1	3	4	6	7	8	10	11	13
32	·5051	5065	5079	5092	5105	5119	5132	5145	5159	5172	13	1	3	4	5	7	8	9	10	12
33	·5185	5198	5211	5224	5237	5250	5263	5276	5289	5302	13	1	3	4	5	6	8	9	10	12
34	·5315	5328	5340	5353	5366	5378	5391	5403	5416	5428	13	1	3	4	5	6	8	9	10	12
35	·5441	5453	5465	5478	5490	5502	5514	5527	5539	5551	12	1	2	4	5	6	7	8	10	11
36	·5563	5575	5587	5599	5611	5623	5635	5647	5658	5670	12	1	2	4	5	6	7	8	10	11
37	·5682	5694	5705	5717	5729	5740	5752	5763	5775	5786	12	1	2	4	5	6	7	8	10	11
38	·5798	5809	5821	5832	5843	5855	5866	5877	5888	5899	11	1	2	3	4	6	7	8	9	10
39	·5911	5922	5933	5944	5955	5966	5977	5988	5999	6010	11	1	2	3	4	6	7	8	9	10
40	·6021	6031	6042	6053	6064	6075	6085	6096	6107	6117	11	1	2	3	4	5	7	8	9	10
41	·6128	6138	6149	6160	6170	6180	6191	6201	6212	6222	10	1	2	3	4	5	6	7	8	9
42	·6232	6243	6253	6263	6274	6284	6294	6304	6314	6325	10	1	2	3	4	5	6	7	8	9
43	·6335	6345	6355	6365	6375	6385	6395	6405	6415	6425	10	1	2	3	4	5	6	7	8	9
44	·6435	6444	6454	6464	6474	6484	6493	6503	6513	6522	10	1	2	3	4	5	6	7	8	9
45	·6532	6542	6551	6561	6571	6580	6590	6599	6609	6618	10	1	2	3	4	5	6	7	8	9
46	·6628	6637	6646	6656	6665	6675	6684	6693	6702	6712	9	1	2	3	4	5	5	6	7	8
47	·6721	6730	6739	6749	6758	6767	6776	6785	6794	6803	9	1	2	3	4	5	5	6	7	8
48	·6812	6821	6830	6839	6848	6857	6866	6875	6884	6893	9	1	2	3	4	4	5	6	7	8
49	·6902	6911	6920	6928	6937	6946	6955	6964	6972	6981	9	1	2	3	4	4	5	6	7	8

x	0	1	2	3	4	5	6	7	8	9	Δ_m +	1 2 3	4 5 6	7 8 9
													ADD	
50	·6990	6998 7007 7016			7024 7033 7042			7050 7059 7067			9	1 2 3	4 4 5	6 7 8
51	·7076	7084 7093 7101			7110 7118 7126			7135 7143 7152			8	1 2 2	3 4 5	6 6 7
52	·7160	7168 7177 7185			7193 7202 7210			7218 7226 7235			8	1 2 2	3 4 5	6 6 7
53	·7243	7251 7259 7267			7275 7284 7292			7300 7308 7316			8	1 2 2	3 4 5	6 6 7
54	·7324	7332 7340 7348			7356 7364 7372			7380 7388 7396			8	1 2 2	3 4 5	6 6 7
55	·7404	7412 7419 7427			7435 7443 7451			7459 7466 7474			8	1 2 2	3 4 5	6 6 7
56	·7482	7490 7497 7505			7513 7520 7528			7536 7543 7551			8	1 2 2	3 4 5	6 6 7
57	·7559	7566 7574 7582			7589 7597 7604			7612 7619 7627			8	1 2 2	3 4 5	6 6 7
58	·7634	7642 7649 7657			7664 7672 7679			7686 7694 7701			8	1 2 2	3 4 5	6 6 7
59	·7709	7716 7723 7731			7738 7745 7752			7760 7767 7774			7	1 1 2	3 4 4	5 6 6
60	·7782	7789 7796 7803			7810 7818 7825			7832 7839 7846			7	1 1 2	3 4 4	5 6 6
61	·7853	7860 7868 7875			7882 7889 7896			7903 7910 7917			7	1 1 2	3 4 4	5 6 6
62	·7924	7931 7938 7945			7952 7959 7966			7973 7980 7987			7	1 1 2	3 3 4	5 6 6
63	·7993	8000 8007 8014			8021 8028 8035			8041 8048 8055			7	1 1 2	3 3 4	5 6 6
64	·8062	8069 8075 8082			8089 8096 8102			8109 8116 8122			7	1 1 2	3 3 4	5 6 6
65	·8129	8136 8142 8149			8156 8162 8169			8176 8182 8189			7	1 1 2	3 3 4	5 6 6
66	·8195	8202 8209 8215			8222 8228 8235			8241 8248 8254			7	1 1 2	3 3 4	5 6 6
67	·8261	8267 8274 8280			8287 8293 8299			8306 8312 8319			6	1 1 2	2 3 4	4 5 5
68	·8325	8331 8338 8344			8351 8357 8363			8370 8376 8382			6	1 1 2	2 3 4	4 5 5
69	·8388	8395 8401 8407			8414 8420 8426			8432 8439 8445			6	1 1 2	2 3 4	4 5 5
70	·8451	8457 8463 8470			8476 8482 8488			8494 8500 8506			6	1 1 2	2 3 4	4 5 5
71	·8513	8519 8525 8531			8537 8543 8549			8555 8561 8567			6	1 1 2	2 3 4	4 5 5
72	·8573	8579 8585 8591			8597 8603 8609			8615 8621 8627			6	1 1 2	2 3 4	4 5 5
73	·8633	8639 8645 8651			8657 8663 8669			8675 8681 8686			6	1 1 2	2 3 4	4 5 5
74	·8692	8698 8704 8710			8716 8722 8727			8733 8739 8745			6	1 1 2	2 3 4	4 5 5
75	·8751	8756 8762 8768			8774 8779 8785			8791 8797 8802			6	1 1 2	2 3 4	4 5 5
76	·8808	8814 8820 8825			8831 8837 8842			8848 8854 8859			6	1 1 2	2 3 4	4 5 5
77	·8865	8871 8876 8882			8887 8893 8899			8904 8910 8915			6	1 1 2	2 3 4	4 5 5
78	·8921	8927 8932 8938			8943 8949 8954			8960 8965 8971			6	1 1 2	2 3 4	4 5 5
79	·8976	8982 8987 8993			8998 9004 9009			9015 9020 9025			6	1 1 2	2 3 4	4 5 5
80	·9031	9036 9042 9047			9053 9058 9063			9069 9074 9079			5	1 1 2	2 3 3	4 4 5
81	·9085	9090 9096 9101			9106 9112 9117			9122 9128 9133			5	1 1 2	2 3 3	4 4 5
82	·9138	9143 9149 9154			9159 9165 9170			9175 9180 9186			5	1 1 2	2 3 3	4 4 5
83	·9191	9196 9201 9206			9212 9217 9222			9227 9232 9238			5	1 1 2	2 3 3	4 4 5
84	·9243	9248 9253 9258			9263 9269 9274			9279 9284 9289			5	1 1 2	2 3 3	4 4 5
85	·9294	9299 9304 9309			9315 9320 9325			9330 9335 9340			5	1 1 2	2 3 3	4 4 5
86	·9345	9350 9355 9360			9365 9370 9375			9380 9385 9390			5	1 1 2	2 3 3	4 4 5
87	·9395	9400 9405 9410			9415 9420 9425			9430 9435 9440			5	0 1 1	2 2 3	3 4 4
88	·9445	9450 9455 9460			9465 9469 9474			9479 9484 9489			5	0 1 1	2 2 3	3 4 4
89	·9494	9499 9504 9509			9513 9518 9523			9528 9533 9538			5	0 1 1	2 2 3	3 4 4
90	·9542	9547 9552 9557			9562 9566 9571			9576 9581 9586			5	0 1 1	2 2 3	3 4 4
91	·9590	9595 9600 9605			9609 9614 9619			9624 9628 9633			5	0 1 1	2 2 3	3 4 4
92	·9638	9643 9647 9652			9657 9661 9666			9671 9675 9680			5	0 1 1	2 2 3	3 4 4
93	·9685	9689 9694 9699			9703 9708 9713			9717 9722 9727			5	0 1 1	2 2 3	3 4 4
94	·9731	9736 9741 9745			9750 9754 9759			9763 9768 9773			5	0 1 1	2 2 3	3 4 4
95	·9777	9782 9786 9791			9795 9800 9805			9809 9814 9818			5	0 1 1	2 2 3	3 4 4
96	·9823	9827 9832 9836			9841 9845 9850			9854 9859 9863			4	0 1 1	2 2 2	3 3 4
97	·9868	9872 9877 9881			9886 9890 9894			9899 9903 9908			4	0 1 1	2 2 2	3 3 4
98	·9912	9917 9921 9926			9930 9934 9939			9943 9948 9952			4	0 1 1	2 2 2	3 3 4
99	·9956	9961 9965 9969			9974 9978 9983			9987 9991 9996			4	0 1 1	2 2 2	3 3 4

x	0	1	2	3	4	5	6	7	8	9	Δ_m +	1 2 3	4 5 6	7 8 9
													ADD	
·00	1000	1002	1005	1007	1009	1012	1014	1016	1019	1021	2	0 0 1	1 1 1	1 2 2
·01	1023	1026	1028	1030	1033	1035	1038	1040	1042	1045	2	0 0 1	1 1 1	1 2 2
·02	1047	1050	1052	1054	1057	1059	1062	1064	1067	1069	2	0 0 1	1 1 1	1 2 2
·03	1072	1074	1076	1079	1081	1084	1086	1089	1091	1094	2	0 0 1	1 1 1	1 2 2
·04	1096	1099	1102	1104	1107	1109	1112	1114	1117	1119	3	0 1 1	1 1 2	2 2 3
·05	1122	1125	1127	1130	1132	1135	1138	1140	1143	1146	3	0 1 1	1 1 2	2 2 3
·06	1148	1151	1153	1156	1159	1161	1164	1167	1169	1172	3	0 1 1	1 1 2	2 2 3
·07	1175	1178	1180	1183	1186	1189	1191	1194	1197	1199	3	0 1 1	1 1 2	2 2 3
·08	1202	1205	1208	1211	1213	1216	1219	1222	1225	1227	3	0 1 1	1 1 2	2 2 3
·09	1230	1233	1236	1239	1242	1245	1247	1250	1253	1256	3	0 1 1	1 1 2	2 2 3
·10	1259	1262	1265	1268	1271	1274	1276	1279	1282	1285	3	0 1 1	1 1 2	2 2 3
·11	1288	1291	1294	1297	1300	1303	1306	1309	1312	1315	3	0 1 1	1 2 2	2 2 3
·12	1318	1321	1324	1327	1330	1334	1337	1340	1343	1346	3	0 1 1	1 2 2	2 2 3
·13	1349	1352	1355	1358	1361	1365	1368	1371	1374	1377	3	0 1 1	1 2 2	2 2 3
·14	1380	1384	1387	1390	1393	1396	1400	1403	1406	1409	3	0 1 1	1 2 2	2 2 3
·15	1413	1416	1419	1422	1426	1429	1432	1435	1439	1442	3	0 1 1	1 2 2	2 2 3
·16	1445	1449	1452	1455	1459	1462	1466	1469	1472	1476	3	0 1 1	1 2 2	2 2 3
·17	1479	1483	1486	1489	1493	1496	1500	1503	1507	1510	4	0 1 1	2 2 2	3 3 4
·18	1514	1517	1521	1524	1528	1531	1535	1538	1542	1545	4	0 1 1	2 2 2	3 3 4
·19	1549	1552	1556	1560	1563	1567	1570	1574	1578	1581	4	0 1 1	2 2 2	3 3 4
·20	1585	1589	1592	1596	1600	1603	1607	1611	1614	1618	4	0 1 1	2 2 2	3 3 4
·21	1622	1626	1629	1633	1637	1641	1644	1648	1652	1656	4	0 1 1	2 2 2	3 3 4
·22	1660	1663	1667	1671	1675	1679	1683	1687	1690	1694	4	0 1 1	2 2 2	3 3 4
·23	1698	1702	1706	1710	1714	1718	1722	1726	1730	1734	4	0 1 1	2 2 2	3 3 4
·24	1738	1742	1746	1750	1754	1758	1762	1766	1770	1774	4	0 1 1	2 2 2	3 3 4
·25	1778	1782	1786	1791	1795	1799	1803	1807	1811	1816	4	0 1 1	2 2 2	3 3 4
·26	1820	1824	1828	1832	1837	1841	1845	1849	1854	1858	4	0 1 1	2 2 2	3 3 4
·27	1862	1866	1871	1875	1879	1884	1888	1892	1897	1901	4	0 1 1	2 2 2	3 3 4
·28	1905	1910	1914	1919	1923	1928	1932	1936	1941	1945	4	0 1 1	2 2 2	3 3 4
·29	1950	1954	1959	1963	1968	1972	1977	1982	1986	1991	4	0 1 1	2 2 2	3 3 4
·30	1995	2000	2004	2009	2014	2018	2023	2028	2032	2037	5	0 1 1	2 2 3	3 4 4
·31	2042	2046	2051	2056	2061	2065	2070	2075	2080	2084	5	0 1 1	2 2 3	3 4 4
·32	2089	2094	2099	2104	2109	2113	2118	2123	2128	2133	5	0 1 1	2 2 3	3 4 4
·33	2138	2143	2148	2153	2158	2163	2168	2173	2178	2183	5	1 1 2	2 3 3	4 4 5
·34	2188	2193	2198	2203	2208	2213	2218	2223	2228	2234	5	1 1 2	2 3 3	4 4 5
·35	2239	2244	2249	2254	2259	2265	2270	2275	2280	2286	5	1 1 2	2 3 3	4 4 5
·36	2291	2296	2301	2307	2312	2317	2323	2328	2333	2339	5	1 1 2	2 3 3	4 4 5
·37	2344	2350	2355	2360	2366	2371	2377	2382	2388	2393	6	1 1 2	2 3 4	4 5 5
·38	2399	2404	2410	2415	2421	2427	2432	2438	2443	2449	6	1 1 2	2 3 4	4 5 5
·39	2455	2460	2466	2472	2477	2483	2489	2495	2500	2506	6	1 1 2	2 3 4	4 5 5
·40	2512	2518	2523	2529	2535	2541	2547	2553	2559	2564	6	1 1 2	2 3 4	4 5 5
·41	2570	2576	2582	2588	2594	2600	2606	2612	2618	2624	6	1 1 2	2 3 4	4 5 5
·42	2630	2636	2642	2649	2655	2661	2667	2673	2679	2685	6	1 1 2	2 3 4	4 5 5
·43	2692	2698	2704	2710	2716	2723	2729	2735	2742	2748	6	1 1 2	2 3 4	4 5 5
·44	2754	2761	2767	2773	2780	2786	2793	2799	2805	2812	6	1 1 2	2 3 4	4 5 5
·45	2818	2825	2831	2838	2844	2851	2858	2864	2871	2877	7	1 1 2	3 3 4	5 6 6
·46	2884	2891	2897	2904	2911	2917	2924	2931	2938	2944	7	1 1 2	3 3 4	5 6 6
·47	2951	2958	2965	2972	2979	2985	2992	2999	3006	3013	7	1 1 2	3 3 4	5 6 6
·48	3020	3027	3034	3041	3048	3055	3062	3069	3076	3083	7	1 1 2	3 4 4	5 6 6
·49	3090	3097	3105	3112	3119	3126	3133	3141	3148	3155	7	1 1 2	3 4 4	5 6 6

x	0	1	2	3	4	5	6	7	8	9	Δ_m +	1 2 3	4 5 6	7 8 9 ADD
·50	3162	3170 3177 3184			3192 3199 3206			3214 3221 3228			7	1 1 2	3 4 4	5 6 6
·51	3236	3243 3251 3258			3266 3273 3281			3289 3296 3304			8	1 2 2	3 4 5	6 6 7
·52	3311	3319 3327 3334			3342 3350 3357			3365 3373 3381			8	1 2 2	3 4 5	6 6 7
·53	3388	3396 3404 3412			3420 3428 3436			3443 3451 3459			8	1 2 2	3 4 5	6 6 7
·54	3467	3475 3483 3491			3499 3508 3516			3524 3532 3540			8	1 2 2	3 4 5	6 6 7
·55	3548	3556 3565 3573			3581 3589 3597			3606 3614 3622			8	1 2 2	3 4 5	6 6 7
·56	3631	3639 3648 3656			3664 3673 3681			3690 3698 3707			8	1 2 2	3 .4 5	6 6 7
·57	3715	3724 3733 3741			3750 3758 3767			3776 3784 3793			9	1 2 3	4 4 5	6 7 8
·58	3802	3811 3819 3828			3837 3846 3855			3864 3873 3882			9	1 2 3	4 4 5	6 7 8
·59	3890	3899 3908 3917			3926 3936 3945			3954 3963 3972			9	1 2 3	4 5 5	6 7 8
·60	3981	3990 3999 4009			4018 4027 4036			4046 4055 4064			9	1 2 3	4 5 5	6 7 8
·61	4074	4083 4093 4102			4111 4121 4130			4140 4150 4159			10	1 2 3	4 5 6	7 8 9
·62	4169	4178 4188 4198			4207 4217 4227			4236 4246 4256			10	1 2 3	4 5 6	7 8 9
·63	4266	4276 4285 4295			4305 4315 4325			4335 4345 4355			10	1 2 3	4 5 6	7 8 9
·64	4365	4375 4385 4395			4406 4416 4426			4436 4446 4457			10	1 2 3	4 5 6	7 8 9
·65	4467	4477 4487 4498			4508 4519 4529			4539 4550 4560			10	1 2 3	4 5 6	7 8 9
·66	4571	4581 4592 4603			4613 4624 4634			4645 4656 4667			11	1 2 3	4 5 7	8 9 10
·67	4677	4688 4699 4710			4721 4732 4742			4753 4764 4775			11	1 2 3	4 5 7	8 9 10
·68	4786	4797 4808 4819			4831 4842 4853			4864 4875 4887			11	1 2 3	4 6 7	8 9 10
·69	4898	4909 4920 4932			4943 4955 4966			4977 4989 5000			11	1 2 3	4 6 7	8 9 10
·70	5012	5023 5035 5047			5058 5070 5082			5093 5105 5117			12	1 2 4	5 6 7	8 10 11
·71	5129	5140 5152 5164			5176 5188 5200			5212 5224 5236			12	1 2 4	5 6 7	8 10 11
·72	5248	5260 5272 5284			5297 5309 5321			5333 5346 5358			12	1 2 4	5 6 7	8 10 11
·73	5370	5383 5395 5408			5420 5433 5445			5458 5470 5483			12	1 2 4	5 6 7	8 10 11
·74	5495	5508 5521 5534			5546 5559 5572			5585 5598 5610			13	1 3 4	5 6 8	9 10 12
·75	5623	5636 5649 5662			5675 5689 5702			5715 5728 5741			13	1 3 4	5 7 8	9 10 12
·76	5754	5768 5781 5794			5808 5821 5834			5848 5861 5875			13	1 3 4	5 7 8	9 10 12
·77	5888	5902 5916 5929			5943 5957 5970			5984 5998 6012			14	1 3 4	6 7 8	10 11 13
·78	6026	6039 6053 6067			6081 6095 6109			6124 6138 6152			14	1 3 4	6 7 8	10 11 13
·79	6166	6180 6194 6209			6223 6237 6252			6266 6281 6295			14	1 3 4	6 7 8	10 11 13
·80	6310	6324 6339 6353			6368 6383 6397			6412 6427 6442			15	1 3 4	6 7 9	10 12 13
·81	6457	6471 6486 6501			6516 6531 6546			6561 6577 6592			15	2 3 5	6 8 9	11 12 14
·82	6607	6622 6637 6653			6668 6683 6699			6714 6730 6745			15	2 3 5	6 8 9	11 12 14
·83	6761	6776 6792 6808			6823 6839 6855			6871 6887 6902			16	2 3 5	6 8 10	11 13 14
·84	6918	6934 6950 6966			6982 6998 7015			7031 7047 7063			16	2 3 5	6 8 10	11 13 14
·85	7079	7096 7112 7129			7145 7161 7178			7194 7211 7228			16	2 3 5	6 8 10	11 13 14
·86	7244	7261 7278 7295			7311 7328 7345			7362 7379 7396			17	2 3 5	7 8 10	12 14 15
·87	7413	7430 7447 7464			7482 7499 7516			7534 7551 7568			17	2 3 5	7 9 10	12 14 15
·88	7586	7603 7621 7638			7656 7674 7691			7709 7727 7745			18	2 4 5	7 9 11	13 14 16
·89	7762	7780 7798 7816			7834 7852 7870			7889 7907 7925			18	2 4 5	7 9 11	13 14 16
·90	7943	7962 7980 7998			8017 8035 8054			8072 8091 8110			18	2 4 5	7 9 11	13 14 16
·91	8128	8147 8166 8185			8204 8222 8241			8260 8279 8299			19	2 4 6	8 10 11	13 15 17
·92	8318	8337 8356 8375			8395 8414 8433			8453 8472 8492			19	2 4 6	8 10 11	13 15 17
·93	8511	8531 8551 8570			8590 8610 8630			8650 8670 8690			20	2 4 6	8 10 12	14 16 18
·94	8710	8730 8750 8770			8790 8810 8831			8851 8872 8892			20	2 4 6	8 10 12	14 16 18
·95	8913	8933 8954 8974			8995 9016 9036			9057 9078 9099			21	2 4 6	8 10 13	15 17 19
·96	9120	9141 9162 9183			9204 9226 9247			9268 9290 9311			21	2 4 6	8 11 13	15 17 19
·97	9333	9354 9376 9397			9419 9441 9462			9484 9506 9528			22	2 4 7	9 11 13	15 18 20
·98	9550	9572 9594 9616			9638 9661 9683			9705 9727 9750			22	2 4 7	9 11 13	15 18 20
·99	9772	9795 9817 9840			9863 9886 9908			9931 9954 9977			23	2 5 7	9 11 14	16 18 21

SQUARES x^2

x	0	1	2	3	4	5	6	7	8	9	Δ_m +	1	2	3	4	5	6	7	8	9
															ADD					
10	1000	1020	1040	1061	1082	1103	1124	1145	1166	1188	21	2	4	6	8	10	13	15	17	19
11	1210	1232	1254	1277	1300	1323	1346	1369	1392	1416	23	2	5	7	9	11	14	16	18	21
12	1440	1464	1488	1513	1538	1563	1588	1613	1638	1664	25	2	5	7	10	12	15	17	20	22
13	1690	1716	1742	1769	1796	1823	1850	1877	1904	1932	27	3	5	8	11	13	16	19	22	24
14	1960	1988	2016	2045	2074	2103	2132	2161	2190	2220	29	3	6	9	12	14	17	20	23	26
15	2250	2280	2310	2341	2372	2403	2434	2465	2496	2528	31	3	6	9	12	15	19	22	25	28
16	2560	2592	2624	2657	2690	2723	2756	2789	2822	2856	33	3	7	10	13	16	20	23	26	30
17	2890	2924	2958	2993	3028	3063	3098	3133	3168	3204	35	3	7	10	14	17	21	24	28	31
18	3240	3276	3312	3349	3386	3423	3460	3497	3534	3572	37	4	7	11	15	18	22	26	30	33
19	3610	3648	3686	3725	3764	3803	3842	3881	3920	3960	39	4	8	12	16	19	23	27	31	35
20	4000	4040	4080	4121	4162	4203	4244	4285	4326	4368	41	4	8	12	16	20	25	29	33	37
21	4410	4452	4494	4537	4580	4623	4666	4709	4752	4796	43	4	9	13	17	21	26	30	34	39
22	4840	4884	4928	4973	5018	5063	5108	5153	5198	5244	45	4	9	13	18	22	27	31	36	40
23	5290	5336	5382	5429	5476	5523	5570	5617	5664	5712	47	5	9	14	19	23	28	33	38	42
24	5760	5808	5856	5905	5954	6003	6052	6101	6150	6200	49	5	10	15	20	24	29	34	39	44
25	6250	6300	6350	6401	6452	6503	6554	6605	6656	6708	51	5	10	15	20	25	31	36	41	46
26	6760	6812	6864	6917	6970	7023	7076	7129	7182	7236	53	5	11	16	21	26	32	37	42	48
27	7290	7344	7398	7453	7508	7563	7618	7673	7728	7784	55	5	11	16	22	27	33	38	44	49
28	7840	7896	7952	8009	8066	8123	8180	8237	8294	8352	57	6	11	17	23	28	34	40	46	51
29	8410	8468	8526	8585	8644	8703	8762	8821	8880	8940	59	6	12	18	24	29	35	41	47	53
30	9000	9060	9120	9181	9242	9303	9364	9425	9486	9548	61	6	12	18	24	30	37	43	49	55
31	9610	9672	9734	9797	9860	9923	9986				63	6	13	19	25	31	38	44	50	57
							999	1005	1011	1018	6	1	1	2	2	3	4	4	5	5
32	1024	1030	1037	1043	1050	1056	1063	1069	1076	1082	6	1	1	2	2	3	4	4	5	5
33	1089	1096	1102	1109	1116	1122	1129	1136	1142	1149	7	1	1	2	3	3	4	5	6	6
34	1156	1163	1170	1176	1183	1190	1197	1204	1211	1218	7	1	1	2	3	3	4	5	6	6
35	1225	1232	1239	1246	1253	1260	1267	1274	1282	1289	7	1	1	2	3	4	4	5	6	6
36	1296	1303	1310	1318	1325	1332	1340	1347	1354	1362	7	1	1	2	3	4	4	5	6	6
37	1369	1376	1384	1391	1399	1406	1414	1421	1429	1436	8	1	2	2	3	4	5	6	6	7
38	1444	1452	1459	1467	1475	1482	1490	1498	1505	1513	8	1	2	2	3	4	5	6	6	7
39	1521	1529	1537	1544	1552	1560	1568	1576	1584	1592	8	1	2	2	3	4	5	6	6	7
40	1600	1608	1616	1624	1632	1640	1648	1656	1665	1673	8	1	2	2	3	4	5	6	6	7
41	1681	1689	1697	1706	1714	1722	1731	1739	1747	1756	8	1	2	2	3	4	5	6	6	7
42	1764	1772	1781	1789	1798	1806	1815	1823	1832	1840	8	1	2	2	3	4	5	6	6	7
43	1849	1858	1866	1875	1884	1892	1901	1910	1918	1927	9	1	2	3	4	4	5	6	7	8
44	1936	1945	1954	1962	1971	1980	1989	1998	2007	2016	9	1	2	3	4	4	5	6	7	8
45	2025	2034	2043	2052	2061	2070	2079	2088	2098	2107	9	1	2	3	4	5	5	6	7	8
46	2116	2125	2134	2144	2153	2162	2172	2181	2190	2200	9	1	2	3	4	5	5	6	7	8
47	2209	2218	2228	2237	2247	2256	2266	2275	2285	2294	10	1	2	3	4	5	6	7	8	9
48	2304	2314	2323	2333	2343	2352	2362	2372	2381	2391	10	1	2	3	4	5	6	7	8	9
49	2401	2411	2421	2430	2440	2450	2460	2470	2480	2490	10	1	2	3	4	5	6	7	8	9
50	2500	2510	2520	2530	2540	2550	2560	2570	2581	2591	10	1	2	3	4	5	6	7	8	9
51	2601	2611	2621	2632	2642	2652	2663	2673	2683	2694	10	1	2	3	4	5	6	7	8	9
52	2704	2714	2725	2735	2746	2756	2767	2777	2788	2798	10	1	2	3	4	5	6	7	8	9
53	2809	2820	2830	2841	2852	2862	2873	2884	2894	2905	11	1	2	3	4	5	7	8	9	10
54	2916	2927	2938	2948	2959	2970	2981	2992	3003	3014	11	1	2	3	4	5	7	8	9	10
55	3025	3036	3047	3058	3069	3080	3091	3102	3114	3125	11	1	2	3	4	6	7	8	9	10
56	3136	3147	3158	3170	3181	3192	3204	3215	3226	3238	11	1	2	3	4	6	7	8	9	10
57	3249	3260	3272	3283	3295	3306	3318	3329	3341	3352	12	1	2	4	5	6	7	8	10	11
58	3364	3376	3387	3399	3411	3422	3434	3446	3457	3469	12	1	2	4	5	6	7	8	10	11
59	3481	3493	3505	3516	3528	3540	3552	3564	3576	3588	12	1	2	4	5	6	7	8	10	11

SQUARES x^2

x	0	1	2	3	4	5	6	7	8	9	Δ_m +	1 2 3	4 5 6	7 8 9
													ADD	
60	3600	3612	3624	3636	3648	3660	3672	3684	3697	3709	12	1 2 4	5 6 7	8 10 11
61	3721	3733	3745	3758	3770	3782	3795	3807	3819	3832	12	1 2 4	5 6 7	8 10 11
62	3844	3856	3869	3881	3894	3906	3919	3931	3944	3956	12	1 2 4	5 6 7	8 10 11
63	3969	3982	3994	4007	4020	4032	4045	4058	4070	4083	13	1 3 4	5 6 8	9 10 12
64	4096	4109	4122	4134	4147	4160	4173	4186	4199	4212	13	1 3 4	5 6 8	9 10 12
65	4225	4238	4251	4264	4277	4290	4303	4316	4330	4343	13	1 3 4	5 7 8	9 10 12
66	4356	4369	4382	4396	4409	4422	4436	4449	4462	4476	13	1 3 4	5 7 8	9 10 12
67	4489	4502	4516	4529	4543	4556	4570	4583	4597	4610	14	1 3 4	6 7 8	10 11 13
68	4624	4638	4651	4665	4679	4692	4706	4720	4733	4747	14	1 3 4	6 7 8	10 11 13
69	4761	4775	4789	4802	4816	4830	4844	4858	4872	4886	14	1 3 4	6 7 8	10 11 13
70	4900	4914	4928	4942	4956	4970	4984	4998	5013	5027	14	1 3 4	6 7 8	10 11 13
71	5041	5055	5069	5084	5098	5112	5127	5141	5155	5170	14	1 3 4	6 7 8	10 11 13
72	5184	5198	5213	5227	5242	5256	5271	5285	5300	5314	14	1 3 4	6 7 8	10 11 13
73	5329	5344	5358	5373	5388	5402	5417	5432	5446	5461	15	1 3 4	6 7 9	10 12 13
74	5476	5491	5506	5520	5535	5550	5565	5580	5595	5610	15	1 3 4	6 7 9	10 12 13
75	5625	5640	5655	5670	5685	5700	5715	5730	5746	5761	15	2 3 5	6 8 9	11 12 14
76	5776	5791	5806	5822	5837	5852	5868	5883	5898	5914	15	2 3 5	6 8 9	11 12 14
77	5929	5944	5960	5975	5991	6006	6022	6037	6053	6068	16	2 3 5	6 8 10	11 13 14
78	6084	6100	6115	6131	6147	6162	6178	6194	6209	6225	16	2 3 5	6 8 10	11 13 14
79	6241	6257	6273	6288	6304	6320	6336	6352	6368	6384	16	2 3 5	6 8 10	11 13 14
80	6400	6416	6432	6448	6464	6480	6496	6512	6529	6545	16	2 3 5	6 8 10	11 13 14
81	6561	6577	6593	6610	6626	6642	6659	6675	6691	6708	16	2 3 5	6 8 10	11 13 14
82	6724	6740	6757	6773	6790	6806	6823	6839	6856	6872	16	2 3 5	6 8 10	11 13 14
83	6889	6906	6922	6939	6956	6972	6989	7006	7022	7039	17	2 3 5	7 8 10	12 14 15
84	7056	7073	7090	7106	7123	7140	7157	7174	7191	7208	17	2 3 5	7 8 10	12 14 15
85	7225	7242	7259	7276	7293	7310	7327	7344	7362	7379	17	2 3 5	7 9 10	12 14 15
86	7396	7413	7430	7448	7465	7482	7500	7517	7534	7552	17	2 3 5	7 9 10	12 14 15
87	7569	7586	7604	7621	7639	7656	7674	7691	7709	7726	18	2 4 5	7 9 11	13 14 16
88	7744	7762	7779	7797	7815	7832	7850	7868	7885	7903	18	2 4 5	7 9 11	13 14 16
89	7921	7939	7957	7974	7992	8010	8028	8046	8064	8082	18	2 4 5	7 9 11	13 14 16
90	8100	8118	8136	8154	8172	8190	8208	8226	8245	8263	18	2 4 5	7 9 11	13 14 16
91	8281	8299	8317	8336	8354	8372	8391	8409	8427	8446	18	2 4 5	7 9 11	13 14 16
92	8464	8482	8501	8519	8538	8556	8575	8593	8612	8630	18	2 4 5	7 9 11	13 14 16
93	8649	8668	8686	8705	8724	8742	8761	8780	8798	8817	19	2 4 6	8 9 11	13 15 17
94	8836	8855	8874	8892	8911	8930	8949	8968	8987	9006	19	2 4 6	8 9 11	13 15 17
95	9025	9044	9063	9082	9101	9120	9139	9158	9178	9197	19	2 4 6	8 10 11	13 15 17
96	9216	9235	9254	9274	9293	9312	9332	9351	9370	9390	19	2 4 6	8 10 11	13 15 17
97	9409	9428	9448	9467	9487	9506	9526	9545	9565	9584	20	2 4 6	8 10 12	14 16 18
98	9604	9624	9643	9663	9683	9702	9722	9742	9761	9781	20	2 4 6	8 10 12	14 16 18
99	9801	9821	9841	9860	9880	9900	9920	9940	9960	9980	20	2 4 6	8 10 12	14 16 18

The decimal point must be inserted by inspection.

Examples:

$$(1 \cdot 43)^2 \doteq 2 \cdot 045 \qquad (6 \cdot 935)^2 \doteq 48 \cdot 09$$
$$(232 \cdot 8)^2 = (2 \cdot 328 \times 10^2)^2 \doteq 5 \cdot 420 \times 10^4$$
$$(0 \cdot 007035)^2 = (7 \cdot 035 \times 10^{-3})^2 \doteq 49 \cdot 49 \times 10^{-6} = 0 \cdot 00004949$$

SQUARE ROOTS $\quad \sqrt{x}$ OR $x^{\frac{1}{2}}$

x	0	1	2	3	4	5	6	7	8	9	Δ_m +	1 2 3	4 5 6	7 8 9
													ADD	
10	1000	1005 1010 1015			1020 1025 1030			1034 1039 1044			5	0 1 1	2 2 3	3 4 4
	3162	3178 3194 3209			3225 3240 3256			3271 3286 3302			16	2 3 5	6 8 10	11 13 14
11	1049	1054 1058 1063			1068 1072 1077			1082 1086 1091			5	0 1 1	2 2 3	3 4 4
	3317	3332 3347 3362			3376 3391 3406			3421 3435 3450			15	1 3 4	6 7 9	10 12 13
12	1095	1100 1105 1109			1114 1118 1122			1127 1131 1136			4	0 1 1	2 2 2	3 3 4
	3464	3479 3493 3507			3521 3536 3550			3564 3578 3592			14	1 3 4	6 7 8	10 11 13
13	1140	1145 1149 1153			1158 1162 1166			1170 1175 1179			4	0 1 1	2 2 2	3 3 4
	3606	3619 3633 3647			3661 3674 3688			3701 3715 3728			14	1 3 4	6 7 8	10 11 13
14	1183	1187 1192 1196			1200 1204 1208			1212 1217 1221			4	0 1 1	2 2 2	3 3 4
	3742	3755 3768 3782			3795 3808 3821			3834 3847 3860			13	1 3 4	5 7 8	9 10 12
15	1225	1229 1233 1237			1241 1245 1249			1253 1257 1261			4	0 1 1	2 2 2	3 3 4
	3873	3886 3899 3912			3924 3937 3950			3962 3975 3987			13	1 3 4	5 6 8	9 10 12
16	1265	1269 1273 1277			1281 1285 1288			1292 1296 1300			4	0 1 1	2 2 2	3 3 4
	4000	4012 4025 4037			4050 4062 4074			4087 4099 4111			12	1 2 4	5 6 7	8 10 11
17	1304	1308 1311 1315			1319 1323 1327			1330 1334 1338			4	0 1 1	2 2 2	3 3 4
	4123	4135 4147 4159			4171 4183 4195			4207 4219 4231			12	1 2 4	5 6 7	8 10 11
18	1342	1345 1349 1353			1356 1360 1364			1367 1371 1375			4	0 1 1	2 2 2	3 3 4
	4243	4254 4266 4278			4290 4301 4313			4324 4336 4347			12	1 2 4	5 6 7	8 10 11
19	1378	1382 1386 1389			1393 1396 1400			1404 1407 1411			4	0 1 1	2 2 2	3 3 4
	4359	4370 4382 4393			4405 4416 4427			4438 4450 4461			11	1 2 3	4 6 7	8 9 10
20	1414	1418 1421 1425			1428 1432 1435			1439 1442 1446			4	0 1 1	2 2 2	3 3 4
	4472	4483 4494 4506			4517 4528 4539			4550 4561 4572			11	1 2 3	4 6 7	8 9 10
21	1449	1453 1456 1459			1463 1466 1470			1473 1476 1480			3	0 1 1	1 2 2	2 2 3
	4583	4593 4604 4615			4626 4637 4648			4658 4669 4680			11	1 2 3	4 5 7	8 9 10
22	1483	1487 1490 1493			1497 1500 1503			1507 1510 1513			3	0 1 1	1 2 2	2 2 3
	4690	4701 4712 4722			4733 4743 4754			4764 4775 4785			11	1 2 3	4 5 7	8 9 10
23	1517	1520 1523 1526			1530 1533 1536			1539 1543 1546			3	0 1 1	1 2 2	2 2 3
	4796	4806 4817 4827			4837 4848 4858			4868 4879 4889			10	1 2 3	4 5 6	7 8 9
24	1549	1552 1556 1559			1562 1565 1568			1572 1575 1578			3	0 1 1	1 2 2	2 2 3
	4899	4909 4919 4930			4940 4950 4960			4970 4980 4990			10	1 2 3	4 5 6	7 8 9
25	1581	1584 1587 1591			1594 1597 1600			1603 1606 1609			3	0 1 1	1 2 2	2 2 3
	5000	5010 5020 5030			5040 5050 5060			5070 5079 5089			10	1 2 3	4 5 6	7 8 9
26	1612	1616 1619 1622			1625 1628 1631			1634 1637 1640			3	0 1 1	1 2 2	2 2 3
	5099	5109 5119 5128			5138 5148 5158			5167 5177 5187			10	1 2 3	4 5 6	7 8 9
27	1643	1646 1649 1652			1655 1658 1661			1664 1667 1670			3	0 1 1	1 2 2	2 2 3
	5196	5206 5215 5225			5235 5244 5254			5263 5273 5282			10	1 2 3	4 5 6	7 8 9
28	1673	1676 1679 1682			1685 1688 1691			1694 1697 1700			3	0 1 1	1 2 2	2 2 3
	5292	5301 5310 5320			5329 5339 5348			5357 5367 5376			9	1 2 3	4 5 5	6 7 8
29	1703	1706 1709 1712			1715 1718 1720			1723 1726 1729			3	0 1 1	1 1 2	2 2 3
	5385	5394 5404 5413			5422 5431 5441			5450 5459 5468			9	1 2 3	4 5 5	6 7 8
30	1732	1735 1738 1741			1744 1746 1749			1752 1755 1758			3	0 1 1	1 1 2	2 2 3
	5477	5486 5495 5505			5514 5523 5532			5541 5550 5559			9	1 2 3	4 5 5	6 7 8

The decimal point must be inserted by inspection.

Examples:

$\sqrt{1.856} \doteq 1.362$ $\qquad$ $\sqrt{217.3} \doteq 14.74$

$\sqrt{27.12} \doteq 5.208$ $\qquad$ $\sqrt{2930} \doteq 54.13$

$\sqrt{0.236} \doteq 0.4858$ $\qquad$ $\sqrt{0.0306} \doteq 0.1749$

SQUARE ROOTS $\sqrt{x}$ OR $x^{\frac{1}{2}}$

x	0	1	2	3	4	5	6	7	8	9	Δ_m +	1 2 3	4 5 6	7 8 9
													ADD	
31	1761	1764	1766	1769	1772	1775	1778	1780	1783	1786	3	0 1 1	1 1 2	2 2 3
	5568	5577	5586	5595	5604	5612	5621	5630	5639	5648	9	1 2 3	4 4 5	6 7 8
32	1789	1792	1794	1797	1800	1803	1806	1808	1811	1814	3	0 1 1	1 1 2	2 2 3
	5657	5666	5675	5683	5692	5701	5710	5718	5727	5736	9	1 2 3	4 4 5	6 7 8
33	1817	1819	1822	1825	1828	1830	1833	1836	1838	1841	3	0 1 1	1 1 2	2 2 3
	5745	5753	5762	5771	5779	5788	5797	5805	5814	5822	9	1 2 3	4 4 5	6 7 8
34	1844	1847	1849	1852	1855	1857	1860	1863	1865	1868	3	0 1 1	1 1 2	2 2 3
	5831	5840	5848	5857	5865	5874	5882	5891	5899	5908	9	1 2 3	4 4 5	6 7 8
35	1871	1873	1876	1879	1881	1884	1887	1889	1892	1895	3	0 1 1	1 1 2	2 2 3
	5916	5925	5933	5941	5950	5958	5967	5975	5983	5992	8	1 2 2	3 4 5	6 6 7
36	1897	1900	1903	1905	1908	1910	1913	1916	1918	1921	3	0 1 1	1 1 2	2 2 3
	6000	6008	6017	6025	6033	6042	6050	6058	6066	6075	8	1 2 2	3 4 5	6 6 7
37	1924	1926	1929	1931	1934	1936	1939	1942	1944	1947	3	0 1 1	1 1 2	2 2 3
	6083	6091	6099	6107	6116	6124	6132	6140	6148	6156	8	1 2 2	3 4 5	6 6 7
38	1949	1952	1954	1957	1960	1962	1965	1967	1970	1972	3	0 1 1	1 1 2	2 2 3
	6164	6173	6181	6189	6197	6205	6213	6221	6229	6237	8	1 2 2	3 4 5	6 6 7
39	1975	1977	1980	1982	1985	1987	1990	1992	1995	1997	2	0 0 1	1 1 1	1 2 2
	6245	6253	6261	6269	6277	6285	6293	6301	6309	6317	8	1 2 2	3 4 5	6 6 7
40	2000	2002	2005	2007	2010	2012	2015	2017	2020	2022	2	0 0 1	1 1 1	1 2 2
	6325	6332	6340	6348	6356	6364	6372	6380	6387	6395	8	1 2 2	3 4 5	6 6 7
41	2025	2027	2030	2032	2035	2037	2040	2042	2045	2047	2	0 0 1	1 1 1	1 2 2
	6403	6411	6419	6427	6434	6442	6450	6458	6465	6473	8	1 2 2	3 4 5	6 6 7
42	2049	2052	2054	2057	2059	2062	2064	2066	2069	2071	2	0 0 1	1 1 1	1 2 2
	6481	6488	6496	6504	6512	6519	6527	6535	6542	6550	8	1 2 2	3 4 5	6 6 7
43	2074	2076	2078	2081	2083	2086	2088	2090	2093	2095	2	0 0 1	1 1 1	1 2 2
	6557	6565	6573	6580	6588	6595	6603	6611	6618	6626	8	1 2 2	3 4 5	6 6 7
44	2098	2100	2102	2105	2107	2110	2112	2114	2117	2119	2	0 0 1	1 1 1	1 2 2
	6633	6641	6648	6656	6663	6671	6678	6686	6693	6701	8	1 2 2	3 4 5	6 6 7
45	2121	2124	2126	2128	2131	2133	2135	2138	2140	2142	2	0 0 1	1 1 1	1 2 2
	6708	6716	6723	6731	6738	6745	6753	6760	6768	6775	7	1 1 2	3 4 4	5 6 6
46	2145	2147	2149	2152	2154	2156	2159	2161	2163	2166	2	0 0 1	1 1 1	1 2 2
	6782	6790	6797	6804	6812	6819	6826	6834	6841	6848	7	1 1 2	3 4 4	5 6 6
47	2168	2170	2173	2175	2177	2179	2182	2184	2186	2189	2	0 0 1	1 1 1	1 2 2
	6856	6863	6870	6877	6885	6892	6899	6907	6914	6921	7	1 1 2	3 4 4	5 6 6
48	2191	2193	2195	2198	2200	2202	2205	2207	2209	2211	2	0 0 1	1 1 1	1 2 2
	6928	6935	6943	6950	6957	6964	6971	6979	6986	6993	7	1 1 2	3 4 4	5 6 6
49	2214	2216	2218	2220	2223	2225	2227	2229	2232	2234	2	0 0 1	1 1 1	1 2 2
	7000	7007	7014	7021	7029	7036	7043	7050	7057	7064	7	1 1 2	3 4 4	5 6 6
50	2236	2238	2241	2243	2245	2247	2249	2252	2254	2256	2	0 0 1	1 1 1	1 2 2
	7071	7078	7085	7092	7099	7106	7113	7120	7127	7134	7	1 1 2	3 4 4	5 6 6
51	2258	2261	2263	2265	2267	2269	2272	2274	2276	2278	2	0 0 1	1 1 1	1 2 2
	7141	7148	7155	7162	7169	7176	7183	7190	7197	7204	7	1 1 2	3 4 4	5 6 6
52	2280	2283	2285	2287	2289	2291	2293	2296	2298	2300	2	0 0 1	1 1 1	1 2 2
	7211	7218	7225	7232	7239	7246	7253	7259	7266	7273	7	1 1 2	3 3 4	5 6 6
53	2302	2304	2307	2309	2311	2313	2315	2317	2319	2322	2	0 0 1	1 1 1	1 2 2
	7280	7287	7294	7301	7308	7314	7321	7328	7335	7342	7	1 1 2	3 3 4	5 6 6

Examples:

$$\sqrt{37450000} = \sqrt{37.45 \times 10^6} \doteq 6.120 \times 10^3 = 6120$$

$$\sqrt{0.0005328} = \sqrt{5.328 \times 10^{-4}} \doteq 2.309 \times 10^{-2} = 0.02309$$

Note that the power of 10 extracted under the root sign must always be even. If this leaves **one** figure before the decimal point, use the **upper** line of a pair; if it leaves **two** figures before the decimal point, use the **lower** line.

SQUARE ROOTS $\sqrt{x}$ OR $x^{\frac{1}{2}}$

x	0	1	2	3	4	5	6	7	8	9	Δ_m +	1 2 3	4 5 6	7 8 9
													ADD	
54	2324	2326	2328	2330	2332	2335	2337	2339	2341	2343	2	0 0 1	1 1 1	1 2 2
	7348	7355	7362	7369	7376	7382	7389	7396	7403	7409	7	1 1 2	3 3 4	5 6 6
55	2345	2347	2349	2352	2354	2356	2358	2360	2362	2364	2	0 0 1	1 1 1	1 2 2
	7416	7423	7430	7436	7443	7450	7457	7463	7470	7477	7	1 1 2	3 3 4	5 6 6
56	2366	2369	2371	2373	2375	2377	2379	2381	2383	2385	2	0 0 1	1 1 1	1 2 2
	7483	7490	7497	7503	7510	7517	7523	7530	7537	7543	7	1 1 2	3 3 4	5 6 6
57	2387	2390	2392	2394	2396	2398	2400	2402	2404	2406	2	0 0 1	1 1 1	1 2 2
	7550	7556	7563	7570	7576	7583	7589	7596	7603	7609	7	1 1 2	3 3 4	5 6 6
58	2408	2410	2412	2415	2417	2419	2421	2423	2425	2427	2	0 0 1	1 1 1	1 2 2
	7616	7622	7629	7635	7642	7649	7655	7662	7668	7675	6	1 1 2	2 3 4	4 5 5
59	2429	2431	2433	2435	2437	2439	2441	2443	2445	2447	2	0 0 1	1 1 1	1 2 2
	7681	7688	7694	7701	7707	7714	7720	7727	7733	7740	6	1 1 2	2 3 4	4 5 5
60	2449	2452	2454	2456	2458	2460	2462	2464	2466	2468	2	0 0 1	1 1 1	1 2 2
	7746	7752	7759	7765	7772	7778	7785	7791	7797	7804	6	1 1 2	2 3 4	4 5 5
61	2470	2472	2474	2476	2478	2480	2482	2484	2486	2488	2	0 0 1	1 1 1	1 2 2
	7810	7817	7823	7829	7836	7842	7849	7855	7861	7868	6	1 1 2	2 3 4	4 5 5
62	2490	2492	2494	2496	2498	2500	2502	2504	2506	2508	2	0 0 1	1 1 1	1 2 2
	7874	7880	7887	7893	7899	7906	7912	7918	7925	7931	6	1 1 2	2 3 4	4 5 5
63	2510	2512	2514	2516	2518	2520	2522	2524	2526	2528	2	0 0 1	1 1 1	1 2 2
	7937	7944	7950	7956	7962	7969	7975	7981	7987	7994	6	1 1 2	2 3 4	4 5 5
64	2530	2532	2534	2536	2538	2540	2542	2544	2546	2548	2	0 0 1	1 1 1	1 2 2
	8000	8006	8012	8019	8025	8031	8037	8044	8050	8056	6	1 1 2	2 3 4	4 5 5
65	2550	2551	2553	2555	2557	2559	2561	2563	2565	2567	2	0 0 1	1 1 1	1 2 2
	8062	8068	8075	8081	8087	8093	8099	8106	8112	8118	6	1 1 2	2 3 4	4 5 5
66	2569	2571	2573	2575	2577	2579	2581	2583	2585	2587	2	0 0 1	1 1 1	1 2 2
	8124	8130	8136	8142	8149	8155	8161	8167	8173	8179	6	1 1 2	2 3 4	4 5 5
67	2588	2590	2592	2594	2596	2598	2600	2602	2604	2606	2	0 0 1	1 1 1	1 2 2
	8185	8191	8198	8204	8210	8216	8222	8228	8234	8240	6	1 1 2	2 3 4	4 5 5
68	2608	2610	2612	2613	2615	2617	2619	2621	2623	2625	2	0 0 1	1 1 1	1 2 2
	8246	8252	8258	8264	8270	8276	8283	8289	8295	8301	6	1 1 2	2 3 4	4 5 5
69	2627	2629	2631	2632	2634	2636	2638	2640	2642	2644	2	0 0 1	1 1 1	1 2 2
	8307	8313	8319	8325	8331	8337	8343	8349	8355	8361	6	1 1 2	2 3 4	4 5 5
70	2646	2648	2650	2651	2653	2655	2657	2659	2661	2663	2	0 0 1	1 1 1	1 2 2
	8367	8373	8379	8385	8390	8396	8402	8408	8414	8420	6	1 1 2	2 3 4	4 5 5
71	2665	2666	2668	2670	2672	2674	2676	2678	2680	2681	2	0 0 1	1 1 1	1 2 2
	8426	8432	8438	8444	8450	8456	8462	8468	8473	8479	6	1 1 2	2 3 4	4 5 5
72	2683	2685	2687	2689	2691	2693	2694	2696	2698	2700	2	0 0 1	1 1 1	1 2 2
	8485	8491	8497	8503	8509	8515	8521	8526	8532	8538	6	1 1 2	2 3 4	4 5 5
73	2702	2704	2706	2707	2709	2711	2713	2715	2717	2718	2	0 0 1	1 1 1	1 2 2
	8544	8550	8556	8562	8567	8573	8579	8585	8591	8597	6	1 1 2	2 3 4	4 5 5
74	2720	2722	2724	2726	2728	2729	2731	2733	2735	2737	2	0 0 1	1 1 1	1 2 2
	8602	8608	8614	8620	8626	8631	8637	8643	8649	8654	6	1 1 2	2 3 4	4 5 5
75	2739	2740	2742	2744	2746	2748	2750	2751	2753	2755	2	0 0 1	1 1 1	1 2 2
	8660	8666	8672	8678	8683	8689	8695	8701	8706	8712	6	1 1 2	2 3 4	4 5 5
76	2757	2759	2760	2762	2764	2766	2768	2769	2771	2773	2	0 0 1	1 1 1	1 2 2
	8718	8724	8729	8735	8741	8746	8752	8758	8764	8769	6	1 1 2	2 3 4	4 5 5

The decimal point must be inserted by inspection.

Examples: $\sqrt{5 \cdot 978} \doteqdot 2 \cdot 445$ $\sqrt{67 \cdot 42} \doteqdot 8 \cdot 211$

$\sqrt{723 \cdot 1} \doteqdot 26 \cdot 89$ $\sqrt{0 \cdot 7591} \doteqdot 0 \cdot 8713$

x	0	1	2	3	4	5	6	7	8	9	Δ_m +	1 2 3	4 5 6	7 8 9 ADD
77	2775	2777	2778	2780	2782	2784	2786	2787	2789	2791	2	0 0 1	1 1 1	1 2 2
	8775	8781	8786	8792	8798	8803	8809	8815	8820	8826	6	1 1 2	2 3 4	4 5 5
78	2793	2795	2796	2798	2800	2802	2804	2805	2807	2809	2	0 0 1	1 1 1	1 2 2
	8832	8837	8843	8849	8854	8860	8866	8871	8877	8883	6	1 1 2	2 3 4	4 5 5
79	2811	2812	2814	2816	2818	2820	2821	2823	2825	2827	2	0 0 1	1 1 1	1 2 2
	8888	8894	8899	8905	8911	8916	8922	8927	8933	8939	6	1 1 2	2 3 4	4 5 5
80	2828	2830	2832	2834	2835	2837	2839	2841	2843	2844	2	0 0 1	1 1 1	1 2 2
	8944	8950	8955	8961	8967	8972	8978	8983	8989	8994	6	1 1 2	2 3 4	4 5 5
81	2846	2848	2850	2851	2853	2855	2857	2858	2860	2862	2	0 0 1	1 1 1	1 2 2
	9000	9006	9011	9017	9022	9028	9033	9039	9044	9050	6	1 1 2	2 3 4	4 5 5
82	2864	2865	2867	2869	2871	2872	2874	2876	2877	2879	2	0 0 1	1 1 1	1 2 2
	9055	9061	9066	9072	9077	9083	9088	9094	9099	9105	6	1 1 2	2 3 4	4 5 5
83	2881	2883	2884	2886	2888	2890	2891	2893	2895	2897	2	0 0 1	1 1 1	1 2 2
	9110	9116	9121	9127	9132	9138	9143	9149	9154	9160	5	1 1 2	2 3 3	4 4 5
84	2898	2900	2902	2903	2905	2907	2909	2910	2912	2914	2	0 0 1	1 1 1	1 2 2
	9165	9171	9176	9182	9187	9192	9198	9203	9209	9214	5	1 1 2	2 3 3	4 4 5
85	2915	2917	2919	2921	2922	2924	2926	2927	2929	2931	2	0 0 1	1 1 1	1 2 2
	9220	9225	9230	9236	9241	9247	9252	9257	9263	9268	5	1 1 2	2 3 3	4 4 5
86	2933	2934	2936	2938	2939	2941	2943	2944	2946	2948	2	0 0 1	1 1 1	1 2 2
	9274	9279	9284	9290	9295	9301	9306	9311	9317	9322	5	1 1 2	2 3 3	4 4 5
87	2950	2951	2953	2955	2956	2958	2960	2961	2963	2965	2	0 0 1	1 1 1	1 2 2
	9327	9333	9338	9343	9349	9354	9360	9365	9370	9375	5	1 1 2	2 3 3	4 4 5
88	2966	2968	2970	2972	2973	2975	2977	2978	2980	2982	2	0 0 1	1 1 1	1 2 2
	9381	9386	9391	9397	9402	9407	9413	9418	9423	9429	5	1 1 2	2 3 3	4 4 5
89	2983	2985	2987	2988	2990	2992	2993	2995	2997	2998	2	0 0 1	1 1 1	1 2 2
	9434	9439	9445	9450	9455	9460	9466	9471	9476	9482	5	1 1 2	2 3 3	4 4 5
90	3000	3002	3003	3005	3007	3008	3010	3012	3013	3015	2	0 0 1	1 1 1	1 2 2
	9487	9492	9497	9503	9508	9513	9518	9524	9529	9534	5	1 1 2	2 3 3	4 4 5
91	3017	3018	3020	3022	3023	3025	3027	3028	3030	3032	2	0 0 1	1 1 1	1 2 2
	9539	9545	9550	9555	9560	9566	9571	9576	9581	9586	5	1 1 2	2 3 3	4 4 5
92	3033	3035	3036	3038	3040	3041	3043	3045	3046	3048	2	0 0 1	1 1 1	1 2 2
	9592	9597	9602	9607	9612	9618	9623	9628	9633	9638	5	1 1 2	2 3 3	4 4 5
93	3050	3051	3053	3055	3056	3058	3059	3061	3063	3064	2	0 0 1	1 1 1	1 2 2
	9644	9649	9654	9659	9664	9670	9675	9680	9685	9690	5	1 1 2	2 3 3	4 4 5
94	3066	3068	3069	3071	3072	3074	3076	3077	3079	3081	2	0 0 1	1 1 1	1 2 2
	9695	9701	9706	9711	9716	9721	9726	9731	9737	9742	5	1 1 2	2 3 3	4 4 5
95	3082	3084	3085	3087	3089	3090	3092	3094	3095	3097	2	0 0 1	1 1 1	1 2 2
	9747	9752	9757	9762	9767	9772	9778	9783	9788	9793	5	1 1 2	2 3 3	4 4 5
96	3098	3100	3102	3103	3105	3106	3108	3110	3111	3113	2	0 0 1	1 1 1	1 2 2
	9798	9803	9808	9813	9818	9823	9829	9834	9839	9844	5	1 1 2	2 3 3	4 4 5
97	3114	3116	3118	3119	3121	3122	3124	3126	3127	3129	2	0 0 1	1 1 1	1 2 2
	9849	9854	9859	9864	9869	9874	9879	9884	9889	9894	5	1 1 2	2 3 3	4 4 5
98	3130	3132	3134	3135	3137	3138	3140	3142	3143	3145	2	0 0 1	1 1 1	1 2 2
	9899	9905	9910	9915	9920	9925	9930	9935	9940	9945	5	1 1 2	2 3 3	4 4 5
99	3146	3148	3150	3151	3153	3154	3156	3158	3159	3161	2	0 0 1	1 1 1	1 2 2
	9950	9955	9960	9965	9970	9975	9980	9985	9990	9995	5	1 1 2	2 3 3	4 4 5

Examples:

$$\sqrt{862300} = \sqrt{86.230 \times 10^4} \doteqdot 9.286 \times 10^2 = 928.6$$

$$\sqrt{0.0927} = \sqrt{9.27 \times 10^{-2}} \doteqdot 3.045 \times 10^{-1} = 0.3045$$

Note that the power of 10 extracted under the root sign must always be even. If this leaves **one** figure before the decimal point, use the **upper** line of a pair; if it leaves **two** figures before the decimal point, use the **lower** line.

The Normal Distribution Function

Z	Φ(Z)	Z	Φ(Z)	Z	Φ(Z)	Z	Φ(Z)	Z	Φ(Z)
0·00	0·5000	0·50	0·6915	1·00	0·8413	1·50	0·9332	2·00	0·97725
·01	·5040	·51	·6950	·01	·8438	·51	·9345	·01	·97778
·02	·5080	·52	·6985	·02	·8461	·52	·9357	·02	·97831
·03	·5120	·53	·7019	·03	·8485	·53	·9370	·03	·97882
·04	·5160	·54	·7054	·04	·8508	·54	·9382	·04	·97932
0·05	0·5199	0·55	0·7088	1·05	0·8531	1·55	0·9394	2·05	0·97982
·06	·5239	·56	·7123	·06	·8554	·56	·9406	·06	·98030
·07	·5279	·57	·7157	·07	·8577	·57	·9418	·07	·98077
·08	·5319	·58	·7190	·08	·8599	·58	·9429	·08	·98124
·09	·5359	·59	·7224	·09	·8621	·59	·9441	·09	·98169
0·10	0·5398	0·60	0·7257	1·10	0·8643	1·60	0·9452	2·10	0·98214
·11	·5438	·61	·7291	·11	·8665	·61	·9463	·11	·98257
·12	·5478	·62	·7324	·12	·8686	·62	·9474	·12	·98300
·13	·5517	·63	·7357	·13	·8708	·63	·9484	·13	·98341
·14	·5557	·64	·7389	·14	·8729	·64	·9495	·14	·98382
0·15	0·5596	0·65	0·7422	1·15	0·8749	1·65	0·9505	2·15	0·98422
·16	·5636	·66	·7454	·16	·8770	·66	·9515	·16	·98461
·17	·5675	·67	·7486	·17	·8790	·67	·9525	·17	·98500
·18	·5714	·68	·7517	·18	·8810	·68	·9535	·18	·98537
·19	·5753	·69	·7549	·19	·8830	·69	·9545	·19	·98574
0·20	0·5793	0·70	0·7580	1·20	0·8849	1·70	0·9554	2·20	0·98610
·21	·5832	·71	·7611	·21	·8869	·71	·9564	·21	·98645
·22	·5871	·72	·7642	·22	·8888	·72	·9573	·22	·98679
·23	·5910	·73	·7673	·23	·8907	·73	·9582	·23	·98713
·24	·5948	·74	·7704	·24	·8925	·74	·9591	·24	·98745
0·25	0·5987	0·75	0·7734	1·25	0·8944	1·75	0·9599	2·25	0·98778
·26	·6026	·76	·7764	·26	·8962	·76	·9608	·26	·98809
·27	·6064	·77	·7794	·27	·8980	·77	·9616	·27	·98840
·28	·6103	·78	·7823	·28	·8997	·78	·9625	·28	·98870
·29	·6141	·79	·7852	·29	·9015	·79	·9633	·29	·98899
0·30	0·6179	0·80	0·7881	1·30	0·9032	1·80	0·9641	2·30	0·98928
·31	·6217	·81	·7910	·31	·9049	·81	·9649	·31	·98956
·32	·6255	·82	·7939	·32	·9066	·82	·9656	·32	·98983
·33	·6293	·83	·7967	·33	·9082	·83	·9664	·33	·99010
·34	·6331	·84	·7995	·34	·9099	·84	·9671	·34	·99036
0·35	0·6368	0·85	0·8023	1·35	0·9115	1·85	0·9678	2·35	0·99061
·36	·6406	·86	·8051	·36	·9131	·86	·9686	·36	·99086
·37	·6443	·87	·8078	·37	·9147	·87	·9693	·37	·99111
·38	·6480	·88	·8106	·38	·9162	·88	·9699	·38	·99134
·39	·6517	·89	·8133	·39	·9177	·89	·9706	·39	·99158
0·40	0·6554	0·90	0·8159	1·40	0·9192	1·90	0·9713	2·40	0·99180
·41	·6591	·91	·8186	·41	·9207	·91	·9719	·41	·99202
·42	·6628	·92	·8212	·42	·9222	·92	·9726	·42	·99224
·43	·6664	·93	·8238	·43	·9236	·93	·9732	·43	·99245
·44	·6700	·94	·8264	·44	·9251	·94	·9738	·44	·99266
0·45	0·6736	0·95	0·8289	1·45	0·9265	1·95	0·9744	2·45	0·99286
·46	·6772	·96	·8315	·46	·9279	·96	·9750	·46	·99305
·47	·6808	·97	·8340	·47	·9292	·97	·9756	·47	·99324
·48	·6844	·98	·8365	·48	·9306	·98	·9761	·48	·99343
·49	·6879	·99	·8389	·49	·9319	·99	·9767	·49	·99361
0·50	0·6915	1·00	0·8413	1·50	0·9332	2·00	0·9772	2·50	0·99379

Z	Φ(Z)	Z	Φ(Z)	Z	Φ(Z)
2·50	0·99379	2·70	0·99653	2·90	0·99813
·51	·99396	·71	·99664	·91	·99819
·52	·99413	·72	·99674	·92	·99825
·53	·99430	·73	·99683	·93	·99831
·54	·99446	·74	·99693	·94	·99836
2·55	0·99461	2·75	0·99702	2·95	0·99841
·56	·99477	·76	·99711	·96	·99846
·57	·99492	·77	·99720	·97	·99851
·58	·99506	·78	·99728	·98	·99856
·59	·99520	·79	·99736	·99	·99861
2·60	0·99534	2·80	0·99744	3·0	0·99865
·61	·99547	·81	·99752	3·1	·99903
·62	·99560	·82	·99760	3·2	·99931
·63	·99573	·83	·99767	3·3	·99952
·64	·99585	·84	·99774	3·4	·99966
2·65	0·99598	2·85	0·99781	3·5	0·99977
·66	·99609	·86	·99788	3·6	·99984
·67	·99621	·87	·99795	3·7	·99989
·68	·99632	·88	·99801	3·8	·99993
·69	·99643	·89	·99807	3·9	·99995
2·70	0·99653	2·90	0·99813	4·0	0·99997

Values of e^{-x} (for use with Poisson Distribution)

x	.00	.01	.02	.03	.04	.05	.06	.07	.08	.09
0.0	1.0000	.9900	.9802	.9704	.9608	.9512	.9418	.9324	.9231	.9139
0.1	0.9048	.8958	.8869	.8781	.8694	.8607	.8521	.8437	.8353	.8270
.2	.8187	.8106	.8025	.7945	.7866	.7788	.7711	.7634	.7558	.7483
.3	.7408	.7334	.7261	.7189	.7118	.7047	.6977	.6907	.6839	.6771
.4	.6703	.6637	.6570	.6505	.6440	.6376	.6313	.6250	.6188	.6126
.5	.6065	.6005	.5945	.5886	.5827	.5769	.5712	.5655	.5599	.5543
.6	.5488	.5434	.5379	.5326	.5273	.5220	.5169	.5117	.5066	.5016
.7	.4966	.4916	.4868	.4819	.4771	.4724	.4677	.4630	.4584	.4538
.8	.4493	.4449	.4404	.4360	.4317	.4274	.4232	.4190	.4148	.4107
.9	.4066	.4025	.3985	.3946	.3906	.3867	.3829	.3791	.3753	.3716
1.0	0.3679	.3642	.3606	.3570	.3535	.3499	.3465	.3430	.3396	.3362
1.1	.3329	.3296	.3263	.3230	.3198	.3166	.3135	.3104	.3073	.3042
.2	.3012	.2982	.2952	.2923	.2894	.2865	.2837	.2808	.2780	.2753
.3	.2725	.2698	.2671	.2645	.2618	.2592	.2567	.2541	.2516	.2491
.4	.2466	.2441	.2417	.2393	.2369	.2346	.2322	.2299	.2276	.2254
.5	.2231	.2209	.2187	.2165	.2144	.2122	.2101	.2080	.2060	.2039
.6	.2019	.1999	.1979	.1959	.1940	.1920	.1901	.1882	.1864	.1845
.7	.1827	.1809	.1791	.1773	.1755	.1738	.1720	.1703	.1686	.1670
.8	.1653	.1637	.1620	.1604	.1588	.1572	.1557	.1541	.1526	.1511
.9	.1496	.1481	.1466	.1451	.1437	.1423	.1409	.1395	.1381	.1367
2.0	0.1353	.1340	.1327	.1313	.1300	.1287	.1275	.1262	.1249	.1237
2.1	0.1225	.1212	.1200	.1188	.1177	.1165	.1153	.1142	.1130	.1119
.2	.1108	.1097	.1086	.1075	.1065	.1054	.1044	.1033	.1023	.1013
.3	.1003	.0993	.0983	.0973	.0963	.0954	.0944	.0935	.0925	.0916
.4	.0907	.0898	.0889	.0880	.0872	.0863	.0854	.0846	.0837	.0829
.5	.0821	.0813	.0805	.0797	.0789	.0781	.0773	.0765	.0758	.0750
.6	.0743	.0735	.0728	.0721	.0714	.0707	.0699	.0693	.0686	.0679
.7	.0672	.0665	.0659	.0652	.0646	.0639	.0633	.0627	.0620	.0614
.8	.0608	.0602	.0596	.0590	.0584	.0578	.0573	.0567	.0561	.0556
9	.0550	.0545	.0539	.0534	.0529	.0523	.0518	.0513	.0508	.0503
3.0	0.0498	.0493	.0488	.0483	.0478	.0474	.0469	.0464	.0460	.0455
3.1	.0450	.0446	.0442	.0437	.0433	.0429	.0424	.0420	.0416	.0412
.2	.0408	.0404	.0400	.0396	.0392	.0388	.0384	.0380	.0376	.0373
.3	.0369	.0365	.0362	.0358	.0354	.0351	.0347	.0344	.0340	.0337
.4	.0334	.0330	.0327	.0324	.0321	.0317	.0314	.0311	.0308	.0305
.5	.0302	.0299	.0296	.0293	.0290	.0287	.0284	.0282	.0279	.0276
.6	.0273	.0271	.0268	.0265	.0260	.0257	.0257	.0255	.0252	.0250
.7	.0247	.0245	.0242	.0240	.0238	.0235	.0233	.0231	.0228	.0226
.8	.0224	.0221	.0219	.0217	.0215	.0213	.0211	.0209	.0207	.0204
.9	.0202	.0200	.0198	.0196	.0194	.0193	.0191	.0189	.0187	.0185
4.0	0.0183									

x	.00	.01	.02	.03	.04	.05	.06	.07	.08	.09

Student's t Critical Points

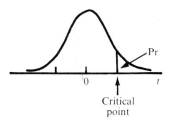

Pr d.f.	.25	.10	.05	.025	.010	.005	.001
1	1.000	3.078	6.314	12.706	31.821	63.657	318.31
2	.816	1.886	2.920	4.303	6.965	9.925	22.326
3	.765	1.638	2.353	3.182	4.541	5.841	10.213
4	.741	1.533	2.132	2.776	3.747	4.604	7.173
5	.727	1.476	2.015	2.571	3.365	4.032	5.893
6	.718	1.440	1.943	2.447	3.143	3.707	5.208
7	.711	1.415	1.895	2.365	2.998	3.499	4.785
8	.706	1.397	1.860	2.306	2.896	3.355	4.501
9	.703	1.383	1.833	2.262	2.821	3.250	4.297
10	.700	1.372	1.812	2.228	2.764	3.169	4.144
11	.697	1.363	1.796	2.201	2.718	3.106	4.025
12	.695	1.356	1.782	2.179	2.681	3.055	3.930
13	.694	1.350	1.771	2.160	2.650	3.012	3.852
14	.692	1.345	1.761	2.145	2.624	2.977	3.787
15	.691	1.341	1.753	2.131	2.602	2.947	3.733
16	.690	1.337	1.746	2.120	2.583	2.921	3.686
17	.689	1.333	1.740	2.110	2.567	2.898	3.646
18	.688	1.330	1.734	2.101	2.552	2.878	3.610
19	.688	1.328	1.729	2.093	2.539	2.861	3.579
20	.687	1.325	1.725	2.086	2.528	2.845	3.552
21	.686	1.323	1.721	2.080	2.518	2.831	3.527
22	.686	1.321	1.717	2.074	2.508	2.819	3.505
23	.685	1.319	1.714	2.069	2.500	2.807	3.485
24	.685	1.318	1.711	2.064	2.492	2.797	3.467
25	.684	1.316	1.708	2.060	2.485	2.787	3.450
26	.684	1.315	1.706	2.056	2.479	2.779	3.435
27	.684	1.314	1.703	2.052	2.473	2.771	3.421
28	.683	1.313	1.701	2.048	2.467	2.763	3.408
29	.683	1.311	1.699	2.045	2.462	2.756	3.396
30	.683	1.310	1.697	2.042	2.457	2.750	3.385
40	.681	1.303	1.684	2.021	2.423	2.704	3.307
60	.679	1,296	1.671	2.000	2.390	2.660	3.232
120	.677	1.289	1.658	1.980	2.358	2.617	3.160
∞	.674	1.282	1.645	1.960	2.326	2.576	3.090

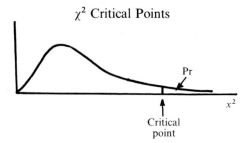

χ^2 Critical Points

Pr d.f.	.250	.100	.050	.025	.010	.005	.001
1	1.32	2.71	3.84	5.02	6.63	7.88	10.8
2	2.77	4.61	5.99	7.38	9.21	10.6	13.8
3	4.11	6.25	7.81	9.35	11.3	12.8	16.3
4	5.39	7.78	9.49	11.1	13.3	14.9	18.5
5	6.63	9.24	11.1	12.8	15.1	16.7	20.5
6	7.84	10.6	12.6	14.4	16:8	18.5	22.5
7	9.04	12.0	14.1	16.0	18.5	20.3	24.3
8	10.2	13.4	15.5	17.5	20.1	22.0	26.1
9	11.4	14.7	16.9	19.0	21.7	23.6	27.9
10	12.5	16.0	18.3	20.5	23.2	25.2	29.6
11	13.7	17.3	19.7	21.9	24.7	26.8	31.3
12	14.8	18.5	21.0	23.3	26.2	28.3	32.9
13	16.0	19.8	22.4	24.7	27.7	29.8	34.5
14	17.1	21.1	23.7	26.1	29.1	31.3	36.1
15	18.2	22.3	25.0	27.5	30.6	32.8	37.7
16	19.4	23.5	26.3	28.8	32.0	34.3	39.3
17	20.5	24.8	27.6	30.2	33.4	35.7	40.8
18	21.6	26.0	28.9	31.5	34.8	37.2	42.3
19	22.7	27.2	30.1	32.9	36.2	38.6	43.8
20	23.8	28.4	31.4	34.2	37.6	40.0	45.3
21	24.9	29.6	32.7	35.5	38.9	41.4	46.8
22	26.0	30.8	33.9	36.8	40.3	42.8	48.3
23	27.1	32.0	35.2	38.1	41.6	44.2	49.7
24	28.2	33.2	36.4	39.4	43.0	45.6	51.2
25	29.3	34.4	37.7	40.6	44.3	46.9	52.6
26	30.4	35.6	38.9	41.9	45.6	48.3	54.1
27	31.5	36.7	40.1	43.2	47.0	49.6	55.5
28	32.6	37.9	41.3	44.5	48.3	51.0	56.9
29	33.7	39.1	42.6	45.7	49.6	52.3	58.3
30	34.8	40.3	43.8	47.0	50.9	53.7	59.7
40	45.6	51.8	55.8	59.3	63.7	66.8	73.4
50	56.3	63.2	67.5	71.4	76.2	79.5	86.7
60	67.0	74.4	79.1	83.3	88.4	92.0	99.6
70	77.6	85.5	90.5	95.0	100	104	112
80	88.1	96.6	102	107	112	116	125
90	98.6	108	113	118	124	128	137
100	109	118	124	130	136	140	149

Index